The Secondary Maths Handbook

Lesley Medcalf

The
Maths
Press

First published in Great Britain in 1998 by
The Maths Press
11 Codrington Road
Bristol
BS7 8ET
0117–949–6414

ISBN 0 9533595 0 6

Designed, typeset and produced by
Action Publishing Technology Limited, Gloucester

Printed in Spain by Mateu Cromo, Madrid

Contents

Contents

Acknowledgements

I would like to thank all colleagues, past and present, who have helped to shape my view of what constitutes good Maths teaching. Particular thanks need to go to Jo Wood, Jane Wall, Alan Sherlock and Brian Hankins for their devotion to proof reading what I thought would be the final manuscript. They suggested many changes which improved the eventual final version considerably.

Introduction

This book sets out to be significantly different from other Maths books!

It aims to explain the underlying reasons behind the theory. It does not present Maths as a series of un-connected hoops which the reader must jump through whether or not they have the slightest idea why they are jumping through these hoops!

Where appropriate, I have indicated the mistakes that pupils often make and the common misconceptions that often stop pupils making further progress. Look out for the CAUTION! boxes as you read through the text, as they will provide you with powerful learning tools.

This book supports the National Curriculum in Maths. It covers enough material to enable the reader to obtain a top grade at Intermediate Level. I start each topic at a point which should be accessible to all readers and develop the ideas contained within each topic so that the reader should find it easy to move on to cover the remaining topics needed for Higher Level GCSE.

Because the book lays good foundations for understanding Maths, the committed reader should be able to go on to take Maths at A Level, where a firm grasp of the ideas covered in this book will ease the transition from GCSE Maths to A Level Maths.

Maths is not a spectator sport! When you are reading the book, make your involvement active, not passive. Have a pencil and paper ready to try the questions that are posed in the text before you move on. If the book belongs to you, add notes in the margin in pencil to make the book your own.

Maths for most people doesn't come quickly. You may need to read a particular section several times, and even come back to it over many weeks, before you think you are happy with the topic. Don't worry if this describes the way you learn Maths – this is perfectly normal and doesn't mean that you are 'no good at Maths'!

I have tried to make the explanations as clear as possible. The lay-out of the page is intended to be visually memorable. Aim to reproduce this style of presentation in your own work.

When you are working on Maths, I suggest you:

- Write down the question that you are working on, so that it forms part of your notes for future reference.

- Show all of your working. Try to take one step at a time and explain your method as you go.

- Make it clear what your final answer is. Check that this is what the question actually asked you to find out.

Try the questions which are in the text, then use the answers in the back of the book intelligently. They are there to help you learn. Looking up the answer and working backwards isn't 'cheating' – it is a sensible approach, providing you are trying to understand how everything fits together.

To help you make maximum use of this book, ask your Maths teacher which sections you should be working on.

Try to explore the work covered in each section, so that you really understand the ideas and could explain them to someone else. If you don't understand something straight away, put a mark in the margin (if it is your own book), but read on anyway! This will help you to get an overview and to see the 'big picture'. When you read the section again later, there will be a good chance that the details will fall into place, once you understand the underlying theory.

The contents are split into five chapters:

1 Number
2 Algebra
3 Shape and Space
4 Statistics
5 Probability

The index at the back of the book will enable you to find a particular topic. For example, if your class is just starting to work on Pythagoras' Theorem, you will be able to look this up in the index and then read the appropriate section.

However, there are some sections, such as Understanding Decimals and Using Decimals to Solve Problems, which every committed reader should work through. In these sections, I pin-point some of the common misconceptions about the way numbers work, which stop people making further progress. All readers should work through the section Using Algebra, where I give examples of why algebra is so powerful and important in the study of Mathematics. This sections will help with GCSE projects, where top grades are obtained only by the use of generalisations using algebra.

Good Luck with your study of Mathematics!

Lesley Medcalf

NUMBER

▲ USING NUMBERS ▼

ADDITION

When adding, you already know that: $3 + 8 = 8 + 3 = 11$

The order of the numbers makes no difference to the answer! Because the order makes no difference when you add two numbers, addition is said to be **commutative.**

Use your calculator to check that: $2 + 13 + 8 + 17 + 23 = 63$
and that: $2 + 8 + 13 + 17 + 23 = 63$

Changing the order makes no difference to the answer, but the second list of numbers is easier to add in your head, as the $2+8$ makes 10 and the $13 + 17$ makes 30.

So, the calculation becomes:

$$
\begin{aligned}
2 + 13 + 8 + 17 + 23 &= 2 + 8 + 13 + 17 + 23 \\
&= (2 + 8) + (13 + 17) + 23 \\
&= 10 + 30 + 23 \\
&= 63
\end{aligned}
$$

This idea is particularly useful for mental arithmetic.

EXAMPLE I

Two elderly teachers have been teaching for 38 years and 35 years. Find the **sum** of their years of teaching experience.

The word **sum** is used here in a very precise way. It means that you need to do an **addition**, in order to find the answer.

Altogether, they have been teaching for $38 + 35 = 73$ years.

QUESTIONS I.I

Find the answers to these additions, without using your calculator. Change the order if this will help!

1. $95 + 7 + 105 + 19 + 33$

2. $125 + 27 + 82 + 35 + 8 + 13$

3. $400 + 72 + 19 + 21 + 28$

4. $222 + 87 + 108 + 33 + 45$

5. Find the sum of 22 and 74.

6. Find the sum of 49 and 23.

SUBTRACTION

This is the type of subtraction which often causes problems!

H	T	U	
7	0	8	
3	4	5	−

You can see that the units column is straight forward: 8 subtract 5 is 3

H	T	U
7	0	8
3	4	5 −
		3

When you look at the tens column, you have to cope with 0 subtract 4, which you cannot evaluate directly. Borrow one of the hundreds from the hundreds column and split it into 10 tens, which you can put into the tens column, like this:

H	T	U
6	10+0	8
3	4	5 −
		3

We can now continue with 10 subtract 4 which is 6 and complete the calculation:

H	T	U
6	10+0	8
3	4	5 −
3	6	3

We can check that this is the correct answer, by adding 363 to 345, like this:

H	T	U
3	6	3
3	4	5 +
7	0	8

We get back to 708, as we should do!

SUBTRACTION IS NOT COMMUTATIVE

With addition, the order of the numbers makes no difference to the answer. Clearly, with subtraction, the order matters crucially.

Look back at the worked example again: $708-345 = 363$

So, if I had £708 in the bank and wrote a cheque for £345 I would have £363 left in the account.

If the order of the numbers is changed, like this: $345-708$, then I get the answer **minus** 363 on my calculator. So, if I had £345 in the bank and wrote a cheque for £708 I am spending money that I don't have. I would be overdrawn by £363. This would appear on my bank statement as '−£363'. Read the section on Negative Numbers for a fuller description of negative numbers.

EXAMPLE I
Find $3008 - 462$.

Set out the calculation as before. I can do "8 subtract 2" straight away, like this:

Th	H	T	U
3	0	0	8
	4	6	2 −
			6

Looking at the tens column, I cannot evaluate "0 subtract 6" directly. This time I cannot borrow one from the hundreds column (there aren't any hundreds!). So, I have to borrow one from the thousands and split it into 10 hundreds, like this:

Th	H	T	U
2	10 + 0	0	8
	4	6	2 −
			6

Now I can borrow a hundred and split it into 10 tens, like this:

Th	H	T	U
2	9	10+0	8
	4	6	2 −
			6

Now I can complete the calculation, like this:

Th	H	T	U
2	9	10+0	8
	4	6	2 −
2	5	4	6

EXAMPLE 2

Two sisters are aged 18 and 13. What is the **difference** in their ages?

Again, the word **difference** is used in a very precise way, mathematically speaking. It means that you need to do a **subtraction**, in order to find the answer. Take the smaller number from the bigger number, like this:

The difference in their ages is found by $18 - 13 = 5$ years.

QUESTIONS 1.2

Try these subtractions, without using your calculator:

1. $308 - 256$ 3. $1009 - 478$

2. $308 - 259$ 4. $2007 - 399$

ADDITION AND SUBTRACTION: INVERSE OPERATIONS

Start with the number 7, add 5 and you get 12.

So, $7 + 5 = 12$

If you now subtract 5 from 12 you get back to 7, which is where you started from!

So, $12 - 5 = 7$

So, "Add 5" followed by "Subtract 5" simply cancel out and leave you where you started.

Also, "Subtract 5" followed by "Add 5" cancel out and leave you where you started.

Addition and Subtraction are said to be **Inverse Operations**.

These ideas will be very important when trying to solve equations later on in the Algebra section.

NUMBER

MULTIPLICATION

Here is the standard method for doing long multiplication without a calculator. Find 237×46.

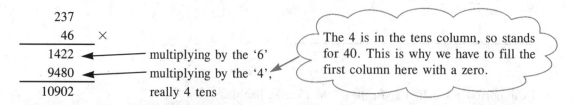

```
  237
   46  ×
 ────────
 1422  ◄────── multiplying by the '6'
 9480  ◄────── multiplying by the '4',
 ────────
10902          really 4 tens
```

> The 4 is in the tens column, so stands for 40. This is why we have to fill the first column here with a zero.

NAPIER'S BONES METHOD FOR MULTIPLICATION

Many pupils enjoy using a different method of doing long multiplication, called **Napier's Bones**. It was devised by a Scottish mathematician called John Napier who lived 1550−1617.

Draw out a grid like this, with enough boxes to put each number in its own square:

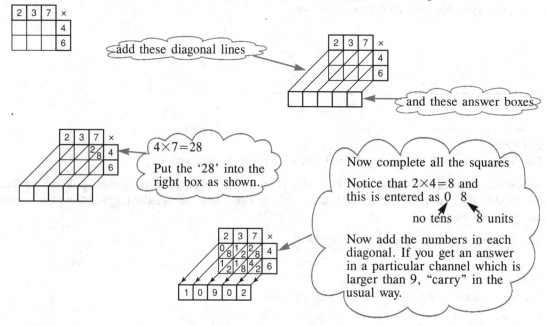

> add these diagonal lines

> and these answer boxes

> $4 \times 7 = 28$
>
> Put the '28' into the right box as shown.

> Now complete all the squares
>
> Notice that $2 \times 4 = 8$ and this is entered as 0 8
>
>   no tens   8 units
>
> Now add the numbers in each diagonal. If you get an answer in a particular channel which is larger than 9, "carry" in the usual way.

Notice that we have got the same answer as before! Now try some long multiplications yourself using both methods. Use some really big numbers!

MULTIPLICATION IS COMMUTATIVE

> $3 \times 5 = 5 \times 3 = 15$
> So, once again, the order makes no difference to the answer. Multiplication is therefore **commutative.**

3 rows of $5 = 15$ 5 rows of $3 = 15$

Use you calculator to find that: $5 \times 27 \times 2 = 270$

Change the order to: $27 \times 5 \times 2$

Now use your calculator to check that: $27 \times 5 \times 2$ also equals 270.

You can use this idea to help you when you are doing mental arithmetic, because

$$\begin{aligned} 5 \times 27 \times 2 &= 27 \times (5 \times 2) \\ &= 27 \times 10 \\ &= 270 \end{aligned}$$

FINDING THE PRODUCT OF TWO NUMBERS

Find the product of 13 and 15.

The word **product** means that you need to **multiply** to find the answer. So, the product of 13 and 15 is $13 \times 15 = 195$

DIVISION

Find: $3096 \div 12$

Set out the division like this: $12\overline{)3\ 0\ 9\ 6}$

Now, 12 into 3, doesn't go. So, try 12 into 30.

At this stage, it might be helpful to write down your 12 times table, like this:

$1 \times 12 = 12$

$2 \times 12 = 24$

$3 \times 12 = 36$

I can stop here, because, already, 36 is too big. 12 goes into 30 twice, with 6 remainder. Add this to your calculation, like this:

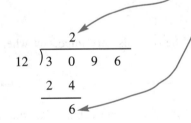

Bring the next digit down, like this:

Now, try 12 into 69. Again it might be helpful to write out your 12 times table, like this:

$1 \times 12 = 12$

$2 \times 12 = 24$

$3 \times 12 = 36$

$4 \times 12 = 48$

$5 \times 12 = 60$

$6 \times 12 = 72$

Stop here as 72 is too big. 12 goes into 69 five times, with 9 remainder. Add this to your calculation.

NUMBER

```
           2  5
   12 )3  0  9  6
       2  4
          6  9
          6  0
             9
```

Bring the next digit down,
like this:

```
           2  5
   12 )3  0  9  6
       2  4
          6  9
          6  0
             9  6
```

Continue the
12 times table,
like this:

$1 \times 12 = 12$

$2 \times 12 = 24$

$3 \times 12 = 36$

$4 \times 12 = 48$

$5 \times 12 = 60$

$6 \times 12 = 72$

$7 \times 12 = 84$

$8 \times 12 = 96$ ◄

12 goes into 96 eight times with no remainder.
So, we can now complete the long division

```
           2  5  8
   12 )3  0  9  6
       2  4
          6  9
          6  0
             9  6
             9  6
                0
```

So, $3096 \div 12 = 258$

DIVISION IS NOT COMMUTATIVE

Check on your calculator that $3096 \div 12 = 258$

Now try $12 \div 3096$! You most definitely do not get 258! The order is very important when dividing, so division is not commutative.

QUESTIONS 1.3
Try these long division, without using your calculator. Set out your working like the worked example.

1. $4788 \div 14$

2. $5235 \div 15$

3. $19584 \div 24$

4. $26976 \div 32$

Now use your calculator to find:

5. $14 \div 4788$

6. $15 \div 5235$

7. $24 \div 19584$

8. $32 \div 26976$

MULTIPLICATION AND DIVISION: INVERSE OPERATIONS

Start with the number 3, multiply by 5 and you get 15. So, $3 \times 5 = 15$

If you now divide 15 by 5, you get back to 3, which is where you started from! So, $15 \div 5 = 3$

So, "Multiply by 5" followed by "Divide by 5" simply cancel out and leave you where you started.

Also, "Divide by 5" followed by "Multiply by 5" cancel out and leave you where you started.

Multiplication and Division are said to be **Inverse Operations**.

We shall return to these ideas when solving equations later on in the section on Algebra.

TIME

The distance between Bristol and Norwich is about 230 miles. Last weekend I made the journey in my car and it took me 5 hours. What was my average speed?

Average Speed = $\dfrac{\text{Total distance travelled}}{\text{Total time taken}}$

Average Speed = $\dfrac{230}{5}$

Average Speed = 46 miles per hour (mph)

EXAMPLE 1
What if the journey had taken me 6 hours altogether?

Use the same formula as before:

Average Speed = $\dfrac{\text{Total distance travelled}}{\text{Total time taken}}$

Average Speed = $\dfrac{230}{6}$

Average Speed = $38 \cdot 3$ mph (to 1 decimal place)

EXAMPLE 2
What if the journey had taken me five and a half hours altogether?

Use the same formula as before:

Average Speed = $\dfrac{\text{Total distance travelled}}{\text{Total time taken}}$

> **CAUTION!**
>
> 5 hours and 30 minutes is not $5 \cdot 30$ on your calculator!
>
> Remember that there are 60 minutes in an hour, so 30 minutes is the same as $\dfrac{30}{60}$ of an hour.
>
> $\dfrac{30}{60} = 30 \div 60 = 0 \cdot 5$
>
> So, 5 hours and 30 minutes is $5 \cdot 5$ hours

Average Speed = $\dfrac{230}{5 \cdot 5} = 230 \div 5 \cdot 5 = 41 \cdot 8$

Average Speed = $41 \cdot 8$ mph (to 1 decimal place)

This looks like the correct answer as it is in between my previous two answers of 46mph and $38 \cdot 3$ mph.

EXAMPLE 3

What if the journey had taken me 5 hours 25 minutes altogether?

Use the same formula as before:

$$\text{Average Speed} = \frac{\text{Total distance travelled}}{\text{Total time taken}}$$

CAUTION!

> 5 hours and 25 minutes is not 5·25 on your calculator!
>
> Remember that there are 60 minutes in an hour, so 25 minutes is the same as $\frac{25}{60}$ of an hour.
>
> $$\frac{25}{60} = 25 \div 60 = 0\cdot416666$$
>
> So, 5 hours 25 minutes is 5·416666666 hours

$$\text{Average Speed} = \frac{230}{5\cdot4166666} = 230 \div 5\cdot4166666$$

Average Speed = 42·5 mph (to 1 decimal place)

This looks like the correct answer. I have taken slightly less time than I did in Example 2, so my average speed is slightly bigger.

QUESTIONS 1.4

1. Change these hours and minutes into hours. The first one has been done for you!

Hours and Minutes	Hours
3 hours 15 minutes	3·25 hours
4 hours 18 minutes	
7 hours 42 minutes	
1 hour 22 minutes	
2 hours 10 minutes	
6 hours 55 minutes	

2 Find the average speed for these journeys (in mph). Give your answers to 1 decimal place.

(a) 240 miles in 4 hour 15 minutes   (c) 175 miles in 2 hour 50 minutes

(b) 190 miles in 3 hour 25 minutes   (d) 170 miles in 3 hour 35 minutes

NEGATIVE NUMBERS

Temperature

On a very hot summer day the temperature could get as high as 30°C.

Recommended room temperature is about 15°C.

Water freezes at 0°C.

In winter, as the temperature drops below zero, we need to use negative numbers.

We use a thermometer to measure temperature. As the weather gets colder, the thermometer might show one degree below zero, like this:

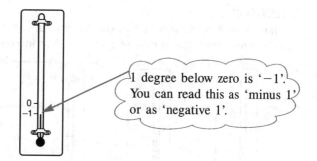

1 degree below zero is '−1'. You can read this as 'minus 1' or as 'negative 1'.

If the thermometer looks like this:

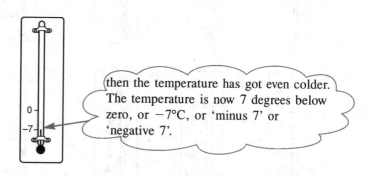

then the temperature has got even colder. The temperature is now 7 degrees below zero, or −7°C, or 'minus 7' or 'negative 7'.

Dealing with Money

I have £7 in my bank balance. If I write a cheque for £10, I am spending money that I don't have(!). The bank will send me a letter to say that I am overdrawn by £3. This would appear on my bank statement as −£3.

So, £7 − £10 = −£3   I would rather have £7 than −£3!

Or, 7 − 10 = −3

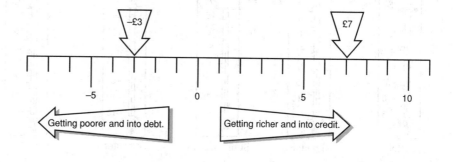

EXAMPLE 1

I owe Susana £8 and I have £5 in my pocket. If I pay her the money I have at the moment, I still owe her £3.

I can write, "I owe Susana £8" as −£8. So, this calculation can be written as −£8 + £5 = −£3

Or: −8 + 5 = −3

EXAMPLE 2

I owe Brian £10 and I owe David £8. What are my total debts?

So, this calculation can be written as −£10 + −£8 = −£18

Or: −10 + −8 = −18

Altogether, I owe £18.

QUESTIONS 1.5

For questions 1 to 4, write down the temperature shown on the thermometers. Put those temperatures in order, with the hottest temperature first in your list.

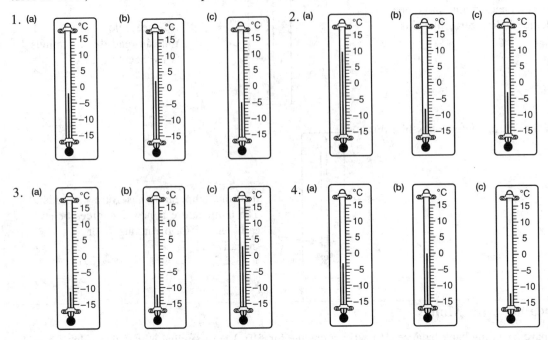

Questions 5 to 10 show the temperatures at different places around the country on a particular day. Find the difference in temperature between the two places. Write down the calculation that you are using to find an answer.

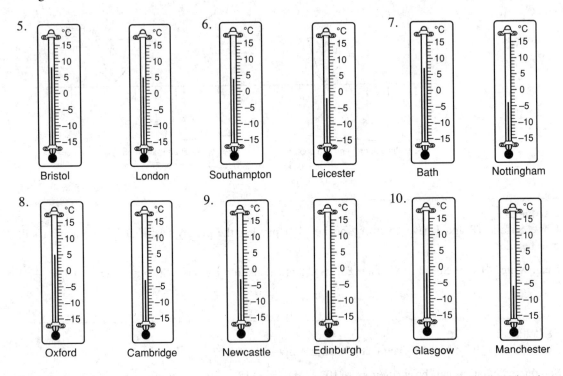

11. I owe the milkman £14 and the newsagents £20. How much do I owe altogether? Write down your calculation.

12. I owe the baby-sitter £9, but have only £4 on me. If I pay her what I can, how much do I still owe her? Write down your calculation.

ADDING AND SUBTRACTING WITH NEGATIVE NUMBERS

Look at your answers to questions 5 to 10. To find the difference in the temperature between the two places you can look at the diagram of the two thermometers to find your answer, or you can subtract. The calculations which you wrote down should look like this:

5. $8 - 5 = 3$

6. $4 - (-2) = 6$

7. $7 - (-4) = 11$

8. $5 - (-3) = 8$

9. $-3 - (-7) = 4$

10. $-2 - (-6) = 4$

> Notice that I can put a bracket round the number and its minus sign if I want to draw attention to the fact that there are two minus signs here.

You can see that, looking at the last 5 answers, subtracting a negative number has the same effect as adding that number.

So,　　$4 - (-2)$ is the same as $4 + 2$ which is 6
So,　　$7 - (-4)$ is the same as $7 + 4$ which is 11
So,　　$5 - (-3)$ is the same as $5 + 3$ which is 8
So,　　$-3 - (-7)$ is the same as $-3 + 7$ which is 4
So,　　$-2 - (-6)$ is the same as $-2 + 6$ which is 4

> Can you explain these results?

You could explain this to a friend by looking at a list of calculations like this:

$7 - 7 = 0$

$7 - 6 = 1$

$7 - 5 = 2$

$7 - 4 = 3$

$7 - 3 = 4$

$7 - 2 = 5$

$7 - 1 = 6$

$7 - 0 = 7$

> None of these calculations should surprise you very much(!).

Now continue the pattern, like this:

$7 - 7 = 0$
$7 - 6 = 1$
$7 - 5 = 2$
$7 - 4 = 3$
$7 - 3 = 4$
$7 - 2 = 5$
$7 - 1 = 6$
$7 - 0 = 7$
$7 - (-1) = 8$
$7 - (-2) = 9$
$7 - (-3) = 10$
$7 - (-4) = 11.$

> And this last calculation is the answer that we have already written down for question 7.

Starting from some calculations where you are sure of the answers and extending the pattern like this is a very good way of confirming your answer to questions involving negative numbers.

If you read 'minus 4' as 'I have a debt of £4', then you could interpret subtracting minus 4 as 'taking away a debt'. If someone takes away a debt for you, you will be better off! So, we add!

SUBTRACTING A NEGATIVE NUMBER

$7 - (-4) = 7 + 4 = 11$

Some people remember this as: "minus minus makes a plus"

QUESTIONS 1.6

Now try these questions. Imagine a situation which would go with the calculation, if this will help you!

1. $-2 + 8 =$	7. $0 - 3 =$	13. $5 - 8 =$	19. $6 - (-6) =$
2. $(-3) + (-7) =$	8. $-2 + 3 =$	14. $0 - (-7) =$	20. $-3 - (-7) =$
3. $8 - 17 =$	9. $-1 - (-6) =$	15. $-6 - 7 =$	21. $-14 + 4 =$
4. $-13 + 7 =$	10. $-5 + 4 =$	16. $-13 - (-7) =$	22. $0 - (-13) =$
5. $5 - 7 =$	11. $0 + (-7) =$	17. $4 + 7 =$	23. $4 + (-7) =$
6. $-8 + 3 =$	12. $-9 + 17 =$	18. $-7 + -4 =$	24. $5 - 13 =$

MULTIPLYING NEGATIVE NUMBERS

The local baby-sitting circle has a standard charge of £6 for one evening's baby-sitting. I have not been very prompt at paying my debts! At the moment: I owe Christine £6.

I owe Raj £6.

I owe Charlotte £6.

Altogether I owe £18.

I could write this as: $-£6 + -£6 + -£6 = -£18$
Or, I could write this as: 3 lots of $-£6 = -£18$
Or: $3 \times -£6 = -£18$
Or: $3 \times -6 = -18$

EXAMPLE 1

My newspaper bill is £7 per week. If I haven't paid the bill for four weeks, how much do I owe the newsagents?

I could write this as: $-£7 + -£7 + -£7 + -£7 = -£28$
Or, I could write this as: 4 lots of $-£7 = -£28$
Or: $4 \times -£7 = -£28$
Or: $4 \times -7 = -28$

Patterns

$4 \times 6 = 24$
$4 \times 5 = 20$
$4 \times 4 = 16$
$4 \times 3 = 12$
$4 \times 2 = 8$
$4 \times 1 = 4$
$4 \times 0 = 0$

None of these calculations should surprise you very much (!).

Now continue this pattern on:

$4 \times 6 = 24$
$4 \times 5 = 20$
$4 \times 4 = 16$
$4 \times 3 = 12$
$4 \times 2 = 8$
$4 \times 1 = 4$
$4 \times 0 = 0$
$4 \times -1 = -4$
$4 \times -2 = -8$
$4 \times -3 = -12$
$4 \times -4 = -16$
$4 \times -5 = -20$
$4 \times -6 = -24$
$4 \times -7 = -28$

This last calculation is the answer that we have already written down for the newspaper bill

Multiplication Square

Fill in the section where we are multiplying positive numbers by positive numbers. We are very sure about these bits!

						6	6	12	18	24	30	36
						5	5	10	15	20	25	30
						4	4	8	12	16	20	24
						3	3	6	9	12	15	18
						2	2	4	6	8	10	12
						1	1	2	3	4	5	6
-6	-5	-4	-3	-2	-1		1	2	3	4	5	6
						-1						
						-2						
						-3						
						-4						
						-5						
						-6						

We know that multiplication is commutative (see the section on multiplication for a reminder here if necessary!). So, we know that:

$$3 \times -6 = -18$$

then, $-6 \times 3 = -18$ as well.

So, we can now fill in the sections, where we are multiplying one negative number by one positive number. Notice that the answers will all be negative.

NUMBER

-36	-30	-24	-18	-12	-6	6	6	12	18	24	30	36
-30	-25	-20	-15	-10	-5	5	5	10	15	20	25	30
-24	-20	-16	-12	-8	-4	4	4	8	12	16	20	24
-18	-15	-12	-9	-6	-3	3	3	6	9	12	15	18
-12	-10	-8	-6	-4	-2	2	2	4	6	8	10	12
-6	-5	-4	-3	-2	-1	1	1	2	3	4	5	6
-6	-5	-4	-3	-2	-1		1	2	3	4	5	6
						-1	-1	-2	-3	-4	-5	-6
						-2	-2	-4	-6	-8	-10	-12
						-3	-3	-6	-9	-12	-15	-18
						-4	-4	-8	-12	-16	-20	-24
						-5	-5	-10	-15	-20	-25	-30
						-6	-6	-12	-18	-24	-30	-36

Now we are left with the last section to complete, where each space is for the answer to a negative number multiplied by a negative number.

To complete this section, we need to continue all the patterns already in the multiplication square. Looking at a particular row and a particular column, these are the numbers which we would like to fill in the square:

-36	-30	-24	-18	-12	-6	6	6	12	18	24	30	36
-30	-25	-20	-15	-10	-5	5	5	10	15	20	25	30
-24	-20	-16	-12	-8	-4	4	4	8	12	16	20	24
-18	-15	-12	-9	-6	-3	3	3	6	9	12	15	18
-12	-10	-8	-6	-4	-2	2	2	4	6	8	10	12
-6	-5	-4	-3	-2	-1	1	1	2	3	4	5	6
-6	-5	-4	-3	-2	-1		1	2	3	4	5	6
	5					-1	-1	-2	-3	-4	-5	-6
	10					-2	-2	-4	-6	-8	-10	-12
	15					-3	-3	-6	-9	-12	-15	-18
24	20	16	12	8	4	-4	-4	-8	-12	-16	-20	-24
	25					-5	-5	-10	-15	-20	-25	-30
	30					-6	-6	-12	-18	-24	-30	-36

To complete these entries, I have assumed, for example, that:

$$(-5) \times (-3) = +15$$

and $\qquad (-6) \times (-4) = +24$

These are sensible assumptions, because we want Mathematics to be about continuing useful patterns. Any other answers in these rows and columns would make life much more difficult, because the answers simply would not fit in with what had gone before! So, we have chosen to make a negative number multiplied by a negative number a positive number.

> **MULTIPLYING TWO NEGATIVE NUMBERS**
>
> So, $(-6) \times (-4) = +24$
>
> Some people remember this as: 'a minus times a minus is a plus'

We can now complete the multiplication square, like this:

−36	−30	−24	−18	−12	−6	6	6	12	18	24	30	36
−30	−25	−20	−15	−10	−5	5	5	10	15	20	25	30
−24	−20	−16	−12	−8	−4	4	4	8	12	16	20	24
−18	−15	−12	−9	−6	−3	3	3	6	9	12	15	18
−12	−10	−8	−6	−4	−2	2	2	4	6	8	10	12
−6	−5	−4	−3	−2	−1	1	1	2	3	4	5	6
−6	−5	−4	−3	−2	−1		1	2	3	4	5	6
6	5	4	3	2	1	−1	−1	−2	−3	−4	−5	−6
12	10	8	6	4	2	−2	−2	−4	−6	−8	−10	−12
18	15	12	9	6	3	−3	−3	−6	−9	−12	−15	−18
24	20	16	12	8	4	−4	−4	−8	−12	−16	−20	−24
30	25	20	15	10	5	−5	−5	−10	−15	−20	−25	−30
36	30	24	18	12	6	−6	−6	−12	−18	−24	−30	−36

DIVIDING NEGATIVE NUMBERS

Now we know how to multiply negative numbers, dividing them isn't too difficult!

Use the multiplication square above to write down all the possibilities involving

multiplying $+4$, -4, $+6$ and -6, like this:

$$4 \times 6 = 24 \qquad (-4) \times 6 = -24$$
$$4 \times (-6) = -24 \qquad (-4) \times (-6) = +24$$

As multiplication and division are inverse operations, we can write down the equivalent statements concerned with division, like this:

Multiplication	Equivalent Division...	...and also....
$4 \times 6 = 24$	$24 \div 4 = 6$	$24 \div 6 = 4$

Multiplication	Equivalent Division...	...and also....
$(-4) \times 6 = -24$	$(-24) \div (-4) = 6$	$(-24) \div 6 = -4$

Multiplication	Equivalent Division...	...and also....
$4 \times (-6) = -24$	$(-24) \div 4 = -6$	$(-24) \div (-6) = 4$

Multiplication	Equivalent Division...	...and also....
$(-4) \times (-6) = +24$	$+24 \div (-4) = -6$	$+24 \div (-6) = -4$

QUESTIONS 1.7

1. Fill in the gaps in these sequences:

(a)   9, 6, 3, 0, −3, _, _, _, _

(b)   8, 5, 2, −1, _, _, _, _

(c)   12, 7, 2, _, _, _, _

(d)   7, 3, −1, _, _, _, _

2. Can you find two numbers whose sum is −7 and whose product is 10?
'Sum', remember, means they add together to make −7.
'Product' means they multiply together to give 10.

3. Fill in the gaps in this table:

Two Numbers	Their Sum	Their Product
	− 1	−42
	+ 1	−42
	− 13	+42
	− 5	−36
	− 13	+36
	− 3	−70

4. Calculate:

(a) $3 \times (-12)$

(b) $16 \div (-4)$

(c) $5 \times (-20)$

(d) $(-36) \div (-6)$

(e) $(-7) \times (-3)$

(f) $48 \div (-12)$

(g) $(-21) \times 4$

(h) $(-100) \div 25$

(i) $(-5) \times (-7)$

(j) $(-56) \div (-7)$

(k) $(-34) \times 2$

(l) $33 \div (-11)$

▲ TYPES OF NUMBER ▼

MULTIPLES

1 × 3 = 3	
2 × 3 = 6	The multiples of 3 are 3, 6, 9, 12, 15, 18,
3 × 3 = 9	21, 24, 27, 30, 33, 36.......
4 × 3 = 12	
5 × 3 = 15	
6 × 3 = 18	... but they don't stop there!
7 × 3 = 21	
8 × 3 = 24	
9 × 3 = 27	The multiples of 3 go on forever.......39, 42, 45, 48, 51, 54..........300,
10 × 3 = 30	303, 306,.......471, 474,....
11 × 3 = 33	
12 × 3 = 36	

Is 874 a multiple of 3?

Calculate 874 ÷ 3 = 291·33333....

As 874 ÷ 3 is not a whole number, 874 is not a multiple of 3.

QUESTIONS 1.8

1. Is 4572 a multiple of 4?

2. Is 6734 a multiple of 6?

3. Is 19024 a multiple of 8?

4. 41211 a multiple of 9?

LOWEST COMMON MULTIPLE (LCM)

What is the Lowest Common Multiple of 6 and 8?

Multiples of 6	Multiples of 8
6	8
12	16
18	24
24	32
30	40
36	48
42	56
48	64

Put a ring round any number which appears in both columns

Multiples of 6	Multiples of 8
6	8
12	16
18	(24)
(24)	32
30	40
36	(48)
42	56
(48)	64

24 is the *smallest* number in both columns, so 24 is the *Lowest* Common Multiple or LCM.

QUESTIONS 1.9

1. Find the Lowest Common Multiple of 14 and 24.

2. Find the Lowest Common Multiple of 12 and 20.

3. Find the Lowest Common Multiple of 18 and 30.

4. Find the Lowest Common Multiple of 9 and 36.

FACTORS

What are the factors of 24?

$1 \times 24 = 24$
$2 \times 12 = 24$ These are the only whole numbers which multiply together to give 24
$3 \times 8 = 24$
$4 \times 6 = 24$ So, the factors of 24 are 1, 2, 3, 4, 6, 8, 12 and 24.

What are the factors of 30?

$1 \times 30 = 30$ These are the only whole numbers which multiply together to give 30
$2 \times 15 = 30$
$3 \times 10 = 30$ The factors of 30 are 1, 2, 3, 5, 6, 10, 15 and 30.
$5 \times 6 = 30$

QUESTIONS 1.10

1. List all the factors of 48.   3. List all the factors of 99.

2. List all the factors of 100.   4. List all the factors of 46.

HIGHEST COMMON FACTOR (HCF)

What is the Highest Common Factor of 24 and 30?

List the factors that we have just found:

Factors of 24	Factors of 30
1	1
2	2
3	3
4	5
6	6
8	10
12	15
24	30

Put a ring round any number which appears in both columns.

Factors of 24	Factors of 30
①	①
②	②
③	③
4	5
⑥	⑥
8	10
12	15
24	30

The number 6 is the *biggest* number in both columns, so 6 is the *Highest* Common Factor or HCF of 24 and 30.

QUESTIONS 1.11

1. Find the Highest Common Factor of 20 and 28.

2. Find the Highest Common Factor of 48 and 50.

3. Find the Highest Common Factor of 36 and 45.

4. Find the Highest Common Factor of 144 and 124.

PRIME NUMBERS

A **prime number** has exactly two factors, 1 and the number itself.

$1 \times 1 = 1$ The number 1 has only one factor, which is 1 itself.
   The number 1 is not a prime number.

$1 \times 2 = 2$ The factors of 2 are 1 and 2.
   So 2 is a prime number.

$1 \times 3 = 3$ The factors of 3 are 1 and 3.
   So 3 is a prime number.

$1 \times 4 = 4$ The factors of 4 are 1, 2 and 4.
$2 \times 2 = 4$ So 4 is not a prime number.

$1 \times 5 = 5$ The factors of 5 are 1 and 5.
   So 5 is a prime number.

$1 \times 6 = 6$ The factors of 6 are 1, 2, 3 and 6
$2 \times 3 = 6$ So 6 is not a prime number.

$1 \times 7 = 7$ The factors of 7 are 1 and 7.
   So 7 is a prime number.

$1 \times 8 = 8$ The factors of 8 are 1, 2, 4 and 8.
$2 \times 4 = 8$ So 8 is not a prime number.

$1 \times 9 = 9$ The factors of 9 are 1, 3 and 9.
$3 \times 3 = 9$ So 9 is not a prime number.

$1 \times 10 = 10$ The factors of 10 are 1, 2, 5 and 10.
$2 \times 5 = 10$ So 10 is not a prime number.

$1 \times 11 = 11$ The factors of 11 are 1 and 11.
   So 11 is a prime number.

$1 \times 12 = 12$ The factors of 12 are 1, 2, 3, 4, 6 and 12.
$2 \times 6 = 12$ So 12 is not a prime number.
$3 \times 4 = 12$

$1 \times 13 = 13$ The factors of 13 are 1 and 13.
   So 13 is a prime number.

$1 \times 14 = 14$ The factors of 14 are 1, 2, 7 and 14.
$2 \times 7 = 14$ So 14 is not a prime number.

So, the first few prime numbers are: 2, 3, 5, 7, 11, 13, ...

Notice that 2 is the only even prime number.

NUMBER

1. Find all the prime numbers between 1 and 100.   3. Is 323 a prime number?

2. Is 143 a prime number?   4. Is 437 a prime number?

WRITING A NUMBER AS A PRODUCT OF PRIME NUMBERS

Write 48 as a product of prime numbers.

The word '**product**' means that we have been asked to find the prime numbers, which **multiply** together to give 48.

You will remember that 2 is the smallest prime number. As 48 is an even number, we can first of all write 48 like this:

$48 = 2 \times 24$

Now 24 is also an even number, so continue the process by writing 24 as 2×12, like this:

$48 = 2 \times 24$
$48 = 2 \times 2 \times 12$

Now 12 is also even, so write 12 as 2×6, like this:

$48 = 2 \times 24$
$48 = 2 \times 2 \times 12$
$48 = 2 \times 2 \times 2 \times 6$

Now 6 is also even, so write 6 as 2×3, like this:

$48 = 2 \times 24$
$48 = 2 \times 2 \times 12$
$48 = 2 \times 2 \times 2 \times 6$
$48 = 2 \times 2 \times 2 \times 2 \times 3$

So, 48 expressed as a product of primes is $48 = 2 \times 2 \times 2 \times 2 \times 3$.

Check that this does multiply together to give 48.

I can also write $48 = 2 \times 2 \times 2 \times 2 \times 3$

as: $48 = 2^4 \times 3$

Look at the section on Index Notation (Powers) for a fuller explanation of this way of writing the final result.

EXAMPLE 2
Express 525 as a product of prime numbers.

This time, 525 is not an even number, so try the next prime number in our list. Does 3 divide into 525 exactly? Yes! $3 \times 175 = 525$.

So, write 525 as: $525 = 3 \times 175$

Does 3 divide exactly into 175? No!
So, try the next prime number in the list.
Does 5 divide exactly into 175?   Yes! $5 \times 35 = 175$.

So, we can continue like this:

$525 = 3 \times 175$

$525 = 3 \times 5 \times 35$

Now, 5 divides exactly into 35, as $5 \times 7 = 35$, so we can complete the expression, like this:

$525 = 3 \times 175$

$525 = 3 \times 5 \times 35$

$525 = 3 \times 5 \times 5 \times 7$

QUESTIONS 1.13

1. Express 50 as a product of prime numbers.

2. Express 52 as a product of prime numbers.

3. Express 60 as a product of prime numbers.

4. Express 858 as a product of prime numbers.

SQUARE NUMBERS

The dots here are all 1 cm apart.

This square has a side of 1 cm.

Its area is therefore $1 \times 1 = 1$ cm^2

This square has a side of 2 cm.

Its area is therefore $2 \times 2 = 4$ cm^2

This square has a side of 3 cm.

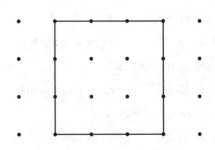

Its area is therefore $3 \times 3 = 9$ cm^2

NUMBER

3×3 is called "3 squared"
We can write 3×3 as 3^2

See the section on Index Notation (Powers) for a fuller explanation of power notation.

$1 \times 1 = 1^2 = 1$
$2 \times 2 = 2^2 = 4$
$3 \times 3 = 3^2 = 9$
$4 \times 4 = 4^2 = 16$
$5 \times 5 = 5^2 = 25$
$6 \times 6 = 6^2 = 36$
$7 \times 7 = 7^2 = 49$
$8 \times 8 = 8^2 = 64$
$9 \times 9 = 9^2 = 81$
$10 \times 10 = 10^2 = 100$

Make sure that you know how your calculator works when finding the square of a number.

So, 1, 4, 9, 16, 25, 36, 49, 64, 81, 100 .... are called **square numbers**.

QUESTIONS 1.14

1. Find the next ten square numbers.

2. Find 23^2

3. Find $6 \cdot 84^2$

4. Find $47 \cdot 4^2$

SQUARE ROOTS

What is the square root of 36?

Trying to find the square root of a number is the same as saying: "If a square has an area of 36, what is the length of the side of the square?"

As $6 \times 6 = 36$ you can see that the square root of 36 must be 6.

It is a square which has a side of length 6 that has an area of 36.

Finding the square root of a number is shown by using the symbol $\sqrt{}$ like this: $\sqrt{36} = 6$

EXAMPLE 2

What is the square root of 40? $\sqrt{40} = ?$

So, this time the square has an area of 40. What is the length of the side of the square?

We already know that: $6 \times 6 = 36$
                and: $7 \times 7 = 49$

So, you can see that this time the length of the square cannot be a whole number. A square of side 6 has an area of 36 and this is too small. A square of side 7 has an area of 49 and this is too big.

Try the length of the side as $6 \cdot 5$:

$6 \cdot 5 \times 6 \cdot 5 = 42 \cdot 25$ ...this is still too big

Try the length of the side as $6 \cdot 4$:

$6 \cdot 4 \times 6 \cdot 4 = 40 \cdot 96$ ...this is still too big

Try the length of the side as $6 \cdot 3$:

$6 \cdot 3 \times 6 \cdot 3 = 39 \cdot 69$ ...this is now too small

Try the length of the side as $6 \cdot 35$:

$6 \cdot 35 \times 6 \cdot 35 = 40 \cdot 3225$ ...this is now slightly too big again.

Try the length of the side as 6·34:

$6 \cdot 34 \times 6 \cdot 34 = 40 \cdot 1956$ ...this is still slightly too big.

Try the length of the side as 6·33:

$6 \cdot 33 \times 6 \cdot 33 = 40 \cdot 0689$ ...this is still slightly too big.

Try the length of the side as 6·32:

$6 \cdot 32 \times 6 \cdot 32 = 39 \cdot 9424$ ...this is now slightly too small.

Try the length of the side as 6·325:

$6 \cdot 325 \times 6 \cdot 325 = 40 \cdot 005625$ ...this is now very close to 40!

So, the square root of 40 is about 6·325.

So, $\sqrt{40} \approx 6 \cdot 325$ The symbol '≈' means 'approximately equal to'.

This method of working towards an answer is called a **trial and improvement** method.

Fortunately, if we need to know a square root, we do not have to go through this lengthy process each time. Your calculator has a 'square root button'. Find the square root symbol on your calculator. Type in 40 and press the square root button.

On my calculator it shows that: $\sqrt{40} \approx 6 \cdot 32455532$

This is all the decimal places that my calculator can show. I still need the '≈' symbol, because even with this many decimal places it is still not an exact answer. In fact, there never will be an exact answer, no matter how many decimal places you have!

QUESTIONS 1.15

1. Find $\sqrt{529}$ 3. Find $\sqrt{200}$ 5. Find $\sqrt{10}$ 7. Find $\sqrt{1000}$

2. Find $\sqrt{961}$ 4. Find $\sqrt{729}$ 6. Find $\sqrt{100}$ 8. Find $\sqrt{10\ 000}$

CUBE NUMBERS

This is a cube with the length of all its sides equal to 1 cm.

The volume of this cube is found from:

$1 \text{ cm} \times 1 \text{ cm} \times 1 \text{ cm} = 1 \text{ cm}^3$

$1 \times 1 \times 1 = 1^3$ ... called "1 cubed" [see the section on Powers and Indices]

This is a cube with the length of all its sides equal to 2 cm.

The volume of this cube is found from:

$2 \times 2 \times 2 = 2^3 = 8 \text{ cm}^3$

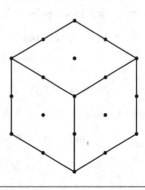

This is a cube with the length of all its sides
equal to 3 cm.

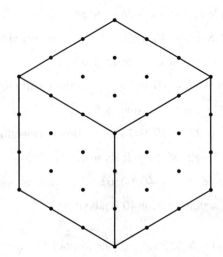

The volume of this cube is found from:
$3 \times 3 \times 3 = 3^3 = 27 \text{ cm}^3$

Continue the list of cube numbers, like this:

$1 \times 1 \times 1 = 1^3 = 1$
$2 \times 2 \times 2 = 2^3 = 8$
$3 \times 3 \times 3 = 3^3 = 27$
$4 \times 4 \times 4 = 4^3 = 64$
$5 \times 5 \times 5 = 5^3 = 125$
$6 \times 6 \times 6 = 6^3 = 216$
$7 \times 7 \times 7 = 7^3 = 343$
$8 \times 8 \times 8 = 8^3 = 512$
$9 \times 9 \times 9 = 9^3 = 729$
$10 \times 10 \times 10 = 10^3 = 1000$

Make sure that you know
how your calculator works
when finding the cube of
a number.

So, 1, 8, 27, 64, 125, 216, 343, 512, 729, 1000 .... are called **cube numbers.**

QUESTIONS 1.16

1. Find the next ten cube numbers.

2. Find $3 \cdot 7^3$

3. Find $6 \cdot 42^3$

4. Find $23 \cdot 8^3$

CUBE ROOTS

What is the cube root of 64?

Trying to find the cube root of a number is the same as saying: "If a cube has a volume of 64, what
is the length of the sides of the cube?"

As $4 \times 4 \times 4 = 64$ you can see that the cube root of 64 must be 4.

It is a cube which has a side of length 4 that has a volume of 64.

Finding the cube root of a number is shown by using the symbol $\sqrt[3]{}$ like this: $\sqrt[3]{64} = 4$

EXAMPLE 2

What is the cube root of 50? $\sqrt[3]{50} = ?$

We already know that: $3 \times 3 \times 3 = 27$

                and: $4 \times 4 \times 4 = 64$

So, $\sqrt[3]{27} = 3$ So, $\sqrt[3]{50}$ must be "3 and a bit".

and $\sqrt[3]{64} = 4$

Fortunately, we do not have to do another trial and improvement method. My calculator has a 'cube root button'. If I type in 50 and press the cube root button, my calculator gives the answer

as: $\sqrt[3]{50} \approx 3.684031499$ So, $\sqrt[3]{50} = 3.68$ (to 2 decimal places)

Make sure you know how your own calculator works when finding the cube root of a number.

QUESTIONS 1.17

1. Find $\sqrt[3]{9261}$ 3. Find $\sqrt[3]{10}$ 5. Find $\sqrt[3]{1000}$ 7. Find $\sqrt[3]{100\ 000}$

2. Find $\sqrt[3]{20}$ 4. Find $\sqrt[3]{100}$ 6. Find $\sqrt[3]{10\ 000}$ 8. Find $\sqrt[3]{1\ 000\ 000}$

TRIANGLE NUMBERS

Triangle numbers are formed by putting stars into triangular formations. Here are the first eight triangle patterns:

Pattern number 1:

1 star

Pattern number 2:

3 stars

Pattern number 3:

6 stars

Pattern number 4:

10 stars

Pattern number 5:

15 stars

Pattern number 6:

21 stars

Pattern number 7:

28 stars

Pattern number 8:

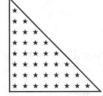

36 stars

So, 1, 3, 6, 10, 15, 21, 28, 36, ... are called **triangle numbers**.

QUESTIONS 1.18

1. Continue the pattern and find the first 20 triangle numbers.

2. Fill your answers into a table like this:

Pattern Number	Numbers of Stars
1	1
2	3
3	6
4	10
5	15
6	21
7	28
8	36
N	S

Add in a difference column, and a second difference column.

Try to find an equation, starting S = , which relates S to N.

Look at the section called Growing Patterns 2 for some help here.

▲ UNDERSTANDING DECIMALS ▼

PLACE VALUE

It is a good idea to remind yourself of the column headings for whole numbers, which look like this:

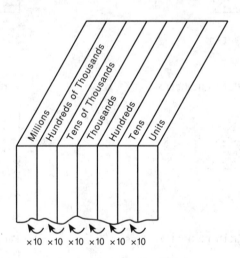

Remember, as you move to the left, each column heading is ten times bigger than the column next to it.

Therefore, as you move to the right, each column heading is ten times smaller than the column next to it!

So, if you take the column heading 'thousands' and divide by 10 you get the next column heading on the right, which is 'hundreds'.

So, if you take the column heading 'hundreds' and divide by 10 you get the next column heading on the right, which is 'tens'.

So, if you take the column heading 'tens' and divide by 10 you get the next column heading on the right, which is 'units' – which comes from the Latin word for one!

Now continue this process. Take 'one' and divide it by 10 and this will give you one ten**th**. Notice the 'th' on the end of the word, to denote that we are not dealing with whole numbers any more, but with parts of a whole number.

So, the next column heading to the right after 'units' is called 'tenths'.

'One tenth' can be written as $\frac{1}{10}$ using fraction notation.

'One tenth' can be written as **0·1** using decimal notation.

We use a decimal point to separate the whole numbers from the parts of numbers. The column headings to the right of the decimal point must continue the pattern of being ten times smaller each time you move to the right.

$$H \quad T \quad U \cdot \frac{1}{10} \quad \frac{1}{100} \quad \frac{1}{1000}$$

So, the column headings go Hundreds, Tens, Units, Ten**ths**, Hundred**ths**, Thousand**ths** ...... and so on .....

THE NUMBER LINE

On a number line, I can represent whole numbers easily enough, like this:

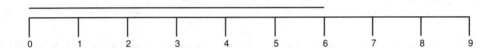

The length of this line will represent 6 units.

What number will the length of this line represent?

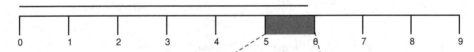

We can see that the length of the line must be more than 5, but less than 6 units.

Or, using symbols: 5 < length < 6

To find the length of this line, we need to zoom in on the number line, to get a closer look. We need to sub-divide the interval between 5 and 6 into tenths, like this:

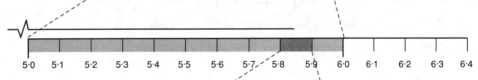

We can see that the length of the line must be more than 5·8, but less than 5·9 units.

Or, using symbols: 5·8 < length < 5·9

If we zoom in once more, taking an even closer look at the number line, we will get an even more accurate answer for the length of the line. We need to sub-divide the interval between 5·8 and 5·9 into hundredths, like this:

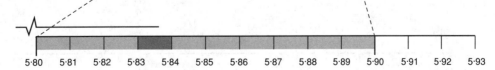

We can see that the length of the line must be more than 5·83, but less than 5·84 units.

Or, using symbols: 5·83 < length < 5·84

This is how decimals work! The more you zoom in, the more decimal places you have. We could, in theory, repeat this process over and over again.

If we zoom in once more, by sub-dividing the region between 5·83 and 5·84 into thousandths, the diagram will look like this:

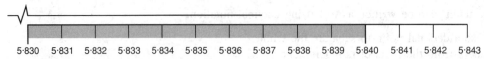

| 5·830 | 5·831 | 5·832 | 5·833 | 5·834 | 5·835 | 5·836 | 5·837 | 5·838 | 5·839 | 5·840 | 5·841 | 5·842 | 5·843 |

We can see that the length of the line is 5·837 units.

Put these numbers under the correct column headings and they look like this:

H	T	U	.	$\frac{1}{10}$	$\frac{1}{100}$	$\frac{1}{1000}$
		5	.	8		
		5	.	8	3	
		5	.	8	3	7

The longer the decimal, the more accurate we are claiming to be.

QUESTIONS 1.19

1. Use a number line to draw in an arrow to show the correct position for each number A and B, in each of these examples. Say which is bigger, A or B.

(a)   A = 7·23
      B = 7·4

(b)   A = 3·4
      B = 3·37

(c)   A = 0·77
      B = 0·8

(d)   A = 4·12
      B = 4·2

2.(a) Write down a number which is bigger than 2·8 but smaller than 2·9

(b) Write down a number which is bigger than 4·5 but smaller than 4·6

(c) Write down a number which is bigger than 1·9 but smaller than 2·0

(d) Write down a number which is bigger than 0·3 but smaller than 0·4

(e) Write down a number which is bigger than 8·87 but smaller than 8·88

(f) Write down a number which is bigger than 0·125 but smaller than 0·126

3. Read off these scales, giving the number indicated by each arrow:

(a)

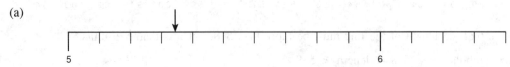

(b)

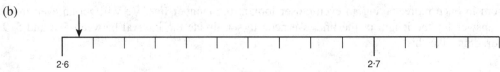

(c)

(d)

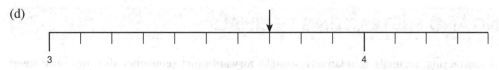

3   4

(e)

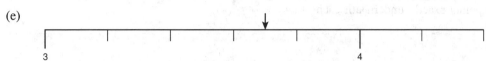

3   4

(f)

6   7

4. (a) Say which is bigger, 0·75 or 0·8

(b) Say which is bigger, 3·5 or 0·87

(c) Say which is bigger, 0·32 or 0·215

(d) Say which is biggest, 0·9 or 0·354 or 0·48

(e) Say which is biggest, 15·9 or 0·967 or 8·248

(f) Say which is bigger, 0·74 or 0·740

(g) Say which is bigger, 0·054 or 0·54

(h) Say which is bigger, 0·023 or 0·2

(i) Say which is biggest, 6·248 or 6·4 or 6·61

(j) Say which is biggest, 11·91 or 12·09 or 12·2

(k) Say which is biggest, 2·95 or 2·9 or 2·85 or 2·88

5. How many different decimals are there between 0·4 and 0·5?

6. How many different decimals are there between 0·43 and 0·44?

7. How many different decimals are there between 0·437 and 0·438?

8. How many different decimals are there between 0·4371 and 0·4372?

9. Write in words how you would say these decimals: (a) 53·68 (b) 0·521

10. Don't use a calculator!

(a) Add 0·1 to 7·9   (d) Take away 0·1 from 8·0

(b) Add 0·1 to 3·97   (e) Take away 0·1 from 12·05

(c) Add 0·01 to 6·39

Now check your answers with a calculator.

11. Fill in the blanks in these sequences;

(a) 0, 0·2, 0·4, 0·6, _____, _____, _____, _____ (adding on 0·2's)

(b) 0·15, 0·30, 0·45, 0·60, _____, _____, _____, _____, _____ (adding on 0·15's)

(c) 4·16, 4·15, 4·14, 4·13, 4·12, _____, _____, _____, _____, _____ (subtracting 0·01's)

12. Say which is the bigger number in each pair, or say "the same".

(a) 54 and 54·0   (d) 0·54 and 0·054

(b) 54 and 054   (e) 0·54 and ·54

(c) 0·54 and 0·540   (f) 54 and 54·000

NUMBER

ADDING AND SUBTRACTING DECIMALS

Adding and subtracting decimals is relatively straight forward! Just remember that you must keep the decimal points exactly underneath each other.

EXAMPLE I
Add $14\cdot94 + 3\cdot735$

T	U	.	$\frac{1}{10}$	$\frac{1}{100}$	$\frac{1}{1000}$	
1	4	.	9	4		
	3	.	7	3	5	+
1	8	.	6	7	5	

If you prefer, you can put a zero into the thousandths column, to make:

T	U	.	$\frac{1}{10}$	$\frac{1}{100}$	$\frac{1}{1000}$	
1	4	.	9	4	0	
	3	.	7	3	5	+
1	8	.	6	7	5	

EXAMPLE 2
Subtract $23\cdot72$ from $56\cdot53$

Set the calculation out as follows:

T	U	.	$\frac{1}{10}$	$\frac{1}{100}$	
5	6	.	5	3	
2	3	.	7	2	−

Now, subtracting from the right, 3 subtract 2 is 1.

Then you come to 5 subtract 7 which cannot be evaluated directly. Use the same method as we did under subtraction when using whole numbers! Take one of the units and write it as ten tenths.

So, the calculation now looks like this:

T	U	.	$\frac{1}{10}$	$\frac{1}{100}$	
5	5	.	10+5	3	
2	3	.	7	2	−
				1	

Now, 15 subtract 7 is 8, and we can complete the calculation, like this:

T	U	.	$\frac{1}{10}$	$\frac{1}{100}$	
5	5	.	10+5	3	
2	3	.	7	2	−
3	2	.	8	1	

EXAMPLE 3

48·7 subtract 23·508

Set out the calculation as before, with the decimal points directly under each other.

T	U	.	$\frac{1}{10}$	$\frac{1}{100}$	$\frac{1}{1000}$	
4	8	.	7			
2	3	.	5	0	8	−

It will help to avoid mistakes to write 48·7 as 48·700 (these represent the **same** number as the zeros stand for no hundredths and no thousandths!)

So, the calculation looks like this:

T	U	.	$\frac{1}{10}$	$\frac{1}{100}$	$\frac{1}{1000}$	
4	8	.	7	0	0	
2	3	.	5	0	8	−

Now, 0 subtract 8 we cannot evaluate directly. This time we must go back as far as the tenths column! Take one of the tenths, and split this into ten lots of hundredths, like this:

T	U	.	$\frac{1}{10}$	$\frac{1}{100}$	$\frac{1}{1000}$	
4	8	.	6	10+0	0	
2	3	.	5	0	8	−

We need to go through this process again. Take one of the hundredths and split it into ten lots of thousandths. The calculation now looks like this:

T	U	.	$\frac{1}{10}$	$\frac{1}{100}$	$\frac{1}{1000}$	
4	8	.	6	9	10+0	
2	3	.	5	0	8	−

Now complete the calculation, like this:

T	U	.	$\frac{1}{10}$	$\frac{1}{100}$	$\frac{1}{1000}$	
4	8	.	6	9	10+0	
2	3	.	5	0	8	−
2	5	.	1	9	2	

QUESTIONS 1.20

Do not use a calculator! Evaluate the following:

1. 32·78 + 54·06

2. 569·04 − 45·6

3. 32·89 + 2·88 + 0·34

4. 7·04 − 3·89

5. 65·3 + 8·56 + 0·003

6. 5·29 − 0·678

7. 44·6 + 12·9 + 2·009

8. 9·72 − 7·000007

9. 200 + 70 + 3 + 0·1 + 0·07 + 0·003

10. 7000 + 40 + 2 + 0·05 + 0·008

NUMBER

11. My ruler was 30 cm long, until I broke it in two pieces! One piece is 12·7 cm long. What is the length of the other piece?

12. My friend tries to break the 12·7 cm piece of ruler into two equal pieces. What length would they be?

13. A story to go with 13 + 7 = 20 could be: "I had 13 felt tip pens. I went shopping and bought 7 more felt tip pens. Now I have 20 pens." Write a suitable story for 3·7 + 8·2

14. Write a suitable story for 29·7 − 18·5

15. Write a suitable story for 30·6 − 19·8

MULTIPLYING DECIMALS

Find the area of these rectangles. Remember that the area of a rectangle = width × length

Area = 3 cm × 4 cm
Area = 12 cm^2

Area = 3 cm × 3 cm
Area = 9 cm^2

Area = 3 cm × 2 cm
Area = 6 cm^2

Area = 3 cm × 1 cm
Area = 3 cm^2

Area = 3 cm × 0·5 cm
Area = 1·5 cm^2

CAUTION!

Many people (adults as well as children!) believe, wrongly, that: "Multiplication always makes things bigger".
But we can see from the last rectangle, that multiplication doesn't always make things bigger!

We have multiplied 3 by 0·5 and the answer is 1·5

$$3 \times 0·5 = 1·5$$

Try these calculations (use your calculator) to multiply one number by another number less than a whole one:

$73 \times 0{\cdot}3$	$678 \times 0{\cdot}42$
$56 \times 0{\cdot}25$	$83{\cdot}65 \times 0{\cdot}7$
$4 \times 0{\cdot}7$	$66{\cdot}9 \times 0{\cdot}004$
$23 \times 0{\cdot}01$	$5{\cdot}8 \times 0{\cdot}09$

You will see from your answers to all of the above calculations that:

> Multiplying by numbers less than 1, makes things smaller.

MULTIPLICATION IS COMMUTATIVE

```
                              *   *   *
*   *   *   *   *             *   *   *
*   *   *   *   *             *   *   *
*   *   *   *   *             *   *   *
                              *   *   *
```

3 lots of 5   5 lots of 3

3 lots of 5 is the same as   5 lots of 3

3×5 $=$ $5 \times 3 = 15$

With multiplication, it does not make any difference to the answer which way round you write the numbers. To describe this, we say that multiplication is **commutative**.

So, for our rectangle:

Area = 3 cm $\times$ 0·5 cm
Area = 1·5 cm^2

So: $3 \times 0{\cdot}5 = 0{\cdot}5 \times 3 = 1{\cdot}5$

Or, in fractions: $3 \times \frac{1}{2} = \frac{1}{2} \times 3 = 1{\cdot}5$

We could think of: $3 \times 0{\cdot}5$

as $3 \times \frac{1}{2}$

or as: 3 lots of a half = one and a half

We could think of: $0{\cdot}5 \times 3$

as: $\frac{1}{2} \times 3$

or as: a half of three = one and a half

The final answer is the same as before. Choose the way which makes most sense to you!

QUESTIONS 1.21

1. Work out the areas of these rectangles without using your calculator.

(a)
8 cm
0·5 cm

(b) 0.25 cm
8 cm

(c)
8 cm
1·5 cm

(d)
0·75 cm
4 cm

Check your answers with your calculator. Did you get the same by both methods? If you made any mistakes, can you see why?

2. Find the areas of these rectangles, using your calculator:

(a)
12 cm
4 cm

(b)
1·2 cm
4 cm

(c)
26 cm
2 cm

(d)
2·6 cm
2 cm

(e)
32 cm
8 cm

(f)
3·2 cm
8 cm

(g)
25 cm
12 cm

(h)
2·5 cm
1·2 cm

(i)
38 cm
24 cm

(j)
3·8 cm
2·4 cm

MULTIPLYING DECIMALS: DECIDING WHERE TO PUT THE DECIMAL POINT!

Look carefully at your answers to question 2 (Questions 1.21). You should have found out that:

(a) $4 \times 12 = 48$

(b) $4 \times 1 \cdot 2 = 4 \cdot 8$

(c) $2 \times 26 = 52$

(d) $2 \times 2 \cdot 6 = 5 \cdot 2$

(e) $8 \times 32 = 256$

(f) $8 \times 3 \cdot 2 = 25 \cdot 6$

(g) $12 \times 25 = 300$

(h) $1 \cdot 2 \times 2 \cdot 5 = 3 \cdot 00$

(i) $24 \times 38 = 912$

(j) $2 \cdot 4 \times 3 \cdot 8 = 9 \cdot 12$

What do you notice? You can see that the answers are in pairs. Both calculations contain the same numbers. The only difference is the position of the decimal points!

Once we know that: $\qquad 24 \times 38 = 912$

then: $\qquad 2 \cdot 4 \times 3 \cdot 8$ must equal $9 \cdot 12$

because $\qquad 2 \cdot 4$ is a bit more than 2

and $\qquad 3 \cdot 8$ is a bit less than 4

So, the final answer must be about 2×4 which is 8, so the decimal point must go after the nine. Putting the decimal point anywhere else doesn't make sense.

The answer to $2 \cdot 4 \times 3 \cdot 8$ could not possibly be: $\qquad 0 \cdot 912$

or: $\qquad 91 \cdot 2$

or: $\qquad 912$

Checking that your answer makes sense in this way is very useful! Try to develop the habit of checking all your answers in Maths, to see that they do actually make sense!

QUESTIONS 1.22

Use the above ideas of estimation and approximation to choose the correct answer for these calculations:

1. Select the correct answer to $6 \cdot 8 \times 2 \cdot 1$
from:
   (a) $0 \cdot 1428$
   (b) $1 \cdot 428$
   (c) $14 \cdot 28$
   (d) $142 \cdot 8$
   (e) 1428

2. Select the correct answer to $13 \times 7 \cdot 7$
from:
   (a) $0 \cdot 1001$
   (b) $1 \cdot 001$
   (c) $10 \cdot 01$
   (d) $100 \cdot 1$
   (e) 1001

3. Select the correct answer to $4 \cdot 6 \times 0 \cdot 8$
from:
   (a) 368
   (b) $36 \cdot 8$
   (c) $3 \cdot 68$
   (d) $0 \cdot 368$

4. Select the correct answer to $0 \cdot 9 \times 0 \cdot 8$
from:
   (a) 720
   (b) 72
   (c) $7 \cdot 2$
   (d) $0 \cdot 72$
   (e) 0.072

Do not use a calculator for questions 5 to 10!

Read the section on long multiplication of whole numbers, if you need a reminder.

5. Multiply 75 by 23. Use your answer to find $7 \cdot 5 \times 2 \cdot 3$

6. Multiply 237 by 91. Use your answer to find $23 \cdot 7 \times 9 \cdot 1$

7. Multiply 735 by 28. Use your answer to find $7 \cdot 35 \times 2 \cdot 8$

8. Multiply 882 by 47. Use your answer to find $8 \cdot 82 \times 4 \cdot 7$

NUMBER

9. Multiply 428 by 35. Use your answer to find $4 \cdot 28 \times 0 \cdot 35$

10. Multiply 297 by 67. Use your answer to find $0 \cdot 297 \times 0 \cdot 67$

MULTIPYING BY 10, 100, 1000 ....

Use your calculator to find answers to these questions:

2×10	$2 \cdot 7 \times 10$
$7 \cdot 1 \times 10$	$0 \cdot 5 \times 10$
$0 \cdot 72 \times 10$	45×10
$0 \cdot 0007 \times 10$	$3 \cdot 0003 \times 10$
$78 \cdot 34 \times 10$	$0 \cdot 624 \times 10$

3×100	$4 \cdot 8723 \times 100$
$4 \cdot 2 \times 100$	$0 \cdot 5 \times 100$
$0 \cdot 6 \times 100$	0.25×100
$20 \cdot 003 \times 100$	308×100
$0 \cdot 00045 \times 100$	23×100

4×1000	$9 \cdot 432 \times 1000$
$4 \cdot 7 \times 1000$	65×1000
$0 \cdot 965 \times 1000$	$3 \cdot 025 \times 1000$
$0 \cdot 0125 \times 1000$	38.56×1000
$5 \cdot 002 \times 1000$	$0 \cdot 125 \times 1000$

How would you describe to someone else the effect of multiplying by 10, 100 and 1000?

CAUTION!

> Many people say, "When you multiply by 10, you add a nought".

You can see from the answers to the above calculations that this isn't a useful rule to apply when you are dealing with decimals.

Look again at the column headings for our number system. (Go back and re-read the section on Place Value, if you need a reminder!)

$$H \quad T \quad U \quad \cdot \quad \tfrac{1}{10} \quad \tfrac{1}{100}$$

$$\begin{array}{ccccc} & 2 & 3 & \cdot & 7 & 1 \\ 2 & 3 & 7 & \cdot & 1 \end{array}$$

When multiplying by 10, you can see that each number must, in effect, move one column to the left.

Two tens, multiplied by ten, becomes 2 hundreds.
Three units, multiplied by ten, becomes 3 tens.
Seven tenths, multiplied by ten, becomes 7 units.
One hundredth, multiplied by ten, becomes 1 tenth.

Write a similar description for what happens when you multiply by 100 and 1000.

DIVIDING DECIMALS

The area of each of these rectangles is 24 cm². Find the length of the marked side.

1.
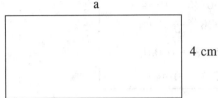

a

4 cm

2.

b

3 cm

3.
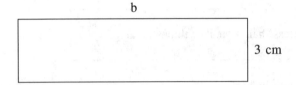

c

2 cm

4.

d

1 cm

5.

e

0·5 cm

Since   Area = Length × Width

          Width = Area ÷ Length

(Read the section on changing the subject of the formula, if you need a reminder here!).

So, you could have calculated the length of the missing side like this, for each example:

Width = Area ÷ Length

    a = 24 ÷ 4 = 6

    b = 24 ÷ 3 = 8

    c = 24 ÷ 2 = 12

    d = 24 ÷ 1 = 24

    e = 24 ÷ 0·5 = 48

CAUTION!

Many pupils (and adults!) wrongly believe, "Division always makes things smaller".

The last example shows that this is not the case!

Use your calculator to evaluate these divisions, where we are dividing one number by other number which is less than one.

$44 \div 0 \cdot 5$	$56 \cdot 36 \div 0 \cdot 34$
$67 \div 0 \cdot 2$	$2 \cdot 9 \div 0 \cdot 8$
$54 \div 0 \cdot 45$	$53 \cdot 8 \div 0 \cdot 001$
$68 \div 0 \cdot 01$	$7 \cdot 3 \div 0 \cdot 44$

You will see from your answers to all of the above calculations that:

> Dividing by numbers less than 1, makes things bigger.

We could read $24 \div 0 \cdot 5$ as "24 divided into halves"

Or, "How many halves are there in 24?"

24 Swiss Rolls cut into halves would give us 48 pieces of cake.

DIVISION IS NOT COMMUTATIVE

A rectangle has area 24 cm² and length 48 cm. To find the width of the rectangle, many pupils would automatically divide 48 by 24, like this:

$$48 \div 24 = 2$$

They believe, wrongly, that you can only ever divide one number by a smaller number.

The answer will be found by applying the formula which we had earlier:

> Width = Area ÷ Length

So,   Width = $24 \div 48 = 0 \cdot 5$

You must therefore be very careful about how you divide! With division, it does make a difference which way round you have the two numbers! So, division is **NOT** commutative.

QUESTIONS 1.23

1. Work out the missing lengths in these rectangles without using your calculator.

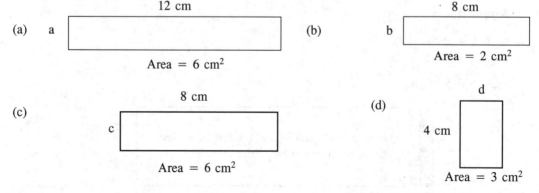

Check your answers with your calculator. Did you get the same by both methods? If you made any mistakes, can you see why?

2. Find the missing lengths of the sides in these rectangles, using your calculator.

Use Width = Area ÷ Length.

(a)

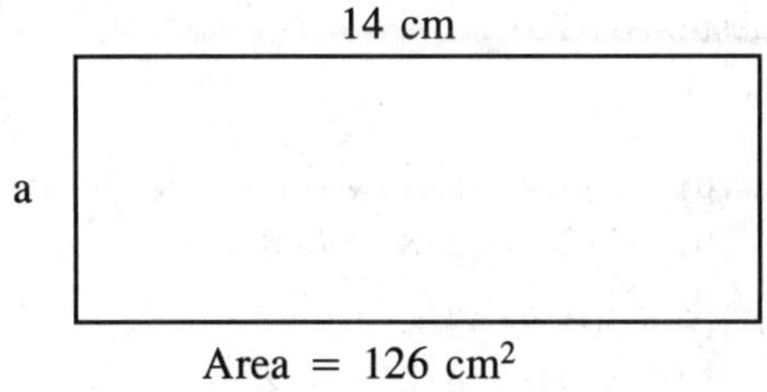

14 cm

a

Area = 126 cm^2

(b)

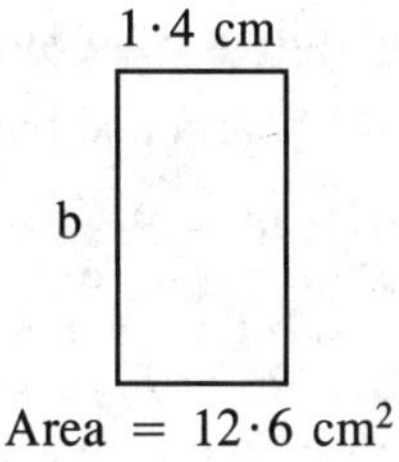

1·4 cm

b

Area = 12·6 cm^2

(c)

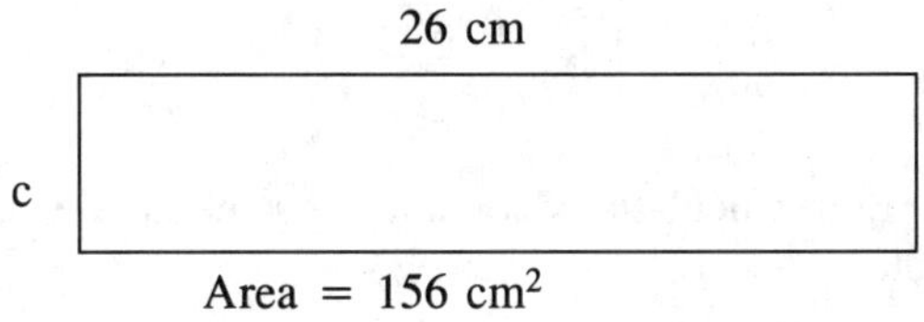

26 cm

c

Area = 156 cm^2

(d)

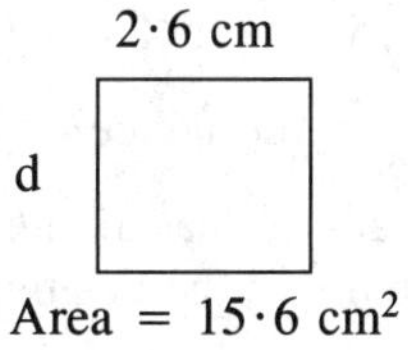

2·6 cm

d

Area = 15·6 cm^2

(e)

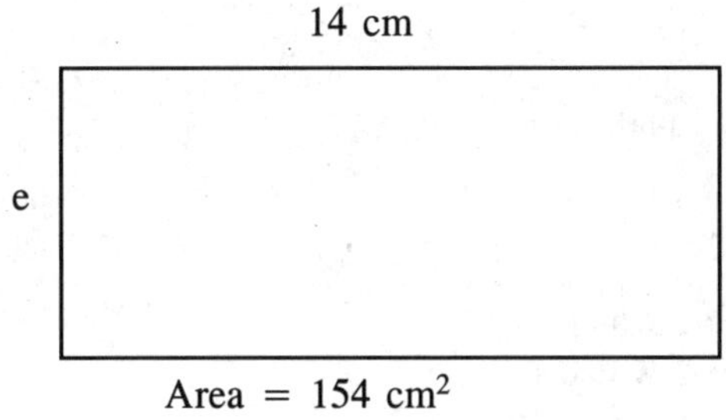

14 cm

e

Area = 154 cm^2

(f)

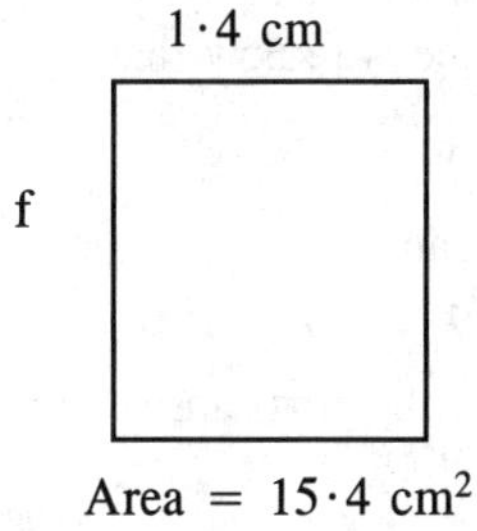

1·4 cm

f

Area = 15·4 cm^2

(g)

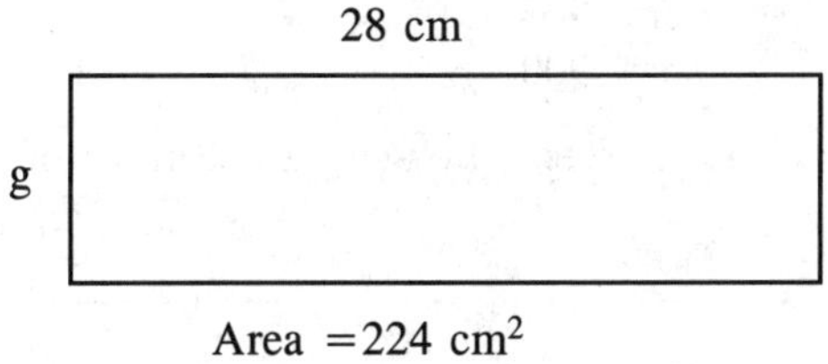

28 cm

g

Area = 224 cm^2

(h)

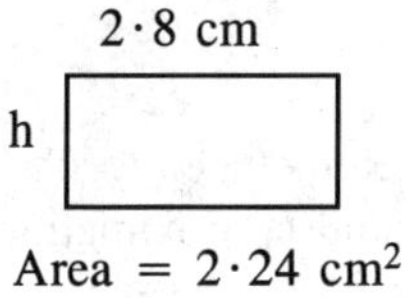

2·8 cm

h

Area = 2·24 cm^2

(i)

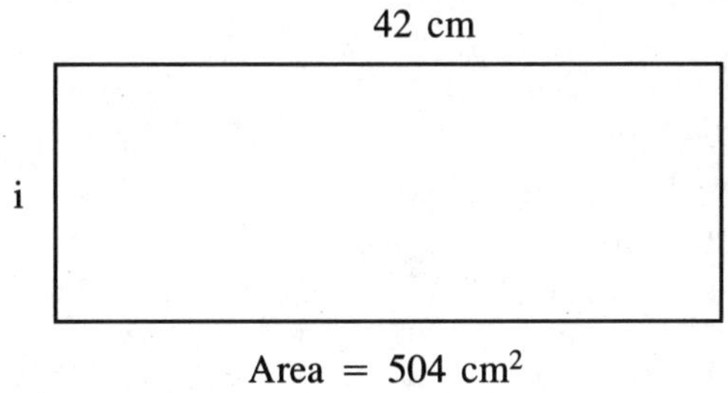

42 cm

i

Area = 504 cm^2

(j)

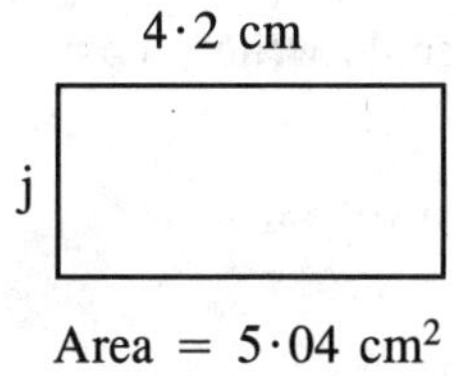

4·2 cm

j

Area = 5·04 cm^2

(k)

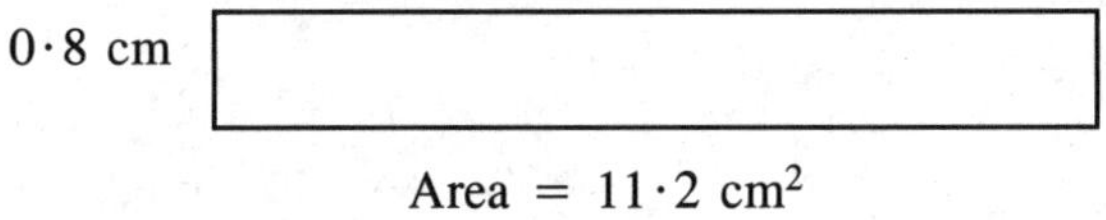

0·8 cm

k

Area = 11·2 cm^2

(l)

0·8 cm

l

Area = 1·12 cm^2

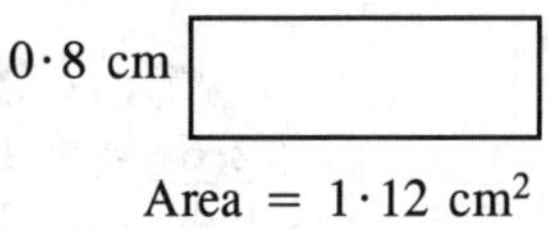

DIVIDING DECIMALS: DECIDING WHERE TO PUT THE DECIMAL POINT!

Look carefully at your answers to question 2 (Questions 1.23).

You should have found out that:

(a) $126 \div 14 = 9$
(b) $12 \cdot 6 \div 1 \cdot 4 = 9$

(c) $156 \div 26 = 6$
(d) $15 \cdot 6 \div 2 \cdot 6 = 6$

(e) $154 \div 14 = 11$
(f) $15 \cdot 4 \div 1 \cdot 4 = 11$

(g) $224 \div 28 = 8$
(h) $2 \cdot 24 \div 2 \cdot 8 = 0 \cdot 8$

(i) $504 \div 42 = 12$
(j) $5 \cdot 04 \div 4 \cdot 2 = 1 \cdot 2$

(k) $11 \cdot 2 \div 0 \cdot 8 = 14$
(l) $1 \cdot 12 \div 0 \cdot 8 = 1 \cdot 4$

What do you notice?

You can see that the numbers come in pairs. Both calculations contain the same numbers; the only difference is the position of the decimal point.

EXAMPLE I
Once we know that: $126 \div 14 = 9$

then: $12 \cdot 6 \div 1 \cdot 4$ must also equal 9

because $12 \cdot 6$ is a bit more than 12
and $1 \cdot 4$ is between 1 and 2

So, the final answer must be between: $12 \div 1$ which is 12
                                                                  and: $12 \div 2$ which is 6.

The final answer to $12 \cdot 6 \div 1 \cdot 4$ could not possibly be: $0 \cdot 9$
                                                                                                       or: 90
                                                                                                       or: 900

Remember to check that your answers do actually make sense, by using these ideas of estimation and approximation.

EXAMPLE I AGAIN
We already know that:

            (a) $126 \div 14 = 9$
and   (b) $12 \cdot 6 \div 1 \cdot 4 = 9$

I could write (a) as: $126 \div 14 = \dfrac{126}{14} = 9$

and (b) as: $12 \cdot 6 \div 1 \cdot 4 = \dfrac{12 \cdot 6}{1 \cdot 4} = 9$

So, $\dfrac{12 \cdot 6}{1 \cdot 4} = \dfrac{126}{14} = 9$

You can see that $12 \cdot 6 \times 10 = 126$ and $1 \cdot 4 \times 10 = 14$

$$\overset{\times 10}{\underset{\times 10}{\dfrac{12 \cdot 6}{1 \cdot 4}}} = \dfrac{126}{14} = 9$$

So, moving from left to right, the top line is ten times bigger, and so is the bottom line. Multiplying the top and the bottom by the same number gives you the same final answer!

Try some easier numbers here to get the feel for what is happening!

If you had 6 sweets to divide between 2 friends, they would get 3 each. If you had 10 times more sweets that would be 60 sweets. If you had ten times more friends, that would be 20 friends. But 60 sweets divided between 20 friends still gives 3 sweets each!

EXAMPLE 2

I can use these ideas to do decimal division without a calculator, like this:

Calculate $67 \cdot 2 \div 1 \cdot 2$

I am not at all keen on dividing by $1 \cdot 2$, so I am going to re-write the calculation like this:

$$67 \cdot 2 \div 1 \cdot 2 = \frac{67 \cdot 2}{1 \cdot 2} \overset{\times 10}{\underset{\times 10}{=}} \frac{672}{12}$$

Now, I can divide by 12, which I am much happier with. I can use long division to calculate $672 \div 12$ as 56, so, the answer to the original question is also 56.

So, $67 \cdot 2 \div 1 \cdot 2 = 56$

Check this makes sense by using the ideas of estimation and approximation that we have used already.

$67 \cdot 2$ is a bit less than 70

$1 \cdot 2$ is between 1 and 2

So, the final answer must be between: $70 \div 1 = 70$

and: $70 \div 2 = 35$

So, an answer of 56 looks to be the right sort of size.

EXAMPLE 3

Evaluate $23 \cdot 98 \div 2 \cdot 6$ without using a calculator.

Again, I am not keen on dividing by $2 \cdot 6$, so I am going to re-write the calculation like this:

$$23 \cdot 98 \div 2 \cdot 6 = \frac{23 \cdot 98}{2 \cdot 6} \overset{\times 10}{\underset{\times 10}{=}} \frac{239 \cdot 8}{26}$$

Now, I can divide by 26, which I am happier with, but there is still a decimal point in the top line. Don't worry! Set out the long division as before, but keep the decimal point in the calculation, like this:

```
              9 · 2 2 3
     26 ) 2 3 9 · 8 0 0 0
          2 3 4
            5   8
            5   2
                6 0
                5 2
                  8 0
                  7 8
                    2
```

This time you can see that the answer doesn't turn out to be nice and convenient. You can keep adding zeros as many times as you like, so the answer can have as many decimal places as you want. In a situation like this, the question might ask you to give your answer correct to 2 decimal places or to 3 decimal places.

So, the answer would be:

$$23 \cdot 98 \div 2 \cdot 6 = 9 \cdot 22 \text{ (to 2 dec pl)}$$

or: $\quad 23 \cdot 98 \div 2 \cdot 6 = 9 \cdot 223 \text{ (to 3 dec pl)}$

(See also the section on Decimal Places and Significant Figures.)

Check that the answer is about the right size: $\qquad$ 23·98 is a bit less than 24

$\qquad\qquad\qquad\qquad\qquad\qquad\qquad\qquad$ 2·6 is between 2 and 3

So, the final answer must be between: $\qquad$ $24 \div 2 = 12$

$\qquad\qquad\qquad\qquad\qquad$ and: $\qquad$ $24 \div 3 = 8$

So, an answer of 9·223 looks about the right size.

EXAMPLE 4

Evaluate $2 \cdot 0789 \div 0 \cdot 006$

Again, I am going to re-write the calculation, multiplying top and bottom by 1000, like this:

$$2 \cdot 0789 \div 0 \cdot 006 = \frac{2 \cdot 0789}{0 \cdot 006} = \frac{2078 \cdot 9}{6}$$

(with ×1000 applied to top and bottom)

```
           3 4 6 · 4 8 3
      6 ) 2 0 7 8 · 9 0 0 0
           1 8
           2 7
           2 4
             3 8
             3 6
               2 9
               2 4
                 5 0
                 4 8
                   2 0
                   1 8
                     2 0
```

You can see that you can multiply the top and the bottom by 10, or by 100, or by 1000 and so on! Whatever makes the calculation easier, provided of course that you multiply top and bottom by the **same** number.

Set out the long division, as before:

Again, the answer isn't working out to be an exact number. You can see that the '3' is going to keep coming up again and again and again. This is called a recurring decimal. We could write it as:

$2 \cdot 0789 \div 0 \cdot 006 = 346 \cdot 48\dot{3}$ $\qquad$ where the dot over the three indicates that the threes go on forever!

So, the answer would be:

$$2 \cdot 0789 \div 0 \cdot 006 = 346 \cdot 5 \text{ (to 1 dec pl)}$$

or: $\quad 2 \cdot 0789 \div 0 \cdot 006 = 346 \cdot 48 \text{ (to 2 dec pl)}$

or: $\quad 2 \cdot 0789 \div 0 \cdot 006 = 346 \cdot 483 \text{ (to 3 dec pl)}$

Go back to the original question: $2 \cdot 0789 \div 0 \cdot 006$

We have a bit more than 2 divided into quite small pieces. It is not surprising that there are quite a lot of them!

QUESTIONS 1.24

Use the above ideas of estimation and approximation to choose the correct answer for these calculations:

1. Select the correct answer to $8 \cdot 6 \div 4 \cdot 3$
   from: (a) $0 \cdot 02$
              (b) $0 \cdot 2$
              (c)   2
              (d)   20
              (e)   200

3. Select the correct answer to $89 \cdot 17 \div 3 \cdot 7$
   from: (a) $0 \cdot 0241$
              (b) $0 \cdot 241$
              (c) $2 \cdot 41$
              (d) $24 \cdot 1$
              (e)   241

2. Select the correct answer to $59 \cdot 22 \div 42 \cdot 3$
   from: (a) $0 \cdot 014$
              (b) $0 \cdot 14$
              (c) $1 \cdot 4$
              (d)   14
              (e)   140

4. Select the correct answer to $1 \cdot 496 \div 4 \cdot 4$
   from: (a) $0 \cdot 0034$
              (b) $0 \cdot 034$
              (c) $0 \cdot 34$
              (d) $3 \cdot 4$
              (e)   34
              (f)   340

Do not use a calculator for questions 5 to 10!

5.   Calculate $6 \cdot 08 \div 0 \cdot 2$

6.   Calculate $67 \cdot 32 \div 0 \cdot 012$

7.   Calculate $174 \cdot 57 \div 3 \cdot 3$

8.   Calculate $227 \cdot 2 \div 0 \cdot 32$

9.   Calculate $137 \cdot 66 \div 4 \cdot 2$

10. Calculate $9 \cdot 355 \div 0 \cdot 45$

DIVIDING BY 10, 100, 1000 ....

Use your calculator to find answers to these questions:

$2 \div 10$	$7 \cdot 2 \div 10$
$3 \cdot 5 \div 10$	$0 \cdot 3 \div 10$
$0 \cdot 73 \div 10$	$25 \div 10$
$0 \cdot 00007 \div 10$	$8 \cdot 00008 \div 10$
$67 \cdot 43 \div 10$	$0 \cdot 582 \div 10$

$5 \div 100$	$7 \cdot 28433 \div 100$
$8 \cdot 3 \div 100$	$54 \div 100$
$0 \cdot 63 \div 100$	$0 \cdot 35 \div 100$
$85 \cdot 005 \div 100$	$809 \div 100$
$0 \cdot 000053 \div 100$	$43 \div 100$

$3 \div 1000$	$7 \cdot 352 \div 1000$
$7 \cdot 4 \div 1000$	$76 \div 1000$
$0 \cdot 683 \div 1000$	$6 \cdot 037 \div 1000$
$0 \cdot 0372 \div 1000$	$37 \cdot 93 \div 1000$
$8 \cdot 002 \div 1000$	$0 \cdot 125 \div 1000$

How would you describe to someone else the effect of dividing by 10, 100 and 1000?

Let's look again at the column headings for our number system. (Go back and re-read the section on Place Value, if you need a reminder!)

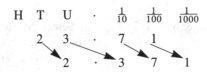

When dividing by 10, you can see that each number must, in effect, move one column to the right.

Two tens, divided by ten, becomes 2 units.
Three units, divided by ten, becomes 3 tenths.
Seven tenths, divided by ten, becomes 7 hundredths.
One hundredth, divided by ten, becomes 1 thousandth.

Write a similar statement for dividing by 100 and by 1000.

WHEN MULTIPLICATION AND DIVISION HAVE THE SAME EFFECT!

Use your calculator to work out answers to the following calculations:

4×2
$4 \div 0 \cdot 5$

$7 \cdot 3 \times 2$
$7 \cdot 3 \div 0 \cdot 5$

23×4
$23 \div 0 \cdot 25$

$45 \cdot 9 \times 4$
$45 \cdot 9 \div 0 \cdot 25$

5×10
$5 \div 0 \cdot 1$

$61 \cdot 73 \times 10$
$61 \cdot 73 \div 0 \cdot 1$

You can see that the calculations in each box give you the same answer!

So: $4 \times 2 = 8$
and: $4 \div 0 \cdot 5 = 8$

You could think of $4 \div 0 \cdot 5$ as being "4 whole ones divided into halves".
This would give you 8 pieces.

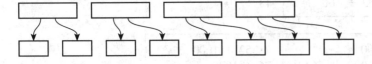

Or, you could think of $4 \div 0 \cdot 5$ as being "How many $0 \cdot 5$'s are there in 4?"
There are 8.

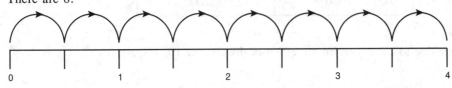

Read the sections on Multiplying Decimals and Dividing Decimals if these results seem surprising! In these two sections, I explained that multiplication doesn't always make things bigger and division doesn't always make things smaller.

So, it is always possible to complete the boxes in a statement like this:

$18 \times \boxed{} = 9$ Where you can multiply 18 by a number to make it smaller.

$18 \times \boxed{0 \cdot 5} = 9$ So, $0 \cdot 5$ will complete the box correctly.

Or a statement such as:

$16 \div \boxed{} = 64$ Where you can divide 16 by a number to make it bigger.

$16 \div \boxed{0 \cdot 25} = 64$ So, $0 \cdot 25$ will complete the box correctly.

EXAMPLE I

Complete this statement, so that multiplying 15 by some number will give the same answer as dividing 15 by a different number. What numbers could go into the two boxes?

$15 \times \boxed{*} = 15 \div \boxed{**}$

One possibility is, for example:

$15 \times \boxed{2} = 15 \div \boxed{0 \cdot 5} = 30$

So, multiplying any number by 2 will give the same answer as dividing the same number by $0 \cdot 5$.

Another possibility is:

$15 \times \boxed{4} = 15 \div \boxed{0 \cdot 25} = 60$

So, multiplying any number by 4 will give the same answer as dividing the same number by $0 \cdot 25$.

QUESTIONS 1.25

Use the same ideas to complete these statements correctly:

Use trial and improvement, if you need to, at least to start with! See if you can find a method.

1. $3 \times \boxed{4} = 3 \div \boxed{}$

2. $13 \times \boxed{0 \cdot 4} = 13 \div \boxed{}$

3. $22 \times \boxed{0 \cdot 8} = 22 \div \boxed{}$

4. $34 \times \boxed{0 \cdot 2} = 34 \div \boxed{}$

5. $12 \times \boxed{4} = 12 \div \boxed{}$

6. $20 \times \boxed{0 \cdot 25} = 20 \div \boxed{}$

7. $13 \times \boxed{} = 13 \div \boxed{2}$

8. $17 \times \boxed{} = 17 \div \boxed{4}$

9. $25 \times \boxed{} = 25 \div \boxed{0 \cdot 5}$

10. $24 \times \boxed{} = 24 \div \boxed{0 \cdot 4}$

NUMBER

Using Fractions

Did you find yourself wanting to use fractions, not decimals, when answering some of these questions?

You have hopefully by now worked out the answers to the above questions, using decimals.
Now look at all the above questions using fractions, as well as decimals, like this:

1.   3   × $\boxed{4}$ =   3   ÷ $\boxed{0\cdot 25}$

1.   3   × $\boxed{4}$ =   3   ÷ $\boxed{\frac{1}{4}}$

Now look at all the other questions two ways, using fractions in one version and decimals in the other:

2.   13   × $\boxed{0\cdot 4}$ =   13   ÷ $\boxed{2\cdot 5}$

2.   13   × $\boxed{\frac{4}{10}}$ =   13   ÷ $\boxed{\frac{10}{4}}$

3.   22   × $\boxed{0\cdot 8}$ =   22   ÷ $\boxed{1\cdot 25}$

3.   22   × $\boxed{\frac{8}{10}}$ =   22   ÷ $\boxed{\frac{10}{8}}$

4.   34   × $\boxed{0\cdot 2}$ =   34   ÷ $\boxed{5}$

4.   34   × $\boxed{\frac{2}{10}}$ =   34   ÷ $\boxed{\frac{10}{2}}$

5.   12   × $\boxed{4}$ =   12   ÷ $\boxed{0\cdot 25}$

5.   12   × $\boxed{4}$ =   12   ÷ $\boxed{\frac{1}{4}}$

6.   20   × $\boxed{0\cdot 25}$ =   20   ÷ $\boxed{4}$

6.   12   × $\boxed{\frac{1}{4}}$ =   20   ÷ $\boxed{4}$

7.   13   × $\boxed{0\cdot 5}$ =   13   ÷ $\boxed{2}$

7.   13   × $\boxed{\frac{1}{2}}$ =   13   ÷ $\boxed{2}$

8.   17   × $\boxed{0.25}$ =   17   ÷ $\boxed{4}$

8.   17   × $\boxed{\frac{1}{4}}$ =   17   ÷ $\boxed{4}$

9.   25   × $\boxed{2}$ =   25   ÷ $\boxed{0\cdot 5}$

9.   25   × $\boxed{2}$ =   25   ÷ $\boxed{\frac{1}{2}}$

10.   24   × $\boxed{2.5}$ =   24   ÷ $\boxed{0\cdot 4}$

10.   24   × $\boxed{\frac{10}{4}}$ =   24   ÷ $\boxed{\frac{4}{10}}$

  A summary of these results is as follows:

Multiplying by:	has the same effect as	Dividing by:
4	has the same effect as	$\frac{1}{4}$
$\frac{4}{10}$	has the same effect as	$\frac{10}{4}$
$\frac{8}{10}$	has the same effect as	$\frac{10}{8}$
$\frac{2}{10}$	has the same effect as	$\frac{10}{2}$
$\frac{1}{4}$	has the same effect as	4
$\frac{1}{2}$	has the same effect as	2
2	has the same effect as	$\frac{1}{2}$
$\frac{10}{4}$	has the same effect as	$\frac{4}{10}$
$\frac{a}{b}$	has the same effect as	$\frac{b}{a}$

By studying when multiplying and dividing **decimals** have the same effect, we have also found out how to divide **fractions**!

$$24 \div \frac{4}{10} = 24 \times \frac{10}{4} = 60$$

> Or, in general: $24 \div \frac{a}{b} = 24 \times \frac{b}{a}$

> **When dividing by a fraction:**
>
> Many people remember the saying: "turn the second number up the other way and multiply", but they never really understand why this works!

▲ USING DECIMALS TO SOLVE PROBLEMS ▼

In this section, there are worked examples which illustrate some of the ways decimals can be used in real-life problems.

EXAMPLE 1A

The cost of some cheese is £7·96 per kg. How much would 1·25 kg of cheese cost?

EXAMPLE 1B

The cost of some cheese is £7·96 per kg. How much would 0·35 kg of cheese cost?

CAUTION!

> Many pupils work their answers out like this:
>
> 1A: £7·95 × 1·25
>
> 1B: £7·96 ÷ 0·35

NUMBER

Most pupils correctly use multiplication for the first problem.

For the second problem, they can see that the answer must be less than £7·96. Some wrongly believe multiplication makes things bigger and division makes things smaller, so choose to divide.

Using your calculator, you find that:

1A: £7·96 × 1·25 = £9·95

1B: £7·96 ÷ 0·35 = £22·74   (to the nearest penny)

This cannot be right as, clearly, the answer to 1B should be less than £9·95!

If you are still uncertain here, you need to re-read the sections on Multiplying Decimals and Dividing Decimals.

The correct answers to these problems are:

Answer to 1A: £7.96 × 1.25 = £9.95

Answer to 1B: £7.96 × 0.35 = £2.79   (to the nearest penny)

> Once you are sure that you should be multiplying, then keep multiplying, however 'difficult' the numbers in the problem!

How do you decide whether to multiply or divide in the first place?
It can be useful to replace the numbers in the original problem by some easier ones.

Suppose the cheese cost £5·00 per kilogram

1 kg would therefore cost:	£5·00 per kg × 1 kg = £5·00
2 kg would therefore cost:	£5·00 per kg × 2 kg = £10·00
3 kg would therefore cost:	£5·00 per kg × 3 kg = £15·00
4 kg would therefore cost:	£5·00 per kg × 4 kg = £20·00
5 kg would therefore cost:	£5·00 per kg × 5 kg = £25·00
6 kg would therefore cost:	£5·00 per kg × 6 kg = £30·00

What would 1·5 kg cost? It would have to be half way between £5·00 and £10·00, so it would cost £7·50

Check on your calculator that £5·00 per kg × 1·5 kg = £7·50

What would 2·5 kg cost? It would have to be half way between £10·00 and £15·00, so it would cost £12·50

Check on your calculator that £5·00 per kg × 2·5 kg = £12·50

What would x kg cost? We can see from the above working that it does not matter what weight of cheese we are buying. We must multiply the cost per kilogram by the weight.

So, the total cost is = £5·00 per kg × x kg = 5x

This is how algebra works, by keeping the formula the same, but changing the value of x (in this case the number of kilograms).

LOOKING AT THE UNITS

Another useful strategy to solve real-life problems is to look at the units involved in the problem:

The cost of the cheese is £7·96 per kilogram, or $\dfrac{\text{Pounds(£)}}{\text{kg}}$

The weight of the cheese is measured in kilograms.

So, the total cost = $\dfrac{\text{Pounds (£)}}{\text{kg}} \times \text{kg} = \text{Pounds (£)}$

You can see that the 'kg' cancel out, leaving the cost in pounds.

EXAMPLE 2

The fuel tank in a small car holds 6·5 gallons of petrol. How many litres is this? Use the conversion fact 1 litre ≈ 0·22 galls.

Start from what you know! And, once again (as in the section on Solving Equations), work on the principle: **"Always do the same to both sides"**.

> 1 litre ≈ 0·22 gallons

To find the number of litres for 1 gallon, divide both sides by 0·22, like this:

÷ 0·22
> 1 litre ≈ 0·22 gallons
> 4·55 litres ≈ 1 gallon
÷ 0·22

Now, multiply both sides by 6·5, like this:

× 6·5
> 4·55 litres ≈ 1 gallon
> 29·58 litres ≈ 6·5 gallon
× 6·5

So, the fuel tank holds 29·58 litres (to two dec pl).

This is a very common technique. See also the same technique being used in the sections on Ratio and Pie Charts.

EXAMPLE 3

The cost of 41·23 litres of petrol is £23·26. What is the price of one litre?

> **CAUTION!** Many pupils write down 41·23 ÷ 23·26 as the answer to this question because they believe (wrongly) that you can only divide one number by a smaller number.

Consider the units involved! If you do calculate 41.23 ÷ 23.26, you have found:

$41\cdot23 \div 23\cdot26 = \dfrac{41\cdot23 \text{ litres}}{\text{£}23\cdot26} = 1\cdot77257 \text{ litres per pound(£)}$

This means that you get 1·77 litres of petrol for each pound(£) you spend (to 2 decimal places).

Now, calculate $23\cdot26 \div 41\cdot23 = \dfrac{\text{£}23\cdot26}{41\cdot23 \text{ litre}} = \text{£}0\cdot564 \text{ per litre (to 3 decimal places)}$

NUMBER

So, this means that you spend £0·564 for each litre that you buy. This is what the original question asked you to find. (This would most often be written as 56·4p.)

Notice that both calculations tell us something interesting: how much petrol you buy for one pound (£) and how much you pay per litre.

By analysing the units we can work out what the answer is telling us. You must always check you have given the answer required by the question.

EXAMPLE 4

My favourite toothpaste comes in two sizes:

The small size contains 50 ml and costs £1·09
The large size contains 125 ml and costs £2·25

Which size is the best value?

FIRST METHOD: Dividing ml by pounds (£)

For the **Small Size** we can calculate:

50 ml ÷ £1·09 = $\dfrac{50\ ml}{£1·09}$ = 45·87 ml per pound(£)

For the **Large Size** we can calculate:

125 ml ÷ £2·25 = $\dfrac{125\ ml}{£2·25}$ = 55·55 ml per pound(£)

You can see that the large size is better value, because you get more millilitres for each pound that you spend.

SECOND METHOD: Dividing pounds (£) by ml

For the **Small Size** we can calculate:

£1·09 ÷ 50 ml = $\dfrac{£1·09}{50\ ml}$ = 0·0218 pounds (£) per ml = 2·18 pence per ml

For the **Large Size** we can calculate:

£2·25 ÷ 125 ml = $\dfrac{£2·25}{125\ ml}$ = 0·018 pounds(£) per ml = 1·8 pence per ml

You can see that the large size still looks better value, because each millilitre costs you 1·8 pence, whereas for the small size each millilitre costs you 2·18 pence.

EXAMPLE 5

Find x and y in the rectangles below, if all three rectangles are **similar**.

[If we keep the rectangles the same shape, they are said to be SIMILAR. See the section on Similar Shapes if you need a reminder here!]

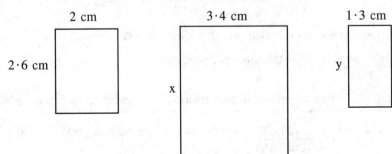

To find the length of side x:

The side which was 2 cm long is now 3·4 cm long.

> 2 cm has become 3·4 cm

Divide both of these numbers by 2, like this:

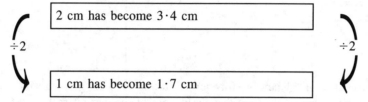

So, to find the length of the side that was 2·6 cm, multiply both sides by 2·6, like this:

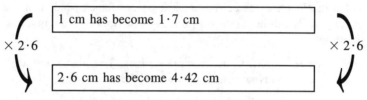

So, the length of side x is 4·42 cm.

To find the length of side y:

The side which was 2 cm long is now only 1·3 cm long.

> 2 cm has become 1·3 cm

Divide both of these numbers by 2, like this:

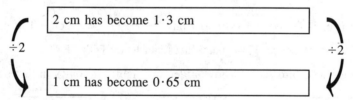

So, to find the length of the side that was 2·6 cm, multiply both sides by 2·6, like this:

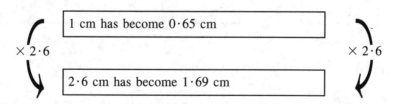

So, the length of side y is 1·69 cm.

QUESTIONS 1.26

1. The cost of some curtain material is £12·56 per metre.
(a) How much would 7·75 metres cost?
(b) How much would 0·7 metres of the material cost to make some cushions?

2. A piece of string is 8 inches long. How long is this in centimetres?
(1cm ≈ 0·4 inches)

3. Find x and y in the rectangles below, where all three rectangles are similar.

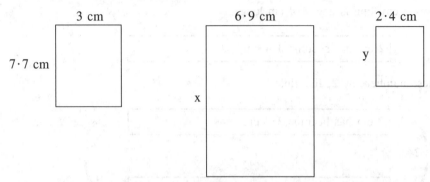

4. A cardboard box contains 24 jars of strawberry jam, where each jar with its jam weighs 490g. How much will the box weigh? (Assume that the weight of the cardboard box is negligible!). Give your answer in kg.

5. James has to wrap some identical parcels. For each parcel James needs a piece of ribbon 0·7 metres long. How many parcels can he wrap from 8 metres of ribbon? How much will be left over? Give your answer in cm.

6. I have bought some planks of wood, to make some shelves. The planks are all 2 metres long. I want the shelves to be 65 cm long. How many shelves can I cut from each plank of wood?

7. I am making a coffee table. I have found the perfect piece of wood in my garage from which to make the four legs. It is 1·7 metres long. If I use all the wood, how long will each table leg be? Give your answer in cm.

8. A 3 metre length of rope is cut into 5 equal lengths. How long is each length? Give your answer in cm.

9. Cheese is priced at £8·28 per kg. What weight of cheese (in kg) can I buy for £10?

10. Dried pears cost £2·30 per pound (weight). How many pounds (weight) of dried pears can I buy for a £10 note?

11. A kilogram of raisins is priced at £5·40. If I buy 2·35 kg, how much will it cost me?

12. A litre of petrol costs 58 pence. How many litres can I buy with £20?

13. I want to buy some wild bird seed for my garden bird table. It comes in three sizes:

1·8 kg for £1.05	1·25 kg for 72p	0·5 kg for 30p

Which of these is the best buy?

14. Which of these pots of wax polish is the best buy?

0·7 litre for £1·20	2·5 litre for £4.15

15. My car's petrol tank is full and the milometer reads 72692 miles. When I next fill the tank up, the milometer reads 72949 miles and I put 41·38 litres of petrol in the tank. How many miles per litre did the car do between refills?

16. On another occasion, I calculate that my car has done 7·3 miles per litre. What is this in miles per gallon? (1litre ≈ 0·22gallons)

▲ *FRACTIONS* ▼

If you had 16 small cakes and 8 people to tea, they could have 2 cakes each, as $16 \div 8 = 2$

If you only had one large cake, like a Swiss roll, you could cut the cake up, into 8 equal pieces.

$1 \div 8 = \frac{1}{8}$

$\frac{1}{8}$

One whole one divided equally between 8 people gives them $\frac{1}{8}$th of the cake each.

A fraction is a part of a whole one, and comes about when you divide.

> Many people forget that $\frac{1}{8}$ means $1 \div 8$.

If you had two Swiss rolls:

And then cut both into 8 equal parts, you would now have:

This would be 16 eighths, or $\frac{16}{8}$

If, whilst you were out of the room, someone came in and ate three pieces of cake, you would be left with $\frac{13}{8}$, like this:

$\frac{13}{8}$, can be written as 1 whole one and 5 eighths left over, or $1\frac{5}{8}$

$\frac{13}{8}$ .... is called a **top heavy fraction** or an **improper fraction**.

$1\frac{5}{8}$ ...... is called a **mixed number**, because it contains both a whole number and a fraction.

EQUIVALENT FRACTIONS

This is one whole Swiss roll:

If I cut it into two equal pieces, then it looks like this:

$\frac{1}{2}$

There are 2 halves in a whole one.

If I cut it into three equal pieces, then it looks like this:

$$\frac{1}{3}$$

There are 3 thirds in a whole one.

If I cut it into four equal pieces, then it looks like this:

$$\frac{1}{4}$$

There are 4 quarters in a whole one.

If I cut it into five equal pieces, then it looks like this:

$$\frac{1}{5}$$

There are 5 fifths in a whole one.

If I cut it into six equal pieces, then it looks like this:

$$\frac{1}{6}$$

There are 6 sixths in a whole one.

If I cut it into eight equal pieces, then it looks like this:

$$\frac{1}{8}$$

There are 8 eighths in a whole one.

If I cut it into ten equal pieces, then it looks like this:

$$\frac{1}{10}$$

There are 10 tenths in a whole one.

If I cut it into twelve equal pieces, then it looks like this:

$$\frac{1}{12}$$

There are 12 twelfths in a whole one.

Putting all the diagrams together, it looks like this:

You can see that some of the dividing lines match up. Put the halves and quarters together:

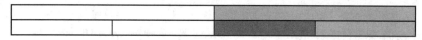

You can see that $\frac{1}{2}$ is the same as $\frac{2}{4}$. These are said to be **equivalent** fractions.

Put the quarters and the twelfths together:

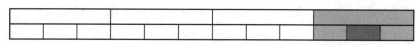

You can see that $\frac{1}{4}$ is the same as $\frac{3}{12}$ And, $\frac{3}{4}$ is the same as $\frac{9}{12}$

You don't have to draw a diagram each time! Look at what we already know:

$$\frac{1}{2} = \frac{2}{4} \qquad \frac{1}{4} = \frac{3}{12} \qquad \frac{3}{4} = \frac{9}{12}$$

The number on the bottom line (which is called the **denominator**), tells you how many equal pieces you have cut the cake into. The top line (which is called the **numerator**), tells you how many of these pieces you have.

If you cut the cake into four equal pieces (into quarters), and then take three of those pieces, you have $\frac{3}{4}$ of the original cake.

If you had cut the cake into 12 equal pieces (3 times as many as before), and then taken 9 of those pieces (again, 3 times as many as before), you have $\frac{9}{12}$ of the original cake, which gives you the same amount of cake as before, like this:

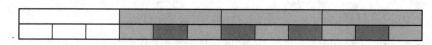

So, $\frac{3}{4} = \frac{9}{12}$ You can find a fraction which is equivalent to another fraction simply by multiplying the numerator and the denominator by the **same** number.

QUESTIONS 1.27

1. Write these fractions as decimals. (You can use your calculator to do the divisions).

(a) $\frac{1}{2}$

(b) $\frac{1}{3}$ and $\frac{2}{3}$

(c) $\frac{1}{4}$, $\frac{2}{4}$ and $\frac{3}{4}$

(d) $\frac{1}{5}$, $\frac{2}{5}$, $\frac{3}{5}$ and $\frac{4}{5}$

(e) $\frac{1}{6}$, $\frac{2}{6}$, $\frac{3}{6}$, $\frac{4}{6}$ and $\frac{5}{6}$

(f) $\frac{1}{7}$, $\frac{2}{7}$, $\frac{3}{7}$, $\frac{4}{7}$, $\frac{5}{7}$ and $\frac{6}{7}$

(g) $\frac{1}{8}$, $\frac{2}{8}$, $\frac{3}{8}$, $\frac{4}{8}$, $\frac{5}{8}$, $\frac{6}{8}$ and $\frac{7}{8}$

(h) $\frac{1}{9}$, $\frac{2}{9}$, $\frac{3}{9}$, $\frac{4}{9}$, $\frac{5}{9}$, $\frac{6}{9}$, $\frac{7}{9}$ and $\frac{8}{9}$

(i) $\frac{1}{10}$, $\frac{2}{10}$, $\frac{3}{10}$, $\frac{4}{10}$, $\frac{5}{10}$, $\frac{6}{10}$, $\frac{7}{10}$, $\frac{8}{10}$ and $\frac{9}{10}$

(j) $\frac{1}{11}$, $\frac{2}{11}$, $\frac{3}{11}$, $\frac{4}{11}$, $\frac{5}{11}$, $\frac{6}{11}$, $\frac{7}{11}$, $\frac{8}{11}$, $\frac{9}{11}$ and $\frac{10}{11}$

(k) $\frac{1}{12}$, $\frac{2}{12}$, $\frac{3}{12}$, $\frac{4}{12}$, $\frac{5}{12}$, $\frac{6}{12}$, $\frac{7}{12}$, $\frac{8}{12}$, $\frac{9}{12}$, $\frac{10}{12}$ and $\frac{11}{12}$

What do you notice about each 'family' of fractions?

Can you spot any patterns?

List any equivalent fractions you can find.

2. Change these top heavy fractions into mixed numbers:

(a) $\frac{5}{2}$　　　(b) $\frac{9}{4}$　　　(c) $\frac{13}{3}$　　　(d) $\frac{23}{5}$　　　(e) $\frac{18}{9}$

(f) $\frac{19}{9}$　　　(g) $\frac{51}{4}$　　　(h) $\frac{32}{3}$　　　(i) $\frac{32}{5}$　　　(j) $\frac{100}{3}$

3. Change these mixed numbers into top heavy fractions.

(a) $2\frac{3}{4}$　　　(b) $3\frac{1}{3}$　　　(c) $4\frac{3}{4}$　　　(d) $5\frac{7}{8}$　　　(e) $4\frac{5}{6}$

(f) $2\frac{1}{5}$　　　(g) $3\frac{4}{5}$　　　(h) $2\frac{4}{7}$　　　(i) $100\frac{1}{3}$　　　(j) $29\frac{3}{8}$

4. Fill in the missing numbers in these equivalent fractions:

(a) $\frac{1}{2} = \frac{*}{10}$　　(b) $\frac{3}{4} = \frac{*}{20}$　　(c) $\frac{18}{20} = \frac{*}{10}$　　(d) $\frac{5}{6} = \frac{*}{24}$　　(e) $\frac{3}{8} = \frac{15}{*}$

(f) $\frac{24}{30} = \frac{*}{5}$　　(g) $\frac{2}{5} = \frac{*}{20}$　　(h) $\frac{5}{8} = \frac{35}{*}$　　(i) $\frac{24}{60} = \frac{*}{5}$　　(j) $\frac{15}{36} = \frac{5}{*}$

CHANGING FRACTIONS TO DECIMALS: RECURRING DECIMALS

You will see from your answers to Question 1 (Questions 1.27) that turning fractions into decimals does not always give a nice tidy answer!

$\frac{1}{3} = 1 \div 3 = 0 \cdot 333333333333\ldots\ldots$

This is called a recurring decimal as the 3's go on forever.

For shorthand, we use a dot over the 3, to show that it is recurring, like this:

$\frac{1}{3} = 1 \div 3 = 0 \cdot 333333333333\ldots\ldots = 0 \cdot \dot{3}$

$\frac{3}{11} = 3 \div 11 = 0 \cdot 27272727\ldots\ldots$

This time the 2 and the 7 keep repeating. To show this, we use two dots over both the 2 and the 7, like this:

$\frac{3}{11} = 3 \div 11 = 0 \cdot 27272727\ldots\ldots = 0 \cdot \dot{2}\dot{7}$

$\frac{3}{22} = 3 \div 22 = 0 \cdot 13636363636\ldots\ldots$

This time, the 1 doesn't repeat at all, but the 3 and the 6 both do, so we write this with a dot over the two numbers which repeat, like this:

$\frac{3}{22} = 3 \div 22 = 0 \cdot 13636363636\ldots\ldots = 0 \cdot 1\dot{3}\dot{6}$

$\frac{2}{7} = 0 \cdot 285714285\ldots\ldots$

This time the string of numbers '285714' keeps on repeating. We show this by putting a dot over just the first and the last numbers which repeat, like this:

$\frac{2}{7} = 0 \cdot 285714285\ldots\ldots = 0 \cdot \dot{2}8571\dot{4}$

QUESTIONS 1.28

1. Look back to Questions 1.27, question number one. Write your answers using the proper notation for recurring decimals, where necessary!

ADDING AND SUBTRACTING FRACTIONS

EXAMPLE 1

I still have $\frac{7}{8}$ of my Swiss roll left over, and my friend arrives with $\frac{3}{8}$ of her Swiss roll, together we have:

$\frac{7}{8} + \frac{3}{8} = \frac{10}{8}$ In pictures:

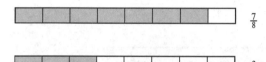
$\frac{7}{8}$

$\frac{3}{8}$

I can put one piece into the gap to make one whole cake, with two pieces left over, like this:

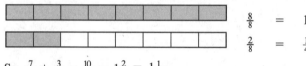
$\frac{8}{8} = 1$

$\frac{2}{8} = \frac{1}{4}$

So, $\frac{7}{8} + \frac{3}{8} = \frac{10}{8} = 1\frac{2}{8} = 1\frac{1}{4}$

Remember that the bottom line tells you how many pieces we cut the cake into originally. We cut the cake into eight equal pieces, so we are working in eighths. It might help to read the question out loud, like this:

$$\frac{7}{8} + \frac{3}{8} = \frac{10}{8}$$

"**Seven** eighths plus **three** eighths must equal **ten** eighths".

We are finding how many pieces of cake there are, of this size:

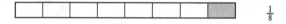
$\frac{1}{8}$

EXAMPLE 2

I still have $\frac{7}{8}$ of my Swiss roll left over and my friend arrives, this time with $\frac{3}{4}$ of her Swiss roll, together we have:

$\frac{7}{8} + \frac{3}{4} = ?$ In pictures:

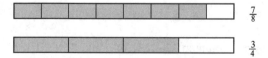
$\frac{7}{8}$

$\frac{3}{4}$

My friend has cut her Swiss roll into 4 equal pieces, not 8 as I have done.

This time we cannot say "seven **eighths** plus three **quarters** equal ten somethings", because there are two different sizes of cake involved.

So, we cut my friend's cake into the same size as mine, like this:

$\frac{7}{8}$

$\frac{3}{4} = \frac{6}{8}$

Now, I can continue as before. Put one piece into the gap to make one whole cake, with 5 pieces left over.

$\frac{8}{8} = 1$

$\frac{5}{8}$

So, $\frac{7}{8} + \frac{3}{4} = \frac{7}{8} + \frac{6}{8} = \frac{13}{8} = 1\frac{5}{8}$

> To add fractions, I must make the denominator (the number on the bottom line) the same in both fractions.

EXAMPLE 3

Add $\frac{7}{8} + \frac{5}{6}$

$\frac{7}{8}$

$\frac{5}{6}$

Again, the cakes have been cut into different size pieces. I need to cut the pieces of cake into smaller bits, so that all the pieces of cake are the same size! To achieve this, I need a new number for the bottom line (the denominator). I need a number that 8 will divide into exactly **and** that 6 will divide into exactly. This is just what you have when you find the Lowest Common Multiple of 6 and 8· (Look back to the section on LCM).

Multiples of 6	Multiples of 8
6	8
12	16
18	(24)
(24)	32
30	40
36	48
42	56
48	64
54	72

24 is the smallest number in both lists, so 24 is the Lowest Common Multiple of 6 and 8. So, I am going to cut both lots of cakes into pieces which are as big as one twenty-fourth of the original cake. Use equivalent fractions to change both fractions into 24ths.

Remember that the strategy is to cut all the pieces of cake into the same size pieces, in this case 24ths.

So, $\frac{7}{8} + \frac{5}{6} = \frac{21}{24} + \frac{20}{24} = \frac{41}{24} = 1\frac{17}{24}$

EXAMPLE 4

Add $\frac{5}{6} + \frac{7}{10}$ You don't need to use diagrams, so long as you understand equivalent fractions!

Step 1: We are looking for the smallest number which 6 **and** 10 will both divided into exactly. So, we need to find the LCM of 6 and 10, which is 30.

Step 2: Change both fractions into equivalent fractions, with a denominator of 30, like this:

Step 3: Change the original question into 30ths, like this:

So, $\frac{5}{6} + \frac{7}{10} = \frac{25}{30} + \frac{21}{30} = \frac{46}{30} = 1\frac{16}{30} = 1\frac{8}{15}$

EXAMPLE 5

$\frac{7}{8} - \frac{3}{10}$ If you have to subtract, then exactly the same ideas apply!

Step 1: Find the LCM of 8 and 10, which is 40.

Step 2: Change both fractions into equivalent fractions, with a denominator of 40, like this:

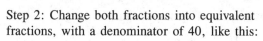

Step 3: Change the original question into 40ths, like this:

So, $\frac{7}{8} - \frac{3}{10} = \frac{35}{40} - \frac{12}{40} = \frac{23}{40}$

EXAMPLE 6

$4\frac{2}{3} + 3\frac{7}{8}$

Step 1: Add the whole numbers first of all: $4\frac{2}{3} + 3\frac{7}{8} = 7\frac{2}{3} + \frac{7}{8}$

Now continue as before:

Step 2: Find the LCM of 3 and 8, which is 24.

Step 3: Change both fractions into equivalent fractions, with a denominator of 24, like this:

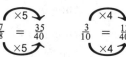

Step 4: Change the original question into 24ths, like this:

$4\frac{2}{3} + 3\frac{7}{8} = 7\frac{2}{3} + \frac{7}{8} = 7\frac{16}{24} + \frac{21}{24} = 7\frac{37}{24} = 8\frac{13}{24}$

EXAMPLE 7

$4\frac{5}{6} - 1\frac{1}{3}$

Step 1: Subtract the whole numbers first: $4\frac{5}{6} - 1\frac{1}{3} = 3\frac{5}{6} - \frac{1}{3}$

Step 2: Find the LCM of 3 and 6, which is 6.

Step 3: Change the fractions into 6ths:

$4\frac{5}{6} - 1\frac{1}{3} = 3\frac{5}{6} - \frac{1}{3} = 3\frac{5}{6} - \frac{2}{6} = 3\frac{3}{6} = 3\frac{1}{2}$

EXAMPLE 8

$4\frac{1}{3} - 1\frac{7}{8}$

Step 1: Subtract the whole numbers first: $4\frac{1}{3} - 1\frac{7}{8} = 3\frac{1}{3} - \frac{7}{8}$

Step 2: Find the LCM of 3 and 8, which is 24.

Step 3: Change both fractions into equivalent fractions, with a denominator of 24, like this:

$4\frac{1}{3} - 1\frac{7}{8} = 3\frac{1}{3} - \frac{7}{8} = 3\frac{8}{24} - \frac{21}{24}$

Step 4: It is not sensible to calculate 8 twenty fourths minus 21 twenty fourths, when I have whole numbers in reserve. So, I take one of the whole ones, and split this into 24ths, like this:

$4\frac{1}{3} - 1\frac{7}{8} = 3\frac{1}{3} - \frac{7}{8} = 3\frac{8}{24} - \frac{21}{24} = 2\frac{(24+8)}{24} - \frac{21}{24} = 2\frac{32}{24} - \frac{21}{24} = 2\frac{11}{24}$

QUESTIONS 1.29

1. Express the first quantity as a fraction of the second. The first is done for you.

(a) Express 8 hours as a fraction of 1 day.

Change 1 day into hours: 1 day = 24 hours

8 hours as a fraction of 24 hours: $\frac{8}{24} = \frac{8 \times 1}{8 \times 3} = \frac{1}{3}$

(b) 90 pence as a fraction of £1   (d) 50 pence as a fraction of £4·50

(c) 35 pence as a fraction of £1   (e) 120° as a fraction of a complete turn.

2. $\frac{1}{2} + \frac{1}{4}$ 10. $\frac{3}{8} + \frac{1}{2}$ 18. $1\frac{3}{4} + \frac{2}{5}$

3. $\frac{1}{6} + \frac{5}{6}$ 11. $\frac{3}{4} - \frac{1}{6}$ 19. $2\frac{1}{2} - \frac{3}{4}$

4. $\frac{2}{9} + \frac{5}{9}$ 12. $\frac{1}{2} + \frac{2}{3} + \frac{3}{4} + \frac{4}{5}$ 20. $3\frac{1}{7} + 1\frac{1}{2}$

5. $\frac{3}{7} - \frac{1}{7}$ 13. $1 - \frac{2}{5}$ 21. $2\frac{4}{7} - \frac{6}{7}$

6. $\frac{5}{8} - \frac{3}{8}$ 14. $1 - \frac{4}{5}$ 22. $1\frac{7}{8} + 2\frac{5}{8}$

7. $\frac{7}{9} - \frac{2}{9}$ 15. $1 - \frac{7}{8}$ 23. $2 - \frac{3}{8}$

8. $\frac{1}{2} + \frac{1}{3}$ 16. $1 - \frac{9}{10}$ 24. $\frac{3}{4} + \frac{3}{8} + \frac{1}{2}$

9. $\frac{2}{3} + \frac{1}{6}$ 17. $1\frac{1}{2} + \frac{2}{3}$ 25. $8\frac{2}{3} - 5\frac{4}{5}$

MULTIPLYING FRACTIONS

EXAMPLE 1   Find $\frac{2}{3} \times \frac{4}{5}$

Take this rectangle:

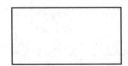

Now, split it into fifths along the length and shade four of the fifths, like this:

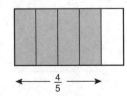

You could read: "Find $\frac{2}{3} \times \frac{4}{5}$" as: "Find two thirds **of** four fifths".

Now split the rectangle into thirds along the width and shade two of the thirds, like this:

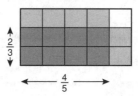

The diagram shows that the heavily shaded area is $\frac{8}{15}$ths of the whole rectangle.

So, $\frac{2}{3} \times \frac{4}{5} = \frac{8}{15}$

QUESTIONS 1.30

Use rectangle diagrams, as we did in Example 1, to find the answers for these calculations:

1. $\frac{1}{2} \times \frac{3}{7}$ [Hint: Draw a rectangle 2 cm by 7 cm]

2. $\frac{3}{8} \times \frac{3}{5}$ [Hint: Draw a rectangle 5 cm by 8 cm]

3. $\frac{5}{8} \times \frac{3}{4}$ [Hint: Draw a rectangle 4 cm by 8 cm]

4. $\frac{2}{5} \times \frac{9}{15}$ [Hint: Draw a rectangle 5 cm by 15 cm]

EXAMPLE 2

Find $\frac{3}{4} \times \frac{7}{12}$

Take this rectangle:

Now, split it into twelfths along the length and shade seven of the twelfths, like this:

You could read: "Find $\frac{3}{4} \times \frac{7}{12}$" as: "Find three quarters of seven twelfths".

Now split the rectangle into quarters along the width and shade three of the quarters, like this:

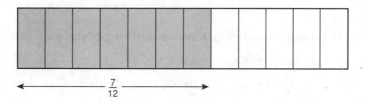

The diagram shows that the heavily shaded area is $\frac{21}{48}$ths of the whole rectangle.

So, $\frac{3}{4} \times \frac{7}{12} = \frac{21}{48}$

But, using what we already know about equivalent fractions, we can write

$\frac{21}{48} = \frac{3 \times 7}{3 \times 16} = \frac{7}{16}$ So, our final answer is $\frac{7}{16}$

It is actually easier to divide the top line and the bottom line by 3, **before** doing the calculation, like this:

$\frac{3}{4} \times \frac{7}{12} = \frac{\cancel{3}^{1}}{4} \times \frac{7}{\cancel{12}_{1} \times 4} = \frac{7}{16}$

EXAMPLE 3
Find $1\frac{2}{3} \times \frac{4}{5}$

We already know from Example 1 that $\frac{2}{3} \times \frac{4}{5} = \frac{8}{15}$

and the diagram that showed this was:

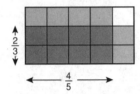 8 parts heavily shaded

And, also:

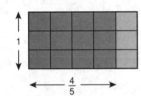 12 parts heavily shaded

So, $1\frac{2}{3} \times \frac{4}{5}$ must equal $\frac{20}{15}$ as there are 20 shaded parts altogether, and we are dealing with 15ths.

So, $1\frac{2}{3} \times \frac{4}{5} = \frac{20}{15} = 1\frac{5}{15} = 1\frac{1}{3}$

EXAMPLE 3 AGAIN
It is probably easier to dispense with diagrams now, and simply change

$1\frac{2}{3}$ into a top heavy fraction and multiply like this:

$1\frac{2}{3} \times \frac{4}{5} = \frac{5}{3} \times \frac{4}{5} = \frac{20}{15} = 1\frac{1}{3}$ or, we could divide first, like this: $1\frac{2}{3} \times \frac{4}{5} = \frac{\cancel{5}^{1}}{3} \times \frac{4}{\cancel{5}_{1}} = \frac{4}{3} = 1\frac{1}{3}$

QUESTIONS 1.31
1. $\frac{1}{2} \times \frac{1}{3}$ 6. $\frac{2}{3} \times \frac{3}{4}$ 11. $1\frac{1}{5} \times 3$ 16. $2\frac{1}{5} \times \frac{3}{11}$

2. $\frac{1}{3} \times \frac{1}{4}$ 7. $\frac{3}{7} \times \frac{5}{6}$ 12. $3\frac{1}{3} \times 5$ 17. $3\frac{4}{5} \times 2\frac{1}{2}$

3. $\frac{2}{3} \times \frac{1}{5}$ 8. $\frac{3}{4} \times \frac{8}{9}$ 13. $3\frac{1}{7} \times \frac{7}{11}$ 18. $2\frac{1}{8} \times 3\frac{1}{5}$

4. $\frac{3}{5} \times \frac{2}{7}$ 9. $\frac{3}{10} \times \frac{5}{12}$ 14. $2\frac{1}{2} \times 3\frac{1}{3}$ 19. $2\frac{1}{4} \times \frac{3}{5}$

5. $\frac{1}{2} \times \frac{4}{5}$ 10. $\frac{8}{15} \times \frac{25}{32}$ 15. $1\frac{3}{4} \times 3\frac{4}{7}$ 20. $3\frac{3}{4} \times 1\frac{2}{3}$

21. A car's petrol tank holds 15 gallons.

(a) If the gauge says that it is $\frac{2}{3}$rds full how much petrol is left in the tank?

(b) If the gauge says that it is $\frac{1}{5}$th full, how much petrol do I need to fill up?

22. A friend's car holds 60 litres of petrol.

(a) If the gauge says that it is $\frac{3}{5}$ths full, how much petrol is in the tank?

(b) If the gauge says that it is $\frac{1}{10}$th full, how much petrol does she need to fill up?

23. Five eighths of the school are girls. There are 1032 pupils in the school all together. How many boys are there?

24. In a sale there is one third off all prices. What is the sale price of a settee, marked at £1845?

25. Abigail, Basil and Caroline share an inheritance of £1800. Abigail gets $\frac{1}{3}$, Basil gets $\frac{1}{4}$ and Caroline gets the rest. How much do they each get?

DIVIDING FRACTIONS

Read the section: When Multiplication and Division have the Same Effect!

This will give you a different perspective on dividing fractions!

EXAMPLE 1

Find $4 \div \frac{1}{3}$ Take four whole ones:

Now divide these 4 whole ones into thirds. How many pieces will there be?

You can see that there are 12 pieces.

So, $4 \div \frac{1}{3} = 12$

EXAMPLE 2

Find $4 \div \frac{2}{3}$

How many $\frac{2}{3}$rds are there in 4?

So, if this is a whole one:

Then, this is $\frac{2}{3}$rds of a whole one:

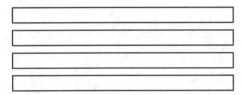

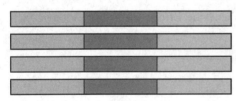

So, the question is asking us to find how many pieces of this size there are in 4 whole ones.

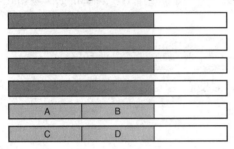

Put A and B together and put C and D together, like this:

So, there are 6 pieces of the right size!

So, $4 \div \frac{2}{3} = 6$

$4 \div \frac{1}{3} = 12$	has the same answer as	$4 \times 3 = 12$
$4 \div \frac{2}{3} = 6$	has the same answer as	$4 \times \frac{3}{2} = 6$

In the section on When Multiplication and Division have the Same Effect, we showed that:

> Dividing by $\frac{a}{b}$ is the same as multiplying by $\frac{b}{a}$.

EXAMPLE 3

The rule above also works when you have whole number involved, like this:

$4\frac{2}{3} \div \frac{1}{3}$ How many thirds are there in $4\frac{2}{3}$?

We already know that there are 12 thirds in 4 whole ones, so there must be 14 in $4\frac{2}{3}$.

To use the rule, first change $4\frac{2}{3}$ into a top heavy fraction

$4\frac{2}{3} \div \frac{1}{3} = \frac{14}{3} \div \frac{1}{3} = \frac{14}{3} \times \frac{3}{1} = 14$

EXAMPLE 4

Find $4\frac{2}{3} \div \frac{2}{3}$ First, change the mixed number into a top heavy fraction, then apply the rule:

$4\frac{2}{3} \div \frac{2}{3} = \frac{14}{3} \div \frac{2}{3} = \frac{14}{3} \times \frac{3}{2} = 7$

QUESTIONS 1.32

1. $\frac{3}{4} \div \frac{3}{5}$

2. $1 \div \frac{3}{4}$

3. $1\frac{1}{3} \div \frac{2}{7}$

4. $\frac{1}{5} \div \frac{1}{5}$

5. $\frac{2}{3} \div \frac{3}{4}$

6. $\frac{1}{3} \div \frac{1}{4}$

7. $\frac{2}{3} \div \frac{5}{6}$

8. $2\frac{3}{4} \div \frac{6}{7}$

9. $1\frac{3}{4} \div \frac{4}{5}$

10. $3\frac{1}{4} \div 4\frac{1}{3}$

11. How many $\frac{3}{4}$ metre lengths of pipe can be cut from a length of pipe 24 metres long?

12. How many $\frac{2}{3}$ metre lengths of ribbon can be cut from a length of ribbon 18 metres long?

▲ ESTIMATION, APPROXIMATION & ACCURACY ▼

This chapter is about giving sensible answers! It is seldom useful to say that my pencil is 16·825 cm long, because I cannot measure that accurately anyway and, of equal importance, no one would want to know the length of my pencil this accurately! When you are working on Maths problems, keep asking yourself the whole time: "Does my answer to this problem make sense for this situation?"

I once watched a pupil spend a very long time to calculate the bill for staying at a hotel for four nights and eating three evening meals. The bill had to include the service charge and VAT. His bill came to £3·92. I asked him if this was a sensible answer. His reply was: "Of course not!" His reasoning was that this was a Maths lesson and that Maths never made any sense! Please do not follow in his footsteps! Whenever you use your calculator, always ask yourself if your answer makes sense or not. We will develop these ideas in the coming sections.

ESTIMATION

It is very useful in life to be good at estimating! People have been known to ask questions such as:

How high is that lamp post?

How long was that enormous slug we saw yesterday?

How many bags of sand will I need to lay my new patio?

How long will it take me to drive from Bristol to Birmingham?

When estimating, you are trying to come up with an answer that will give someone else a rough idea of the size you are talking about. I estimate that the slug that I saw yesterday was about 12 cm long. There is no point in estimating the slug to be 11·7 cm long – I simply cannot claim to be that exact! I didn't want to pick it up and actually measure it (I don't even like slugs, to tell you the truth). Even if I had tried to measure it, the length of a slug varies according to whether it is stretching itself or not!

QUESTIONS 1.33

1. Estimate the floor area of your bedroom. Check your estimate by taking measurements then working it out.

2. Estimate the floor area of your Maths classroom. Check your estimate by taking measurements then working it out.

3. Estimate the volume of a mug of coffee. Use a measuring jug to check your estimate. Now estimate the volume of other kitchen containers and check your answers by measuring.

4. Find two different household containers. Estimate how many times you need to fill the smaller

NUMBER

container with water to completely fill the bigger container. Now do the experiment. How close were you? Ask some adults to estimate as well. Are adults any better at estimating volume than children? Investigate!

APPROXIMATION

EXAMPLE 1

When using your calculator to find: $\dfrac{600 \times 80}{40}$

it is a good idea to know what sort of size answer you are expecting. You can find an approximate answer by rounding the numbers of the original calculation either up or down. Do this to make the new version as easy as possible! Don't make life any harder than it has to be! I'm going to change the original calculation to:

$\dfrac{600 \times 80}{40}$ Now I can do some mental arithmetic to find the answer to this new calculation. I can divide top and bottom by 40, so the answer to my new simplified version must be:

$$\frac{600 \times 2 \times \cancel{40}^{1}}{\cancel{40}_{1}} \quad = \quad 600 \times 2 = 1200$$

So, the answer to the original question must also be around 1200.

When I do it on my calculator, I find that: $\dfrac{609 \times 78}{42} = 1131$

So, you can see that my approximate answer of 1200 was reasonably close to the actual answer of the original question.

EXAMPLE 2

Find an approximate answer to $738 \cdot 7 \times 21 \cdot 9$

Again, replace the original numbers by nice, easy ones. You could change the original to:

	740×22
or	740×20
or	700×22
or	700×20

Now use a calculator to evaluate all of these as well as the original version, like this:

	740×22	$= 16\ 280$
or	740×20	$= 14\ 800$
or	700×22	$= 15\ 400$
or	700×20	$= 14\ 000$
	$738 \cdot 7 \times 21 \cdot 9$	$= 16\ 177 \cdot 53$

You can see that all of these approximations are close to the value of the original. Notice that, if all I am interested in is an approximate answer, then I may as well choose:

either $740 \times 20 = 14800$
or $700 \times 20 = 14000$

as both of these are easy to do in my head.

EXAMPLE 3

(a) What is 432 to the nearest 10?

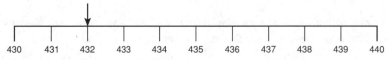

432 to the nearest 10 is 430

(b) What is 437 to the nearest 10?

437 to the nearest 10 is 440

(c) What is 435 to the nearest 10?

435 is exactly half way between 430 and 440, so you could give either answer, but usually most people choose to round up and give the answer as 440.

(d) What is 435 to the nearest 100?

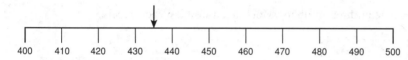

435 to the nearest 100 is 400

QUESTIONS 1.34

1. Some of these calculations are wrong! Decide which calculations are wrong without using your calculator!

(a) $7 \cdot 4876 \times 53 \cdot 7 = 402 \cdot 08412$

(b) $436 \times 89 \cdot 4 = 3897 \cdot 84$

(c) $291 \times 489 = 14229$

(d) $42 \times 62 \cdot 1 \times 92 \cdot 5 = 241258 \cdot 5$

(e) $95 \times 45 \cdot 7 \times 239 \cdot 77 = 10409 \cdot 61455$

(f) $1566 \cdot 24 \div 20 \cdot 8 = 7 \cdot 53$

(g) $5007 \cdot 42 \div 89 \cdot 1 = 56 \cdot 2$

(h) $22 \cdot 96 \div 0 \cdot 8 = 0 \cdot 287$

(i) $1666 \cdot 7865 \div 2 \cdot 935 = 567 \cdot 9$

(j) $1 \cdot 755 \div 0 \cdot 045 = 39$

2. Choose the best approximate answer for each of these calculations:

(a) 31×58 is about   (i)   18
      or   (ii)   180
      or   (iii)   1800

(b) $6217 \div 28$ is about   (i)   2
      or   (ii)   20
      or   (iii)   200
      or   (iv)   2000

(c) $\dfrac{521 \times 39}{11 \cdot 03}$ is about   (i)   2
      or   (ii)   20
      or   (iii)   200
      or   (iv)   2000

(d) $\sqrt{3 \cdot 97} \times 4 \cdot 0887$ is about   (i)   0·08
      or   (ii)   0·8
      or   (iii)   8
      or   (iv)   80

3. Find an approximate answer to these calculations:

(a) $391 \times 2 \cdot 9$
(f) $861 \div 10 \cdot 98$

(b) $69 \cdot 54 \times 0 \cdot 51$
(g) $274 \cdot 9 \div 213$

(c) $429 \times 2 \cdot 98$
(h) $274 \cdot 9 \div 2 \cdot 13$

(d) $2 \cdot 00003 \times 98 \cdot 7$
(i) $274 \cdot 9 \div 0 \cdot 0213$

(e) $\sqrt{78} \times 3 \cdot 1$
(j) $\dfrac{29 \times 98}{0 \cdot 9}$

Now do these calculations using your calculator. How accurate were you?

4. At the Post Office I buy 28 stamps at 38p each. I have several £10 notes and £5 notes in my wallet. How much should I hand over to pay for the stamps?

5. For approximately how many seconds have you been alive?

6. Find approximately how many heartbeats you have per day.

7. (a) Give 283 to the nearest 10
(d) Give $3 \cdot 6$ to the nearest whole number

(b) Give 3487 to the nearest 100
(e) Give £$3 \cdot 586$ to the nearest penny

(c) Give 15 675 to the nearest 1000
(f) Give £$32 \cdot 355$ to the nearest penny

8. £485 is divided equally between three brothers. How much do they each receive:

(a) to the nearest penny?
(b) to the nearest ten pence?
(c) to the nearest pound?

ACCURACY

When I can't sleep at nights I count sheep. I usually get as far as 49 or 50 before I actually fall asleep. The number of sheep increases one at a time. You cannot count "one and a half sheep". The number of sheep is said to be a **discrete** variable, because it can have only whole number values. So, **counting** the total number of sheep in the field is (usually!) no problem.

When I need to **measure** anything, this is altogether different! The other day in my garage I was looking for a long bolt. I went to my box of spare parts and started to measure the length of the bolts which were in the box.

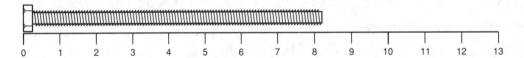

The length of the bolt is 8 cm **to the nearest cm**.

If I use a ruler with finer graduations, I can say that the length of the bolt is $8 \cdot 2$ cm **to one decimal place**.

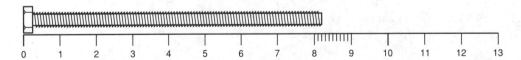

In theory, I could use a finer ruler still and obtain an even more accurate reading for the length of the bolt. In practice, for this example, finding the length of the bolt to one decimal place is definitely good enough. However, $8 \cdot 2$ cm is not the exact length of the bolt. You can never measure something exactly, no matter how careful you are being! At some stage you need to say that this is accurate enough and stop there. (It is a good idea to say how accurate you have been – in this case, we have measured to one decimal place.) So, **measuring** is a difficult task as length is a **continuous** variable and (unlike counting sheep) does not increase by a whole number each time.

Look back at the section on the Number Line. You will see in that section how we kept zooming in to obtain ever more decimal places, demonstrating the denseness of decimals, just as we could do when measuring something.

EXAMPLE 2
My local hardware shop sells bolts. I have selected a bolt from the box labelled, "6 cm long (to the nearest cm)".

The shop is not claiming that the bolts are exactly 6 cm long. There will be some variation in the length of the bolts. You can see that the bolt that I have selected is not quite 6 cm long, it is about 5·8 cm long.

The shop keeper has carefully sorted the bolts into boxes, like this:

If I take a bolt from the 6 cm box, the shortest it could be is 5·5 cm. If it was any shorter it would have gone into the 5 cm box. The longest it could be would be just less than 6·5 cm. If it was any longer it would have gone into the 7 cm box.

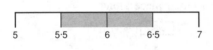

So, bolts labelled **"6 cm (to the nearest cm)"** **are between 5·5 cm and 6·5 cm in length**. This is most precisely shown using symbols as:

$$5·5 \text{ cm} \leqslant \text{length} < 6·5 \text{ cm}$$

EXAMPLE 3
The hardware shop also sells much more expensive bolts which are made to a more consistent length. The shop advertises these bolt as 6·0 cm long.

When people are using Mathematical ideas precisely, 6·0 cm is definitely different from 6 cm!

Remember that a bolt labelled "6 cm (to the nearest cm)" is not 5 cm or 7 cm, so it must be **between** 5·5 cm and 6·5 cm.

But a bolt labelled "6·0 cm (to one decimal place)" is not 5·9 cm (we know this, because otherwise we would have labelled the bolt 5·9 cm, which we haven't!). The bolt isn't as big as 6·1 cm either, so it must be greater than or equal to 5·95 cm, but just less than 6·05 cm.

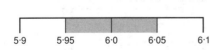

So, bolts labelled **"6·0 cm in length"** are **between 5·95 cm and 6·05** cm in length. This is most precisely shown using symbols as:

$$5·95 \text{ cm} \leqslant \text{length} < 6·05 \text{ cm}$$

QUESTIONS 1.35
1. A garden furniture catalogue gives the height of a garden table to be 75 cm to the nearest cm.
(a) What is the shortest the table could be?

(b) What is the tallest the table could be?

2. Nina's teacher measures her height as 152·5 cm to the nearest half centimetre. (a) What is the shortest Nina could be? (b) What is the tallest Nina could be?

3. A manufacturing firm labels a particular component as 3·8 cm long (to one decimal place).

(a) What is the shortest the component could be?

(b) What is the longest the component could be?

4. A firm making parts for the computer industry labels a metal rectangle as 2·3 cm by 4·7 cm, where both measurements are given correct to one decimal place.

(a) What is the smallest the two measurements could be?

(b) What is the largest the two measurements could be?

(c) What is the smallest area that this rectangle could have?

(d) What is the largest area that this rectangle can have?

ACCURACY 2: Decimal Places and Significant Figures

People will make use of Decimal Places and Significant Figures, when they want to be precise about how accurate they are being.

EXAMPLE I

A very sensitive instrument measures the thickness of a human hair to be 0·3825 mm. Give 0·3825 mm to (a) 1 decimal place (b) 2 decimal places (c) 3 decimal places.

(a) 1 decimal place:

0·3825 to 1 decimal place will be either 0·3 or 0·4

To decide whether it is 0·3 or 0·4, consider the next decimal place along....

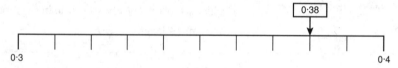

So, 0·3825 to 1 decimal place is 0·4 as the arrow is nearer to 0·4 than 0·3

(b) 2 decimal places:

0·3825 to 2 decimal places will be either 0·38 or 0·39

To decide whether it is 0·38 or 0·39, consider the next decimal place along....

So, 0·3825 to 2 decimal place is 0·38 as the arrow is nearer to 0·38 than 0·39

(c) 3 decimal places:

0·3825 to 3 decimal places will be either 0·382 or 0·383
To decide whether it is 0·382 or 0·383, consider the next decimal place along....

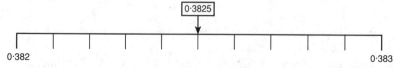

So, 0·3825 to 3 decimal places could be either 0·382 or 0·383, as the arrow is exactly half-way, but it is usual to round up in this situation, to get 0·383.

EXAMPLE 2

The distance of Saturn from the Sun is reckoned to be 1 427 000 000 km.

Give 1 427 000 000 km to (a) 1 significant figure (b) 2 significant figures (c) 3 significant figures.

(a) 1 significant figure

1 427 000 000 to 1 significant figure will be either 1 000 000 000
or 2 000 000 000.

As before, look at the next figure along, which is a '4', so take the smaller value.

So, 1 427 000 000 to 1 significant figure is 1 000 000 000

(b) 2 significant figures

1 427 000 000 to 2 significant figures will be either   1 400 000 000
or   1 500 000 000.

Look at the next figure along, which is a '2', so take the smaller value.

So, 1 427 000 000 to 2 significant figures is 1 400 000 000

(c) 3 significant figures

1 427 000 000 to 3 significant figures will be either   1 420 000 000
or   1 430 000 000.

Look at the next figure along, which is a '7', so take the larger value.

So, 1 427 000 000 to 3 significant figures is 1 430 000 000

EXAMPLE 3

Give 0·0057381 to (a) 1 significant figure (b) 2 significant figures (c) 3 significant figures.

(a) 1 significant figure

0·0057381 to 1 significant figure will be either 0·005
or 0·006

> Notice that I have not counted the two zeros here. They are called 'place holders' and make sure that the final answer that I give is of the right size.

Look at the next figure along, which is a '7', so take the larger value.

So, 0·0057381 to 1 significant figure is 0·006

(b) 2 significant figures

0·0057381 to 2 significant figures will be either   0·0057
or   0·0058

Look at the next figure along, which is a '3', so take the smaller value.

So, 0·0057381 to 2 significant figures is 0·0057

(c) 3 significant figures

0·0057381 to 3 significant figures will be either   0·00573
or   0·00574

Look at the next figure along, which is an '8', so take the larger value.

So, 0·0057381 to 3 significant figures is 0·00574

EXAMPLE 4

I am told that the area of a rectangle is exactly 45 cm² and its length is measured as 7·1 cm. What is the width of the rectangle?

Width × Length = Area

So, Width = Area ÷ Length
　　Width = 45 cm² ÷ 7·1 cm
　　Width = 6·338028169 cm

This is the answer according to my calculator. Don't give this as your final answer, as you cannot possibly measure the width of a rectangle this accurately!

Your final answer could reasonably be given as 6·3 (to 1 dec pl) or 6·3 (to 2 sig figs).

QUESTIONS 1.36

1. Complete this table:

Number	1 decimal place	2 decimal places	3 decimal places
23·9355			
344·29611			
37·02698			
0·07924			
0·6047			

2. Complete this table:

Number	1 significant figure	2 significant figures	3 significant figures
34·875			
1689·63			
20 832			
1·06428			
0·0043923			

3. $\dfrac{8·826 \times 16·33}{4·81}$

(a) Find an approximate value for the above without using your calculator.

(b) Now use you calculator. Write down all the figures in the calculator display.

(c) How good was your approximation?

(d) Give your answer to (b) to 1 decimal place.

(e) Give your answer to (b) to 2 decimal places.

(f) Give your answer to (b) to 3 significant figures.

4. I am told that the exact area of a rectangle is 250 cm² and its length is measured as 18·7 cm. What is the width of the rectangle (a) to 1 decimal place (b) to 2 significant figures?

▲ *INDEX NOTATION (POWERS)* ▼

3	=	3
3 × 3	=	9
3 × 3 × 3	=	27
3 × 3 × 3 × 3	=	81
3 × 3 × 3 × 3 × 3	=	243
3 × 3 × 3 × 3 × 3 × 3	=	729
3 × 3 × 3 × 3 × 3 × 3 × 3	=	2187
3 × 3 × 3 × 3 × 3 × 3 × 3 × 3	=	6561
3 × 3 × 3 × 3 × 3 × 3 × 3 × 3 × 3	=	19683
3 × 3 × 3 × 3 × 3 × 3 × 3 × 3 × 3 × 3	=	59049

The numbers in the last column 3, 9, 27, 81, 243, 729 and so on, have been formed by multiplying three by itself a certain number of times. These numbers are called "**powers of three**".

When you are multiplying a number by itself you can use a Mathematical shorthand to save writing out a long string of figures, like this:

$3 \times 3 = 3^2$	and is called "3 squared"
$3 \times 3 \times 3 = 3^3$	and is called "3 cubed"
$3 \times 3 \times 3 \times 3 = 3^4$	and is called "3 to the power 4"
$3 \times 3 \times 3 \times 3 \times 3 = 3^5$	and is called "3 to the power 5" … and so on!

So, writing our earlier list as powers, we have:

3		$= 3^1$	=	3
3 × 3		$= 3^2$	=	9
3 × 3 × 3		$= 3^3$	=	27
3 × 3 × 3 × 3		$= 3^4$	=	81
3 × 3 × 3 × 3 × 3		$= 3^5$	=	243
3 × 3 × 3 × 3 × 3 × 3		$= 3^6$	=	729
3 × 3 × 3 × 3 × 3 × 3 × 3		$= 3^7$	=	2187
3 × 3 × 3 × 3 × 3 × 3 × 3 × 3		$= 3^8$	=	6561
3 × 3 × 3 × 3 × 3 × 3 × 3 × 3 × 3		$= 3^9$	=	19683
3 × 3 × 3 × 3 × 3 × 3 × 3 × 3 × 3 × 3		$= 3^{10}$	=	59049

Notice that we have labelled 3 as 3^1 as this fits in with the pattern of powers.

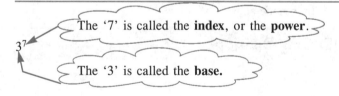

3^7

The '7' is called the **index**, or the **power**.

The '3' is called the **base**.

Note that the plural of index is indices!

$3^7 = 3 \times 3 \times 3 \times 3 \times 3 \times 3 \times 3 = 2187$

To find that 3^7 equals 2187 you can use your calculator 'power' button. Make sure that you know how your own calculator works when calculating powers.

CALCULATIONS USING INDICES: Multiplication

Number	Number written as a power
81	3^4
27 ×	3^3 ×
2187	3^7

NUMBER

QUESTIONS 1.37

Complete these calculations, filling in all the gaps:

1.

Number	Number written as a power
243	$3^?$
9 ×	$3^? \times$
	$3^?$

2.

Number	Number written as a power
729	$3^?$
3 ×	$3^? \times$
	$3^?$

3.

Number	Number written as a power
2187	$3^?$
27 ×	$3^? \times$
	$3^?$

4.

Number	Number written as a power
243	$3^?$
81 ×	$3^? \times$
	$3^?$

What do you notice about these calculations?

Look back at the earlier example:

Number	Number written as a power	Number written long hand
81	3^4	$3 \times 3 \times 3 \times 3$
27 ×	$3^3 \times$	$3 \times 3 \times 3$
2187	3^7	$3 \times 3 \times 3 \times 3 \times 3 \times 3 \times 3$

So, $3^4 \times 3^3 = 3^{4+3} = 3^7$

Three to the power **four** multiplied by three to the power **three** equals three to the power **seven**. $(4 + 3 = 7)$

> When multiplying, simply add the powers!

Check that this works for the questions you have done above.

CALCULATIONS USING INDICES: Division

$$6561 \div 27 = \frac{6561}{27} = 243$$

Now write the same calculation using powers:

$$3^8 \div 3^3 = \frac{3^8}{3^3} = \frac{\overset{1}{\cancel{3}} \times \overset{1}{\cancel{3}} \times \overset{1}{\cancel{3}} \times 3 \times 3 \times 3 \times 3 \times 3}{\underset{1}{\cancel{3}} \times \underset{1}{\cancel{3}} \times \underset{1}{\cancel{3}}} = 3 \times 3 \times 3 \times 3 \times 3 = 3^5$$

Dividing 3's top and bottom.

QUESTIONS 1.38

Do these divisions, exactly as the worked example above, putting in all the equivalent steps. Use both methods for each question!

1. $243 \div 27$

2. $59049 \div 81$

3. $19683 \div 2187$

4. $6561 \div 3$

What do you notice about these calculations?

EXAMPLE 2

$19683 \div 243 = \dfrac{19683}{243} = 81$

Writing the same calculation using powers:

$$3^9 \div 3^5 = \frac{3^9}{3^5} = \frac{\overset{1}{\cancel{3}} \times \overset{1}{\cancel{3}} \times \overset{1}{\cancel{3}} \times \overset{1}{\cancel{3}} \times \overset{1}{\cancel{3}} \times 3 \times 3 \times 3 \times 3}{\underset{1}{\cancel{3}} \times \underset{1}{\cancel{3}} \times \underset{1}{\cancel{3}} \times \underset{1}{\cancel{3}} \times \underset{1}{\cancel{3}}} = 3^4$$

> Again, dividing 3's top and bottom.

So, $3^9 \div 3^5 = 3^{9-5} = 3^4$

Three to the power **nine** divided by three to the power **five** equals three to the power **four**. $(9 - 5 = 4)$

> When dividing, simply subtract the powers!

Check that this works for the questions you have done above.

THE POWER 0

EXAMPLE 1

Consider the calculation $3^5 \div 3^5$

So, applying the above rule for dividing, we should subtract the powers, like this:

$3^5 \div 3^5 = 3^{5-5} = 3^0$

What does 3^0 mean?

$3^5 \div 3^5$ must also equal $243 \div 243$ which equals 1

So, 3^0 must equal 1.

EXAMPLE 2

What about taking powers of a number other than 3?

Consider the calculation $5^2 \div 5^2$

Again, applying the above rule for dividing, we should subtract the powers, like this:

$5^2 \div 5^2 = 5^{2-2} = 5^0$

So, what does 5^0 mean?

$5^2 \div 5^2 = 25 \div 25 = 1$

So, again 5^0 must equal 1.

We have shown that 3^0 must equal 1.

And that 5^0 must also equal 1.

The two examples above show that it does not matter what the base is at all!

> Any number to the power 0 must always equal 1
>
> $x^0 = 1$

NUMBER

NEGATIVE POWERS

Consider the calculation $729 \div 243$

Using your calculator: $729 \div 243 = 3$

Using index notation:

$$729 \div 243 = 3^6 \div 3^5 = \frac{\overset{1}{\cancel{3}} \times \overset{1}{\cancel{3}} \times \overset{1}{\cancel{3}} \times \overset{1}{\cancel{3}} \times \overset{1}{\cancel{3}} \times 3}{\underset{1}{\cancel{3}} \times \underset{1}{\cancel{3}} \times \underset{1}{\cancel{3}} \times \underset{1}{\cancel{3}} \times \underset{1}{\cancel{3}}} = 3^{6-5} = 3^1 = 3$$

Now, consider the calculation $243 \div 729$

Remember that the answer to this calculation will not be 3 as well, because we have already found that division is not commutative. (See the section on Division for a reminder here.)

Using your calculator: $243 \div 729 = 0 \cdot 333333333$

Using index notation: $243 \div 729 = 3^5 \div 3^6 = 3^{5-6} = 3^{-1}$

So, what does 3^{-1} mean?

$$243 \div 729 = 3^5 \div 3^6 = \frac{\overset{1}{\cancel{3}} \times \overset{1}{\cancel{3}} \times \overset{1}{\cancel{3}} \times \overset{1}{\cancel{3}} \times \overset{1}{\cancel{3}}}{\underset{1}{\cancel{3}} \times \underset{1}{\cancel{3}} \times \underset{1}{\cancel{3}} \times \underset{1}{\cancel{3}} \times \underset{1}{\cancel{3}} \times 3} = \frac{1}{3}$$

> Dividing 3's top and bottom again.

So, you can see that 3^{-1} means $\frac{1}{3}$

Your calculator has confirmed this answer, of course, because $0 \cdot 333333333$ is the decimal equivalent to the fraction $\frac{1}{3}$.

(You can check that this is so, if you need a reminder, by doing $1 \div 3$ on your calculator.)

EXAMPLE 2
Consider the calculation $729 \div 81$

Using your calculator: $729 \div 81 = 9$

Using index notation:

$$729 \div 81 = 3^6 \div 3^4 = \frac{\overset{1}{\cancel{3}} \times \overset{1}{\cancel{3}} \times \overset{1}{\cancel{3}} \times \overset{1}{\cancel{3}} \times 3 \times 3}{\underset{1}{\cancel{3}} \times \underset{1}{\cancel{3}} \times \underset{1}{\cancel{3}} \times \underset{1}{\cancel{3}}} = 3^{6-4} = 3^2 = 9$$

Now, consider the calculation $81 \div 729$

Again, this calculation will not give you 9 as before.

Using your calculator: $81 \div 729 = 0 \cdot 111111111$

Using index notation: $81 \div 729 = 3^4 \div 3^6 = 3^{4-6} = 3^{-2}$

So, what does 3^{-2} mean?

$$81 \div 729 = 3^4 \div 3^6 = \frac{\overset{1}{\cancel{3}} \times \overset{1}{\cancel{3}} \times \overset{1}{\cancel{3}} \times \overset{1}{\cancel{3}}}{\underset{1}{\cancel{3}} \times \underset{1}{\cancel{3}} \times \underset{1}{\cancel{3}} \times \underset{1}{\cancel{3}} \times 3 \times 3} = \frac{1}{3 \times 3} = \frac{1}{3^2}$$

So, you can see that 3^{-2} means $\frac{1}{3^2} = \frac{1}{9}$

Your calculator has confirmed this answer, of course, because $0 \cdot 111111111$ is the decimal equivalent to the fraction $\frac{1}{9}$.

You can check that this is so, if you need a reminder, by doing $1 \div 9$ on your calculator.

EXAMPLE 3

Consider the calculation $2187 \div 81$

Using your calculator: $2187 \div 81 = 27$

Using index notation:

$$2187 \div 81 = 3^7 \div 3^4 = \frac{\cancel{3} \times \cancel{3} \times \cancel{3} \times \cancel{3} \times 3 \times 3 \times 3}{\cancel{3} \times \cancel{3} \times \cancel{3} \times \cancel{3}} = 3^{7-4} = 3^3 = 27$$

Now, consider the calculation $81 \div 2187$

Again, this calculation will not give you 27 as before.

Using your calculator: $81 \div 2187 = 0 \cdot 037037037$

Using index notation: $81 \div 2187 = 3^4 \div 3^7 = 3^{4-7} = 3^{-3}$

So, what does 3^{-3} mean?

$$81 \div 2187 = 3^4 \div 3^7 = \frac{\cancel{3} \times \cancel{3} \times \cancel{3} \times \cancel{3}}{\cancel{3} \times \cancel{3} \times \cancel{3} \times \cancel{3} \times 3 \times 3 \times 3} = \frac{1}{3 \times 3 \times 3} = \frac{1}{3^3}$$

So, you can see that 3^{-3} means $\frac{1}{3^3} = \frac{1}{27}$

Check that your calculator has confirmed this answer, by doing the calculation $1 \div 27$ to show that you do obtain $0 \cdot 037037037$

So far we have found that:

Positive Power	Negative Power	
$3^1 = 3$	3^{-1} means $\frac{1}{3}$	$\frac{1}{3}$ is the **reciprocal** of 3
$3^2 = 9$	3^{-2} means $\frac{1}{3^2} = \frac{1}{9}$	$\frac{1}{9}$ is the reciprocal of 9
$3^3 = 27$	3^{-3} means $\frac{1}{3^3} = \frac{1}{27}$	$\frac{1}{27}$ is the reciprocal of 27

In general: 3^{-n} means $\frac{1}{3^n}$

THE POWER $\frac{1}{2}$

Consider $9^{\frac{1}{2}} \times 9^{\frac{1}{2}}$

As we are multiplying, we know that we should add the powers, like this:

$9^{\frac{1}{2}} \times 9^{\frac{1}{2}} = 9^1 = 9$

So, something multiplied by the **same thing** equals nine.
But, we know that 3×3 equals 9. So, the something must be 3!

So, $9^{\frac{1}{2}}$ must equal 3.
So, $9^{\frac{1}{2}}$ is exactly the same as finding the square root of 9!
So, $9^{\frac{1}{2}} = \sqrt{9} = 3$

NUMBER

In general:

$$n^{\frac{1}{2}} = \sqrt{n}$$

QUESTIONS 1.39

1. (i) Write these expression using index notation.
   (ii) Find the value of each expression.
   (iii) Use the power button on your calculator to check your answer to (ii).

(a) $5 \times 5 \times 5 \times 5 \times 5 \times 5 \times 5 \times 5$
(b) $8 \times 8 \times 8 \times 8 \times 8$
(c) $10 \times 10 \times 10 \times 10 \times 10$
(d) $2 \times 2 \times 2 \times 2 \times 2 \times 2 \times 2 \times 2 \times 2 \times 2$

2. Give the answer to each of the following calculations, (i) leaving your answer in index form, (ii) finding the value of each expression.

(a) $3^8 \times 3^7$
(b) $2^5 \times 2^7$
(c) $10^3 \times 10^5$
(d) $2^3 \times 2^4 \times 2^5$

(e) $3^8 \div 3^2$
(f) $2^9 \div 2^5$
(g) $10^6 \div 10$
(h) $2^4 \div 2^5$

(i) $2^3 \div 2^8$
(j) $10^3 \div 10^7$
(k) $\dfrac{10^3 \times 10^5}{10^7}$

(l) $\dfrac{2^6 \times 2^5}{2^2 \times 2^3}$

3. Are these statements true or false?

(a) $5^2 = 2^5$
(b) $4^2 = 2^4$

(c) $9^2 = 3^4$
(d) $3^2 + 3^4 = 729$

4. Write these expressions as fractions:

(a) 2^{-1}
(b) 2^{-2}

(c) 2^{-3}
(d) 4^{-2}

(e) 10^{-1}
(f) 10^{-2}

5. Find the value of these expressions:

(a) $100^{\frac{1}{2}}$
(b) $16^{\frac{1}{2}}$

(c) $64^{\frac{1}{2}}$
(d) $144^{\frac{1}{2}}$

INDICES USING ALGEBRA

All of the rules we have discovered so far work equally well when you are using algebra.

$a^1 = a$
$a^2 = a \times a$ called "a squared"
$a^3 = a \times a \times a$ called "a cubed"
$a^4 = a \times a \times a \times a$ called "a to the power 4"
$a^5 = a \times a \times a \times a \times a$ called "a to the power 5"
$a^6 = a \times a \times a \times a \times a \times a$ and so on ...
$a^7 = a \times a \times a \times a \times a \times a \times a$
$a^8 = a \times a \times a \times a \times a \times a \times a \times a$
$a^9 = a \times a \times a \times a \times a \times a \times a \times a \times a$
$a^{10} = a \times a \times a \times a \times a \times a \times a \times a \times a \times a$

Remember: $5a^2$ equals $5 \times a \times a$
                 $5a^2$ does **not** equal $(5a) \times (5a)$
                 $(5a)^2$ is what you need for $(5a) \times (5a)$

Look at the section in Algebra called Substituting In (Order of Operations) if you need a reminder of this.

$6ab^4$ means $6 \times a \times b \times b \times b \times b$

Notice that only the 'b' is raised to the power 4.

EXAMPLE 1

Simplify this expression: $3ab^4 \times 4a^3b^5$

$3ab^4 \times 4a^3b^5 = 3 \times a \times b^4 \times 4 \times a^3 \times b^5$

$3ab^4 \times 4a^3b^5 = 3 \times 4 \times a \times a^3 \times b^4 \times b^5$ .... re-arranging to put the numbers together, the a's together and the b's together.

$3ab^4 \times 4a^3b^5 = (3 \times 4) \times (a \times a^3) \times (b^4 \times b^5)$

$3ab^4 \times 4a^3b^5 = 12a^4b^9$

EXAMPLE 2

Find (a) $(5^2)^3$ (b) $(x^2)^3$ (c) $(x^a)^b$

(a) $(5^2)^3$ $= (5^2) \times (5^2) \times (5^2)$
            $= (5 \times 5) \times (5 \times 5) \times (5 \times 5)$
            $= 5^6$ ....Simply multiply the powers $2 \times 3 = 6$

(b) $(x^2)^3$ $= (x^2) \times (x^2) \times (x^2)$
            $= (x \times x) \times (x \times x) \times (x \times x)$
            $= x^6$ ....Simply multiply the powers $2 \times 3 = 6$

(c) $(x^a)^b$ $= x^{(a \times b)} = x^{ab}$ ....Simply multiply the powers $a \times b = ab$

QUESTIONS 1.40

1. If $a = 2$ and $b = 3$, work out the value of the following expressions:

(a) $a^2 \times a^3$

(b) a^5

(c) $3a^2$

(d) $(3a)^2$

(e) $a^2 + b^2$

(f) $(a + b)^2$

(g) $(2a^3b^2)^2$

(h) $6a^2b^3 + 2a^2b^3$

(i) $(a + b)^{-2}$

(j) $(ab)^{-2}$

2. Simplify these expressions:

(a) $a^3 \times 6a^2$

(b) $a^3 \times 6a^2b$

(c) $\dfrac{16x^4}{2x^3}$

(d) $\dfrac{3a^5}{a^2}$

(e) $\dfrac{3a^2}{a^5}$

(f) $\dfrac{6a^3b^4 \times 2ab^7}{3ab \times 4a^4b^3}$

(g) $\dfrac{16a^2b^6 \times 5a^2b^3}{3ab^2 \times 2a^3b}$

(h) $\dfrac{16a^2b^6 + 4a^2b^3}{2a^3b}$

(i) $(x^2y^3)^2$

(j) $(x^2y^3)^3$

STANDARD INDEX FORM

When I multiply 6000000 by 8000000 on my calculator, it gives the answer as:

$$\boxed{4 \cdot 8 \quad 13}$$

This is short for $4 \cdot 8 \times 10^{13}$

Don't forget to put in the '$\times 10$' and make the 13 the power when you write your answer down.

Try multiplying 6000000 by 8000000 on **your** calculator. What does your calculator give as the answer? Different makes of calculator have different ways of displaying large numbers. Make sure that you are familiar with the way your calculator works!

NUMBER

Using paper and pencil methods, you can work out that the answer must be 48000000000000, but the calculator simply hasn't got enough spaces on its display to give the whole of this number, so it uses a shorthand instead.

Writing 48000000000000 as $4 \cdot 8 \times 10^{13}$ is called using **Standard Index Form** or just **Standard Form.**

When you have a very large number such as 48000000000000, it does become quite difficult to read it correctly and you could easily mis-read the number of zeros. Using Standard Index Form, you can see directly that if you start with $4 \cdot 8$, you would have to move the decimal point 13 times to get to 48000000000000, as the 13 appears as the power of 10.

If you want to write 48000000000000 long hand, people often group the digits in threes, (starting at the right-hand end), like this:

48 000 000 000 000

A number in Standard Index Form is defined to be:

A number between 1 and 10	$\times$	A power of ten

Or, using algebra:

$$A \times 10^n$$

Where A must be between 1 and 10. Strictly speaking, A can be equal to 1, but it must be just less than 10.

This is most neatly written as: $1 \leqslant A < 10$

STANDARD FORM USING NEGATIVE POWERS

Look back at the section on negative powers for a reminder that:

$$10^{-1} = \tfrac{1}{10} \quad = 0 \cdot 1$$
$$10^{-2} = \tfrac{1}{100} \quad = 0 \cdot 01$$
$$10^{-3} = \tfrac{1}{1000} \quad = 0 \cdot 001$$
$$10^{-4} = \tfrac{1}{10000} \quad = 0 \cdot 0001$$

So, for example:
$$30000 = 3 \times 10000 = 3 \times 10^4$$
$$3000 = 3 \times 1000 = 3 \times 10^3$$
$$300 = 3 \times 100 = 3 \times 10^2$$
$$30 = 3 \times 10 = 3 \times 10^1$$
$$3 = 3 \times 1 = 3 \times 10^0$$
$$0 \cdot 3 = 3 \times 0 \cdot 1 = 3 \times 10^{-1}$$
$$0 \cdot 03 = 3 \times 0 \cdot 01 = 3 \times 10^{-2}$$
$$0 \cdot 003 = 3 \times 0 \cdot 001 = 3 \times 10^{-3}$$
$$0 \cdot 0003 = 3 \times 0 \cdot 0001 = 3 \times 10^{-4}$$

Remember that $10^0 = 1$

We can link these ideas in with the column headings described in the section on Place Value in Understanding Decimals. All of the column headings can be written in terms of powers of ten, like this:

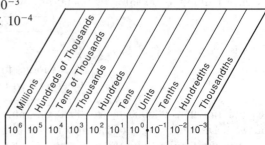

You can write any number in Standard Index form, but it is especially useful for very large or very small numbers.

So, an every day number, such as $7 = 7 \times 10^0$ in Standard Index Form.

A very large number:
The distance of Uranus from the Sun is $2 \cdot 87 \times 10^9$ km = 2 870 000 000

A very small number:
The mass of an electron is about $9 \cdot 1 \times 10^{-31}$ kg = 0·000 000 000 000 000 000 000 000 000 91

Make sure that you know how your calculator deals with numbers expressed in Standard Form.

EXAMPLE 1
Multiply 3×10^2 by 4×10^3 and give your answer in Standard Index Form.

$$3 \times 10^2 \times 4 \times 10^3 = 3 \times 4 \times 10^2 \times 10^3$$
$$= (3 \times 4) \times (10^2 \times 10^3)$$
$$= 12 \times 10^5 \quad \text{Remember that you add the powers when multiplying}$$

CAUTION!

> 12×10^5 is **not** the final answer and will not get you full marks in an exam! It is not in Standard Index Form, because the 12 is now bigger than ten, so it is outside the given limits.

So, $\quad 12 \times 10^5 = 1 \cdot 2 \times 10^1 \times 10^5 \quad$ ....writing 12 as $1 \cdot 2 \times 10^1$
$$= 1 \cdot 2 \times 10^6$$

So, the final answer is $1 \cdot 2 \times 10^6$ as this is in Standard Index Form.

QUESTIONS 1.41
1. Fill in the gaps in this table:

Calculation	Calculator Display on your calculator	Standard Index Form
3000 × 5 000 000		
20 000 × 80 000 000		
250 000 × 3 000 000		
54 000 000 × 3 200 000		
0·000000004 ÷ 20 000		
20 000 ÷ 0·000000004		
6400 ÷ 0·000000004		
0·000000065 ÷ 20 000		

2. Are these numbers in Standard Index Form? If they aren't, re-write them so they are:

(a) $3 \cdot 178463 \times 10^{-6}$

(b) 31×10^{-9}

(c) $0 \cdot 9998 \times 10^6$

(d) $10 \cdot 2 \times 10^{-3}$

3. Fill in the gaps in this table:

Number	Standard Index Form
23 000	
485 000 000 000	
3·71	
	$2·73 \times 10^{-7}$
	$4·93 \times 10^5$
	$3·9 \times 10^3$
0·00000000098	
	$5·26 \times 10^{-8}$
0·000000000562	
	$5·982 \times 10^6$

4. Work out these calculations, giving your answer in Standard Index Form.

(a) $2·54 \times 10^5 \times 7·45 \times 10^3$

(b) $7·8 \times 10^3 \times 9·54 \times 10^7$

(c) $\dfrac{8·4 \times 10^6}{2·1 \times 10^2}$

(d) $\dfrac{9·2 \times 10^7}{2 \times 10^3}$

(e) $8·5 \times 10^{13} \times 4·32 \times 10^{-5}$

(f) $\dfrac{9·5 \times 10^{11}}{8·5 \times 10^{-6}}$

5. Write these numbers in order of size, starting with the smallest:

$a = 4·2 \times 10^3$
$b = 2·8 \times 10^4$
$c = 9·1 \times 10^{-2}$
$d = 5679$

6. The speed of light is about $2·998 \times 10^5$ km/s.
The distance of the Earth from the Sun is about $1·5 \times 10^8$ km.
Find how long it takes light to reach Earth from the Sun.
(Speed = Distance ÷ Time)

▲ PERCENTAGES ▼

A percentage tells you "an amount out of 100".

A percentage can be written as a fraction out of 100.

So, 45 per cent means 45 out of 100 or $\dfrac{45}{100}$ and is written as 45%.

Most examinations are marked out of 100. In this case your final mark will be your percentage score. When marks are given as a percentage it is easy to compare different subjects, like this:

Subject	marks out of 100	Percentage
Maths	78	78%
Technology	91	91%
Science	83	83%
English	35	35%
Music	23	23%
Drama	38	38%

You can see at a glance where this person has strengths and weaknesses!

The half-yearly exams, however, have been marked out of different amounts:

Subject	Mark
Maths	$\frac{41}{50}$
Technology	$\frac{178}{200}$
Science	$\frac{18}{20}$
English	$\frac{27}{50}$
Music	$\frac{19}{25}$
Drama	$\frac{6}{10}$

It is now much harder to see where this person's strengths and weaknesses are!

We can turn all the marks into marks out of one hundred, like this:

Subject	Mark	Equivalent Mark out of 100	Method	Percentage
Maths	$\frac{41}{50}$	$\frac{82}{100}$	multiply top and bottom by 2	82%
Technology	$\frac{178}{200}$	$\frac{89}{100}$	divide top and bottom by 2	89%
Science	$\frac{18}{20}$	$\frac{90}{100}$	multiply top and bottom by 5	90%
English	$\frac{27}{50}$	$\frac{54}{100}$	multiply top and bottom by 2	54%
Music	$\frac{19}{25}$	$\frac{76}{100}$	multiply top and bottom by 4	76%
Drama	$\frac{6}{10}$	$\frac{60}{100}$	multiply top and bottom by 10	60%

The percentage column now shows at a glance that English and Drama are the subjects that need some attention!

QUESTIONS 1.42

Find the percentage scores for these pupils:

1. Tony:

Subject	Mark	Mark out of 100	Percentage
Maths	$\frac{35}{50}$		
Technology	$\frac{139}{200}$		
Science	$\frac{15}{20}$		
English	$\frac{39}{50}$		
Music	$\frac{23}{25}$		
Drama	$\frac{9}{10}$		

2. Shreeti:

Subject	Mark	Mark out of 100	Percentage
Maths	$\frac{47}{50}$		
Technology	$\frac{189}{200}$		
Science	$\frac{19}{20}$		
English	$\frac{19}{50}$		
Music	$\frac{11}{25}$		
Drama	$\frac{3}{10}$		

3. During the month of June, at a particular test centre, 87% of those people who took their driving test passed. What percentage failed their test during the month of June?

FRACTIONS, DECIMALS & PERCENTAGES

Fractions	$\frac{1}{2}$	$\frac{3}{4}$	$\frac{1}{10}$		$\frac{3}{20}$			$\frac{5}{8}$		
Decimals				0·7		0·375		0·65		0·22
Percentages			30		85				40	

Try to complete the gaps in the table. Can you find a method to move between fractions, decimals and percentages?

CHANGING FRACTIONS TO DECIMALS

Pupils often forget that $\frac{3}{4}$ means $3 \div 4$

Use your calculator to evaluate $3 \div 4$

The answer on your calculator is $0 \cdot 75$

CHANGING DECIMALS TO PERCENTAGES

To change $0 \cdot 75$ to a percentage, simply multiply by 100, to give 75%.

Look back at the section on Decimals if you need a reminder here, as $0 \cdot 75$ means 75 hundredths.

$0 \cdot 75 = \dfrac{75}{100} = 75\%$

CHANGING FRACTIONS TO PERCENTAGES

The History exam is marked out of 40. Abigail has scored 27 marks out of 40.

So, $\frac{27}{40}$ means $27 \div 40 = 0 \cdot 675$

Now take $0 \cdot 675$ and multiply by 100

So, Abigail's percentage is $0 \cdot 675 \times 100 = 67 \cdot 5\%$

Notice that this method will cope with the fraction, no matter how 'difficult' the numbers are! For example, the Economics exam is marked out of 37 marks! Leanne has scored 25 marks out of 37.

So, $\frac{25}{37}$ means $25 \div 37 = 0 \cdot 675675675.....$

Now take $0 \cdot 675675675...$ and multiply by 100

So, Leanne's percentage is $0 \cdot 675675675 \times 100 = 67 \cdot 6$ (to 1 dec. pl.)

CHANGING DECIMALS TO FRACTIONS

$0 \cdot 7 = \dfrac{7}{10}$ $\qquad\qquad$ $0 \cdot 24 = \dfrac{24}{100}$ $\qquad\qquad$ $0 \cdot 375 = \dfrac{375}{1000}$ $\qquad$ and so on!

We must now get our fractions in their simplest form.

$\dfrac{24}{100} = \dfrac{2 \times 12}{2 \times 50} = \dfrac{12}{50} = \dfrac{2 \times 6}{2 \times 25} = \dfrac{6}{25}$

$\dfrac{375}{1000} = \dfrac{5 \times 75}{5 \times 200} = \dfrac{75}{200} = \dfrac{5 \times 15}{5 \times 40} = \dfrac{15}{40} = \dfrac{5 \times 3}{5 \times 8} = \dfrac{3}{8}$

CHANGING PERCENTAGES TO FRACTIONS

Percentages are simply fractions, where the bottom line (the denominator) is 100.

So, 87% means $\frac{87}{100}$

Notice that it makes no difference how 'difficult' the numbers are. Simply put your percentage over 100, like this:

17% means $\frac{17}{100}$

24% means $\frac{24}{100}$ .... which we already know is $\frac{6}{25}$

NUMBER

87·5% means $\frac{87·5}{100}$

This doesn't look correct, because we have a decimal within a fraction. The best way to cope here is to multiply top and bottom by 10, so that I have made the top line into a whole number, like this:

$$\frac{87·5}{100} = \frac{875}{1000}$$

Now, we can divide top and bottom, as before, like this:

$$\frac{875}{1000} = \frac{5 \times 175}{5 \times 200} = \frac{175}{200} = \frac{5 \times 35}{5 \times 40} = \frac{5 \times 7}{5 \times 8} = \frac{7}{8}$$

CHANGING PERCENTAGES TO DECIMALS

87% means $\frac{87}{100}$ which means $87 \div 100 = 0·87$

45·8% means $\frac{45·8}{100}$ which means $45·8 \div 100 = 0·458$

So, you should now be able to complete the earlier table, to look like this:

Fractions	$\frac{1}{2}$	$\frac{3}{4}$	$\frac{1}{10}$	$\frac{3}{10}$	$\frac{7}{10}$	$\frac{3}{20}$	$\frac{17}{20}$	$\frac{3}{8}$	$\frac{5}{8}$	$\frac{13}{20}$	$\frac{2}{5}$	$\frac{11}{50}$
Decimals	0·5	0·75	0·1	0·3	0·7	0·15	0·85	0·375	0·625	0·65	0·4	0·22
Percentages	50	75	10	30	70	15	85	37·5	62·5	65	40	22

EXAMPLE 1

In the election for parent governors at my school, the votes cast were as follows:

Elaine Hammley 204
Nicholas Winter 187
Peter Figuieredo 237

Find the percentage of the votes cast that each person received.

Firstly, find the total number of votes cast, like this: $204 + 187 + 237 = 628$

So, the percentage of the votes polled by each person is calculated like this:

Elaine Hammley: $\frac{204}{628} \times 100 = 32·5\%$ (to one decimal place)

Nicholas Winter: $\frac{187}{628} \times 100 = 29·8\%$ (to one decimal place)

Peter Figuieredo: $\frac{237}{628} \times 100 = 37·7\%$ (to one decimal place)

Notice that these percentages add to 100%, as we have accounted for all the votes cast. [Sometimes, your answers might not add to 100% **exactly**, as we have rounded each answer up or down to one decimal place.]

QUESTIONS 1.43
1. Fill in the gaps in this table:

Fractions	$\frac{1}{4}$			$\frac{9}{10}$			$\frac{7}{8}$	$\frac{1}{3}$	$\frac{2}{3}$		$\frac{23}{48}$	
Decimals		0·6			0·35					0·54		
Percentages			80			65						17·5

2. At a local election, the votes cast were as follows:

Chris Peters   2724
Ian Anderson   1892
Rosalind Griffiths   2934

Find the percentage of the vote that each candidate received.

FINDING A PERCENTAGE OF AN AMOUNT

EXAMPLE 1: SALE PRICES: In a sale, a shop might advertise "15% off everything!"

A camera costs £225 before the sale starts. What will it cost when the 15% discount is deducted?

So, we need to find 15% of £225 $15\% = \dfrac{15}{100}$

"of" here means times or multiply, as in '6 lots of 7'

So,   15% of £225

$$= \dfrac{15}{100} \times £225$$

You can use your calculator to evaluate this. Type into your calculator

either: $15 \times 225 \div 100$

or: $15 \div 100 \times 225$

Check that both give the same answer!

$$\dfrac{15}{100} \times £225 = £33 \cdot 75$$

So, the sale price must be $£225 - £33 \cdot 75 = £191 \cdot 25$

EXAMPLE 2: COMPOUND INTEREST
On the 1st of January, I invested £300 at 5% interest. The interest is paid a year later. What is my investment worth at the end of the first year?

I must find 5% of £300 and add this amount on to the £300.

So,   5% of £300

$$= \dfrac{5}{100} \times £300 = £15$$

So, a year later, the investment is worth $£300 + £15 = £315$

What is the investment worth after two years? I'll assume here that I don't put any more money in or take any out!

> **CAUTION!**
>
> The answer to this question is **not** £330!
>
> This seems like the logical answer, but, for the second year I receive interest on the original £300 **and** on the extra £15 interest. This is called **compound interest.**

So, I must find 5% of **£315** and add this on to the £315.

NUMBER

So,   5% of £315

$$= \frac{5}{100} \times £315 = £15 \cdot 75$$

So, after two years the investment is now worth £315 + £15·75 , which equals £330·75 altogether.

EXAMPLE 3: DEPRECIATION

A new car costs £9500. A year later, the car is worth much less(!). This is called depreciation. It is estimated that the depreciation is 18% each year.

What is the value of the car at the end of the first year?

I must find 18% of £9500 and subtract this from £9500.

So,   18% of £9500 $= \frac{18}{100} \times £9500 = £1710$

So, after the end of the first year, the car is now worth £9500 − £1710 = £7790.

What is the car worth at the end of the second year?

> **CAUTION!**
> The answer to this question is not found by £7790 subtract £1710.
> (So, the answer is **not** £7790 − £1710 = £6080)
> The depreciation is now 18% of **£7790**.

So, $\frac{18}{100} \times £7790 = £1402 \cdot 20$

The depreciation is less this year, because the car itself is already worth less. So after the end of two years the car is now worth £7790 − £1402·20 = £6387·80

EXAMPLE 4: VAT

A computer costs £1700 before VAT is added. What is the cost of the computer after VAT is added on?

At the time of writing, VAT is at the rate of 17·5% .

I must calculate 17·5% of £1700 and add this amount on to £1700 for the final amount.

So,   17·5% of £1700

$$= \frac{17 \cdot 5}{100} \times £1700 = £297 \cdot 50$$

> Notice that it doesn't matter that VAT is such an awkward amount as 17·5%! Just do the same type of calculation as you did before.

So, the computer will cost £1700 + £297·50 = £1997·50

THE SCALE FACTOR METHOD

All of the examples in the previous section can be done by the scale factor method!

EXAMPLE 1: SALE PRICES

Sale: "15% off everything"!

A camera costs £225 before the sale starts. What will it cost when the 15% discount is deducted?

Scale Factor	$= 100\% - 15\%$	...we start with 100% and the sale takes 15% off
	$= 85\%$	.....that leaves 85% of the original price to pay
	$= \dfrac{85}{100}$	
Scale Factor	$= 0\cdot85$	

So, the **Sale Price** $=$ **Old Price** $\times$ **Scale Factor**
$= £225 \times 0\cdot85$
$= £191\cdot25$ ... as before

EXAMPLE 2: COMPOUND INTEREST

I have invested £300 on the 1st of January at 5% interest. The interest is paid a year later. What is my investment worth at the end of the first year?

Scale Factor	$= 100\% + 5\%$	...I start with 100% and the bank adds on 5%
	$= 105\%$	...I have more than I started with ...
	$= \dfrac{105}{100}$	
Scale Factor	$= 1\cdot05$	

So, the **New Amount** $=$ **Old Amount** $\times$ **Scale Factor**
$= £300 \times 1\cdot05$
$= £315\cdot00$ ......as before

Notice that once I have calculated the Scale Factor, then I can find the value of the investment at the end of the second year straight away, like this:

Value of the investment at $=$ **Value of the investment at** $\times$ **Scale Factor**
the end of the second year   **the end of the first year**

$= £315\cdot00 \times 1\cdot05$
$= £330\cdot75$ ......as before

Notice that I can now keep multiplying by the scale factor, to find the value of the investment after 3 years, 4 years and so on, like this:

Value after 3 years $=$ **Value after 2 years** $\times$ **Scale Factor**
$= £330\cdot75 \times 1\cdot05$
$= £347\cdot2875$
$= £347\cdot29$ ...... to the nearest penny

Value after 4 years $=$ **Value after 3 years** $\times$ **Scale Factor**
$= £347\cdot29 \times 1\cdot05$
$= £364\cdot6545$
$= £364\cdot65$ ...... to the nearest penny

EXAMPLE 3: DEPRECIATION

A new car costs £9500. A year later, the car is worth much less(!). This is called depreciation. It is estimated that the depreciation is 18% each year.

What is the value of the car at the end of the first year?

Scale Factor	$= 100\% - 18\%$	...we start with 100% but the car loses 18% of its value
	$= 82\%$	.....that leaves 82% of the original value of the car
	$= \dfrac{82}{100}$	
Scale Factor	$= 0\cdot82$	

So, **Value after 1 year** = **Value when new** × **Scale Factor**
= £9500 × 0·82
= £7790 ...as before

Notice that I can now, as in example 2, keep multiplying by the scale factor to find the value of the car after 2 years or after 3 years, like this:

Value after 2 years = **Value after 1 year** × **Scale Factor**
= £7790 × 0·82
= £6387·80 ...as before

Value after 3 years = **Value after 2 years** × **Scale Factor**
= £6387·80 × 0·82
= £5237·996
= £5238·00 ...to the nearest penny

We have made the assumption here that the depreciation will stay at 18% for each year. This assumption might not be realistic, because as a car gets older, it probably loses less of its value each year.

EXAMPLE 4: VAT

A computer costs £1700 before VAT is added. What is the cost of the computer after VAT is added on?

Scale Factor = 100% + VAT
= 100% + 17·5%
= 117·5%
= $\frac{117·5}{100}$
= 1·175

New Price = **Old Price** × **Scale Factor**
= £1700 × 1·175
= £1997·50 ...as before

Notice that the scale factor method is an excellent way to add on VAT! If you worked in a shop where you had to add on the VAT to the many different goods you were selling, all you need to do is to multiply the Old Price by the Scale Factor each time. So, all you have to do is to multiply by 1·175 each time.

QUESTIONS 1.44

(Use which ever method you like for questions 1 to 6)

1. Three partners in a business agree to share any profits so that Archibald gets 45%, Becky gets 30% and Clarence gets 25%. This year they make £8750 profit. How much does each one get?

2. I have invested some money at 7% interest. If I put £550 in the account, how much money do I have altogether at the end of the first year?

3. A particular make of new car loses about 15% of its value each year. Alan paid £17 000 for a new car. What is the car worth when it is one year old? What will the car be worth at the end of the second year?

4. A television costs £650. The shop has a sale, where all prices are reduced by 15%. What is the cost of the television in the sale?

5. The cost of a computer is £1050 excluding VAT. What is the cost of the computer when VAT is added on?

6. Four business partners agree to share any profit so that Amy gets 20%, Brian gets 25%, Christopher gets 40% and Debbie gets 15%. This year they make £32 000. How much does each one get?

USE THE SCALE FACTOR METHOD FOR THE QUESTIONS THAT FOLLOW!

7. A new car costs £22 000. Its value falls by 14% each year.

   (a) Calculate how much the car is worth after 1 year.
   (b) Calculate how much the car is worth after 2 years.
   (c) Calculate how much the car is worth after 3 years.

8. I invest some money at 6% interest. I put £12 000 in at the start of one year and I don't take any money out or put any more in.

   (a) How much is my investment worth at the end of 1 year?
   (b) How much is my investment worth at the end of 2 years?
   (c) How much is my investment worth at the end of 3 years?

9. These are the costs of some goods before VAT is added on. Calculate the costs of the goods including VAT:

   (a) double bed £500   (c) garden table and chairs £450
   (b) table and chairs £850   (d) settee £950

10. What is £420 increased by 16%?

REVERSE PERCENTAGES

My local bicycle shop has a sale: "20% off all bikes". During the sale, I buy a new bicycle for £384. What did the bicycle cost before the sale started?

> **CAUTION!**
>
> Many pupils don't read this sort of question carefully enough! They see that the sale has led to a 20% reduction, so they find 20% of £384 and add this amount on to £384. This does not lead to the correct answer!

The question has asked us to find the cost of the bicycle before the sale started. The shopkeepers have found 20% of this amount (which, obviously, we don't actually know yet!) and taken this off the cost of the bicycle.

What we do know is that, for a sale, we can find the scale factor, like this:

Scale Factor = 100% − 20% ...we start with 100% and the sale takes off 20%
             = 80% ... that leaves 80% of the original price to pay
             = $\frac{80}{100}$
Scale Factor = 0·8

Now we can use the same formula as before:

| Sale Price = Old Price × Scale Factor |

Now, this time we know the Sale Price (£384) and the Scale Factor (0·8). Substitute in what we know, like this:

Sale Price = Old Price × Scale Factor
    £384 = Old Price × 0·8

So, to find the Old Price, we must divide both sides by 0·8. (See the sections on solving equations if you need a reminder here.)

£384 ÷ 0·8 = Old Price
£480   = Old Price

> You can check that this is the correct answer, by finding 20% of £480 and taking that amount away from £480, to leave you £384.

So, the cost of the bicycle was £480 before the sale!

QUESTIONS 1.45

1. I buy a coat in a sale where the shop has reduced everything by 20%. I paid £96 for the coat. How much did the coat cost before the sale?

2. I buy a sweat shirt from a shop where they have a sale with 10% off all marked prices at the moment. I pay £40·50 for the sweat shirt. What was its price before the sale?

3. At my local furniture shop they have a sale with 15% off everything. I take this chance to buy a new dining room table and I pay them £340 for it. How much did the table cost before the sale?

4. I have been staying at a hotel for my holidays. The food has been delicious and I have put some weight on! My weight has increased by 8% and I now weigh 54 kg. What did I weigh before the holiday?

5. So I now weigh 54 kg! If I go down to my local gymnasium and start exercising and work off 8% of my weight, what will I weigh then?

6. A friend of mine has been to a health farm. He has told me that he has lost 10% of his previous weight and now weighs 72 kg. What did he weigh before?

7. A computer costs £1645 after VAT at 17·5% has been added. What was the cost of the computer before VAT was added?

8. A shop advertises a video at £376 including VAT. What is the cost of the video excluding VAT?

9. A camcorder costs £564 including VAT. What is the cost of the camcorder excluding VAT?

10. A new car costs £18 800 after VAT is added on. What is the cost of the car before VAT is included?

TWO-WAY TABLES

A Two-Way table is a convenient way of storing information. Below is a Two-Way table showing the numbers of students at a local college, put into these categories.

	Male	Female
Arts	259	348
Science	643	481

It is called a Two-Way table, because the information goes in two directions! Going across, students are put into the male column or the female column. Going down, students are either put into the Arts row or into the Science row.

We can usefully add a row and column total, like this:

	Male	Female	Total
Arts	259	348	607
Science	643	481	1124
Total	902	829	

I can add the grand total of 1731, which gives the number of students who attend the college, like this:

	Male	Female	Total
Arts	259	348	607
Science	643	481	1124
Total	902	829	1731

I can use the table to help answer questions, such as:

What percentage **of the science students** is female?

As I have been asked about the science students, I am going to draw a loop around the Science part of the table, like this:

	Male	Female	Total
Arts	259	348	607
Science	643	481	1124
Total	902	829	1731

The percentage of Science Students who are female $= \dfrac{\text{Number of female scientists}}{\text{Total number of scientists}} \times 100 = \dfrac{481}{1124} \times 100$

The percentage of Science Students who are female $= 42 \cdot 8\%$ (to 1 dec pl)

What percentage of **male students** studies the arts?

As I have been asked about male students, I am going to draw a loop around the male student section of the table, like this:

	Male	Female	Total
Arts	259	348	607
Science	643	481	1124
Total	902	829	1731

The percentage of male students who study the arts $= \dfrac{\text{Number of male arts students}}{\text{Total number of male students}} \times 100 = \dfrac{259 \times 100}{902}$

The percentage of Male Students who study the arts $= 28 \cdot 7\%$ (to 1 dec pl)

QUESTIONS 1.46

1. I asked the whole of Year 7 whether they are right-handed or left-handed, and recorded their replies in a Two-Way table, like this:

	Boys	Girls	Total
Right-handed	118	78	196
Left-handed	17	25	42
Total	135	103	238

(a) Of the boys, what percentage is left-handed?

(b) What percentage of left-handed people are girls?

2. I carried out a survey of students in Year 12, to find out how many are vegetarians, and recorded the results in a Two-Way table, like this:

	Males	Females	Total
Vegetarian	27	52	79
Meat-eating	131	117	248
Total	158	169	327

(a) What percentage of the females is vegetarian?

(b) Of the vegetarians, what percentage is male?

3. The Headteacher has done some research to find out the destination of all the pupils from last year's Year 11. This is how she has recorded her findings:

	Stayed on	Further education at another school or college	Work	Looking for work	Total
Males	85	8	18	12	123
Females	102	5	5	3	115
Totals	187	13	23	15	238

(a) What is the percentage of males still looking for work?

(b) Of those who stayed on, what percentage is female?

(c) What percentage of the females went out to work?

PERCENTAGE PROFIT & LOSS

A young business man called Henry has opened a shop selling pictures, pottery and hand-made jewellery. He decides to make £25 profit on each item that he buys in from local artists and crafts people.

So, when he buys a pottery vase for £25, he wants to sell it for £50.

When he buys a pair of silver earrings for £100, he wants to sell them for £125.

He realises that he has invested £100 to make £25 profit for the earrings, but that he has invested only £25 to make £25 profit for the vase.

We need to define Percentage Profit to help Henry understand his business venture more fully!

$$\text{Percentage Profit} = \frac{\text{Actual Profit}}{\text{What it cost Henry originally}} \times 100$$

For the vase, the percentage profit $= \dfrac{£25}{£25} \times 100 = 100\%$

For the earrings, the percentage profit $= \dfrac{£25}{£100} \times 100 = 25\%$

Businesses usually try to set their prices so that their percentage profit stays about the same, no matter how much money the items cost in the first place. So, Henry needs to re-assess his policy of making £25 profit on every item, regardless of how much that item is costing him in the first place.

If he charged £37·50 for the vase and £150 for the earrings, the percentage profit would then be calculated like this:

For the vase, the actual profit is £37·50 − £25 = £12·50

So, the percentage profit $= \dfrac{£12 \cdot 50}{£25} \times 100 = 50\%$

For the earrings, the actual profit is £150 − £100 = £50

So, the percentage profit $= \dfrac{£50}{£100} \times 100 = 50\%$

Henry would now make 50% profit on both items.

This formula can be adapted for other situations, such as making a loss. Henry buys a water colour from a local artist for £80, but it doesn't sell! He keeps reducing the price, until the picture finally sells for £45. So, we can give the Percentage Loss as:

$$\text{Percentage Loss} = \frac{\text{Actual Loss}}{\text{What it cost Henry originally}} \times 100$$

Henry has made an actual loss of £35.

So, the Percentage Loss $= \dfrac{£35}{£80} \times 100 = 43 \cdot 75\%$

PERCENTAGE INCREASE AND DECREASE

I have read in the newspaper that a company executive has had a pay increase! His salary was £255 000, but has now gone up to £330 000.

His actual increase is £75 000.

Re-writing the formula, to give the Percentage Increase, like this:

$$\text{Percentage Increase} = \frac{\text{Actual Increase}}{\text{What it was originally}} \times 100$$

So, the Percentage Increase $= \dfrac{£75\ 000}{£255\ 000} \times 100 = 29 \cdot 4\%$ to 1 dec place

We can also give the Percentage Decrease, like this:

$$\text{Percentage Decrease} = \frac{\text{Actual Decrease}}{\text{What it was originally}} \times 100$$

QUESTIONS 1.47

1. Find the percentage profit or loss for these items that Henry sells in his shop:

Item	What Henry paid for the item	What Henry sold it for
Painting	£50	£70
Silver ring	£20	£37·50
Statue	£125	£180
Vase	£40	£35
Water colour	£18	£25
Pottery table lamp	£38	£55
Silver pendant	£60	£55
Water colour	£85	£70

2. A car dealer bought a car in at an auction for £6755, then sold it the next week at her show-rooms for £8150. What percentage profit did she make?

3. A rectangle measures 5 cm by 12 cm.
   (a) What is the area of the rectangle?
   (b) Increase the length of each side by 10% (Use the Scale Factor Method). What is the length of each side now?
   (c) Find the new area. Write down all decimal places in your answer.
   (d) What is the increase in area?
   (e) What is the percentage increase in area?
   (f) Can you explain your answer to (e)?

4. A rectangle measures 7 cm by 18 cm.
   (a) What is the area of the rectangle?
   (b) Increase the length of each side by 10% (Use the Scale Factor Method). What is the length of each side now?
   (c) Find the new area. Write down all decimal places in your answer.
   (d) What is the increase in area?
   (e) What is the percentage increase in area?
   (f) Can you explain your answer to (e)?
   (g) Can you explain your answers to both question 3 and 4?!

5. I have just read in a newspaper that, because of speculation about a takeover bid, Manchester United's shares have increased in value on the Stock Market. At the end of the day, the shares were worth 513 pence each, a rise of 61 pence. What percentage increase is this? Give your answer to one decimal place.

6. The excitement also rubbed off on Tottenham Hotspur shares, which gained 11 pence to finish at 450 pence. What percentage increase is this?
   Give your answer to one decimal place.

7. Chelsea's shares also went up 2 pence to 86 pence. What percentage increase is this? Give your answer to one decimal place.

▲ RATIO AND PROPORTION ▼

Two friends decide to set up their own business. Abigail puts in £3000 to start the business, but Bruce puts in only £2000. So, they decide that at the end of the first year of business, they will share their profits (assuming that they make any!) to take account of the fact that Abigail has put in more money than Bruce.

Abigail : Bruce

£3000 : £2000

£3 × 1000 : £2 × 1000

Which we can write as   3 : 2   ..... in its simplest form.

£3000:£2000 is called a ratio, because I am comparing two amounts of money.
3:2 is £3000:£2000 in its simplest form.

You can divide ratios in exactly the same way as you can divide fractions.

If they make only £5 profit, you can easily see that Abigail will get £3 and Bruce will get £2. If they make a profit which is a multiple of £5, the profit is easy to calculate, like this:

Profit	Abigail	Bruce
£5	£3	£2
£10 = £5 × 2	£3 × 2 = £6	£2 × 2 = £4
£15 = £5 × 3	£3 × 3 = £9	£2 × 3 = £6
£20 = £5 × 4	£3 × 4 = £12	£2 × 4 = £8
£25 = £5 × 5	£3 × 5 = £15	£2 × 5 = £10

and so on ...

We need a method which will work no matter what the profit is!

Suppose that the profit they earn in the first year is £641.

Put the money in to 5 equal piles. To do this I need to divide £641 by 5, like this:

£641 ÷ 5 = £128·20

| £128·20 | £128·20 | £128·20 | £128·20 | £128·20 |

Now, remember that the ratio is: Abigail: Bruce
                                      3: 2

So, whatever amount of money is in each pile, Abigail will get three piles and Bruce will get two piles, like this:

Abigail   Bruce

So, Abigail will get £128·20 × 3 = £384·60

And, Bruce will get £128·20 × 2 = £256·40

Sometimes you will be asked to express the ratio of Abigail:Bruce in the form 1:n.

Abigail:Bruce
3:2

So, I must divide both parts of the ratio by 3, like this:

Abigail: Bruce

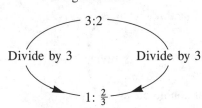

3:2

Divide by 3   Divide by 3

$1: \frac{2}{3}$

This means for every £1 Abigail takes, Bruce can take only $\frac{2}{3}$rds of a pound (67p to the nearest penny).

Sometimes you will be asked to express the ratio of Abigail:Bruce in the form m:1.

Abigail:Bruce
3:2

So, I must divide both parts of the ratio by 2, like this:

Abigail: Bruce

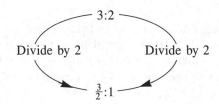

3:2

Divide by 2   Divide by 2

$\frac{3}{2}:1$

This means for every £1 Bruce takes, Abigail can take $\frac{3}{2}$ pounds = £1·50.

EQUIVALENT RATIOS

So, all these ratios are equivalent:

$$\text{Abigail: Bruce}$$
$$3000:2000$$
$$3:2$$
$$1:\frac{2}{3}$$
$$\frac{3}{2}:1$$

To get from one ratio to the next, I have multiplied or divided both sides by the same number.

PROPORTION

I have just looked up how to make a pudding called Crème Brûlée in my recipe book. I need these ingredients:

> half a pint of double cream (285 ml)
> 3 egg yolks
> 1 tablespoon of caster sugar
> 2 level teaspoons of cornflour
> 3 oz granulated sugar

I have 4 eggs in the fridge, which I would like to use up! How much double cream should I use, to keep the mixture right?

> 3 eggs go with 285 ml of double cream

I can divide both sides by 3, to find the amount of double cream needed for 1 egg, like this:

3 eggs go with 285 ml double cream

divide by 3   divide by 3

1 egg goes with 95 ml double cream

Now I need to find the amount of double cream needed for 4 eggs. So, I can multiply both sides by 4, like this:

1 egg goes with 95 ml double cream

multiply by 4   multiply by 4

4 eggs go with 380 ml double cream

So, if I am going to use up 4 eggs, to make more of the mixture, I must use 380 ml of double cream. I must increase the quantities of all the other ingredients in the same way. The amount of each ingredient must stay in the same **proportion** as the original recipe. See if you can find the quantities of the other ingredients which I will need for my 4 egg version of the recipe.

MAPS AND SCALES

My Ordnance Survey map has a scale of 1:50 000.

This means that 1 cm on the map represents 50 000 cm in reality.

Map : Reality
1 cm : 50 000 cm   [100 cm = 1 m ... so, divide by 100 to change cm to m]
1 cm : 500 m   [1000m = 1 km ... so, divide by 1000 to change m to km]
1 cm : 0·5 km

EXAMPLE 1

The straight line distance between Ruddington and Plumtree is 7 cm on the map. How far apart are they in reality?

Map : Reality
1 cm : 50 000 cm   ...dividing by 100
1 cm : 500 m   ...dividing by 1000
1 cm : 0·5 km

multiply by 7   multiply by 7

7 cm : 3·5 km

So, Ruddington and Plumtree are 3·5 km apart in reality.

EXAMPLE 2

If two places are 17 km apart in reality, how far apart will they appear on the map?

Again, start from what you know:

Map : Reality
1 cm : 50 000 cm   ...dividing by 100
1 cm : 500 m   ....dividing by 1000
1 cm : 0·5 km

multiply by 2   multiply by 2

2 cm : 1 km

Multiply both sides by 2, to make the right-hand side equal to 1 km.

2 cm : 1 km

multiply by 17   multiply by 17

34 cm : 17 km

The two places will be 34 cm apart on the map.

QUESTIONS 1.48

1. Write each of the following ratios in their simplest form. The first one is done for you!
   (a) 1 week : 1 day
       7 days : 1 day   ....write both sides in the same units!
          7 : 1

   (b) 20 minutes : 2 hours   (e) 20 metres : 1 km   (h) 200 ml : 1 litre
   (c) 20 minutes : 2 days   (f) 200 grams : 1 kg   (i) 250 ml : 3 litres
   (d) £5 : 40p   (g) 250 grams : 1·2 kg   (j) 48 cm : 5 metres

2. Express the following ratios in the form 1:n
   (a) 3 : 18
   (b) 2 : 21
   (c) 5 : 24
   (d) 0·5 : 10
   (e) 12 : 156
   (f) 0·4 : 24
   (g) 12 : 3
   (h) 10 : 7
   (i) 16 :0·8
   (j) 0·18 : 76

3. Express the following ratios in the form n:1
   (a) 22 : 2   (b) 32 : 0·5   (c) 56 : 5   (d) 26 : 0·6

4. (a) Divide £600 in the ratio 1 : 2
   (b) Divide £600 in the ratio 2 : 3
   (c) Divide £350 in the ratio 4 : 3
   (d) Divide £572 in the ratio 9 : 2
   (e) Divide £1150 in the ratio 11 : 14
   (f) Divide £600 in the ratio 1 : 2 : 3
   (g) Divide £600 in the ratio 2 : 3 : 5
   (h) Divide £672 in the ratio 5 : 7 : 2
   (i) Divide £1125 in the ratio 5 : 9 : 1
   (j) Divide £612·50 in the ratio 5 : 8 : 12

5. I have bought a bottle of concentrated fruit juice. On the label it says that the contents of the bottle must be diluted with one part of the concentrate to seven parts of water. If I wish to make up a litre of juice ready to drink, how much water do I need? How much of the concentrated juice do I need?

6. **Five** miles is about the same as **eight** kilometres. (a) In a French town I see a sign saying that the speed limit is 60 km per hour. What is this in miles per hour, approximately? (b) What is 70 mph in km per hour, approximately?

7. A recipe for spaghetti Bolognese uses 10 ounces of spaghetti for 4 people. How much spaghetti will I need to feed (a) 2 people (b) 3 people (c) 5 people (d) 17 people?

8. The mass of 5·8 cm³ of a metal is 95g. What is the mass of 12·7 cm³? What is the volume of 128g of the same metal?

9. A train is travelling at a steady speed and covers 30 km in 24 minutes. How far will it travel in 40 minutes if it continues to travel at the same speed?

10. A model is made of a real yacht, using a scale of 1 : 50. The boom on the model is 12 cm long. (a) How long is the boom on the real yacht? The length of the real yacht is 9 metres. (b) How long is the model?

11. The scale on a map is given as 1 : 25 000. (a) Two places are 3 cm apart on the map. How far apart are they in reality? (b) Two other places are 19 km apart in reality. How far apart will they be on the map?

12. My road map of Europe has a scale of 1 : 4 000 000. (a) On the map, the distance between Paris and Marseille is 16·5 cm. How far apart are they in reality? (b) As the crow flies, Madrid is 12·5 cm away from Barcelona on the map. How far apart are they in reality?

ALGEBRA

▲ *PRACTISING ALGEBRA* ▼

SIMPLIFYING

Algebra uses letters for numbers!
To understand how algebra works, you must be very clear about how numbers work!

Using Numbers
You can see that: $3 + 3 + 3 + 3 + 3 = 15 = 5 \times 3$
                                                       $= 5$ lots of three

Using Algebra
If $a = 3$, we
could write this as: $a + a + a + a + a = 5 \times a$
                                                    $= 5$ lots of a

We usually shorten $5 \times a$ even more to be just $5a$

EXAMPLE I

Using Numbers:

Add $3 + 3 + 3 + 3 + 3$ to $3 + 3 + 3$

$(3 + 3 + 3 + 3 + 3) + (3 + 3 + 3) = 3 + 3 + 3 + 3 + 3 + 3 + 3 + 3$
      5×3 $+$ 3×3 $=$ 8×3
        15           $+$ 9 $=$ 24   (which is correct)

Using Algebra:

Add $a + a + a + a + a$ to $a + a + a$

$(a + a + a + a + a) + (a + a + a) = a + a + a + a + a + a + a + a$
        5a $+$ 3a $=$ 8a

Check that if $a = 3$, then you get an answer of $8a = 8 \times 3 = 24$ as before.

COLLECTING LIKE TERMS

It is always a good idea to make the algebra in your final answer as simple as possible. Suppose you had an answer of:

$7a + 2b + 5a + 3b$

You can re-write this, by putting all the a's together and all the b's together:

$(7a + 5a) + (2b + 3b)$ This is called **collecting like terms**

So, we can write this as: $(7a + 5a) + (2b + 3b) = 12a + 5b$

Using Numbers: Check that this makes sense by trying some numbers. Put $a = 2$ and $b = 3$.

$7a + 2b + 5a + 3b = (7 \times 2) + (2 \times 3) + (5 \times 2) + (3 \times 3)$
                                $=$ 14 $+$ 6 $+$ 10 $+$ 9
                                $=$ 39

Or, collect like terms first, then substitute in the values of a and b:

$$12a + 5b = (12 \times 2) + (5 \times 3)$$
$$= \quad 24 \quad + \quad 15$$
$$= \quad 39 \quad \text{(as before!)}$$

EXAMPLE 2
Simplify the following: $8a - (-7a)$

$8a - (-7a) = 8a + 7a = 15a$ [Read the notes on negative numbers]

EXAMPLE 3
Simplify the following: $5a + 7$

> **CAUTION!**
>
> $5a + 7$ does NOT equal $12a$!
>
> Check by trying a number to show that this does not work. When $a = 2$, the algebraic expression $5a + 7$ equals $10 + 7$ which is 17.
> $12a$, however, is 12×2 which equals 24, not 17.
> So, $5a + 7$ does not give the same as $12a$.

So, $5a + 7$ is already in the simplest form it can be.

EXAMPLE 4
Simplify the following: $3a \times 4$

You can think of this algebraic expression as being three numbers multiplied together:

$3a \times 4 = 3 \times a \times 4$ ......but when you multiply the order makes no difference to the answer.

So, rearrange the order: $3 \times a \times 4 = 3 \times 4 \times a$
$$= 12a$$

So, $3a \times 4 = 12a$ ....which looks much tidier!

EXAMPLE 5
Simplify the following: $4a \times (-5a)$

$$4a \times (-5a) = 4 \times a \times (-5) \times a$$
$$= 4 \times (-5) \times a \times a$$
$$= -20a^2$$

EXAMPLE 6
Simplify the following: $4a \times 7c \times 3b$

$$4a \times 7c \times 3b = 4 \times 7 \times 3 \times a \times c \times b$$
$$= 84abc \quad \text{........notice that the letters are usually written in alphabetical order.}$$

EXAMPLE 7
Simplify the following: $7ab - 5ab$

You can think of this as: '7 lots of ab minus 5 lots of ab.' This must equal 2 lots of ab.

So, $7ab - 5ab = 2ab$

Check this makes sense by trying some numbers:

If $a = 3$ and $b = 5$, then:

$$7ab - 5ab = (7 \times 3 \times 5) - (5 \times 3 \times 5)$$
$$= 105 \quad - \quad 75$$
$$= 30$$

And, $2ab = 2 \times 3 \times 5 = 30$ ....as before!

EXAMPLE 8

Simplify the following: $\quad 6a \div 2$

$6a \div 2 = 3a$

Check this makes sense:

$(a + a + a + a + a + a) \div 2 = (a + a + a)$

Or:

$$\frac{6 \times a}{2} = \frac{3 \times 2 \times a}{2} = 3a \qquad ......\text{because I can divide by 2 top and bottom...}$$

EXAMPLE 9

Simplify the following: $\quad (-56ab) \div 6b$

$$(-56ab) \div 6b \quad = \frac{-56 \times a \times b}{6 \times b}$$

$$= \frac{2 \times -28 \times a \times b}{2 \times 3 \times b} \quad ....\text{I have left the minus sign with the 28 as I can see that I am going to cancel the two 2's.......}$$

$$= \frac{\cancel{2} \times -28 \times a \times \cancel{b}}{\cancel{2} \times 3 \times \cancel{b}} \quad .....\text{I can now divide the two b's and the two 2's.....}$$

$$= \frac{-28a}{3}$$

QUESTIONS 2.1

Simplify the following algebraic expressions where possible:

1. $5a + 7a$
2. $5a + 7$
3. $4a + 5b + 2a + b$
4. $3a - a$
5. $3a - a + 4b$
6. $3a - a - 4b$
7. $7a + 2b - 5a + b$
8. $30a - 4b + 5c + 2a - 5b + 5c$
9. $4a - 7b - 8a - (-9b)$
10. $7 - a + 23 - (-5b) + c$
11. $3a \times 7$
12. $5a \times 8$
13. $5a \times 8a$
14. $5a \times (-8a)$
15. $3a \times 5b \times 8c$
16. $3a \times 5b \times (-8c)$
17. $3a \times (-5b) \times (-8c)$
18. $(-3a) \times (-5b) \times (-8c)$
19. $3a^2 + 5a^2 + 7a$
20. $7a^2 - 5a^2 + 7a - 3a$
21. $8a \div 2$
22. $18ab \div 3$
23. $18ab \div 3a$
24. $18ab \div 3ab$
25. $18ab \div (-3a)$
26. $42abc \div 18c$
27. $15abc + 7ab + 9abc - 3abc$
28. $15abc + 7ab + 9abc - (-3abc)$
29. $7ab^2 - 5ab^2 + ab^2$
30. $13a^2b^2 - ab^2$

Now substitute the values $a = 2$, $b = 3$ and $c = 5$ into all of the above algebraic expressions AND into your answers. For each question these should, of course, give you the same numerical value!

SUBSTITUTING IN (Order of Operations)

Area of a Rectangle = Width × Length
A = W × L

> This formula works for all rectangles. So, I can find the area of a given rectangle, if I am told the width and the length.

So, suppose that I am told that W = 12 cm and L = 28 cm, then:

A = W × L
A = 12 cm × 28 cm
A = 336 cm² ......this is an example of **substituting in values**......

A second rectangle has W = 13·7 cm and L = 25·3 cm

So, A = W × L
A = 13·7 cm × 25·3 cm
A = 346·61 cm²

> So, the formula for the area of a rectangle will work for all rectangles, no matter how 'difficult' the lengths involved!

What is the formula for the perimeter of the rectangle below?

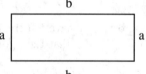

Perimeter = a + b + a + b
Perimeter = 2a + 2b
Perimeter = 2(a + b)

> You should be able to see that these three equations are equivalent. If not, read the sections on simplifying, collecting like terms and factorising.

If a = 3 cm and b = 8 cm, these three equations should all give the same numerical value for the perimeter.

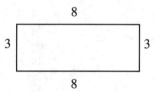

Version 1:   Perimeter = a + b + a + b
                 Perimeter = 3 + 8 + 3 + 8 = 22 cm

Version 2:   Perimeter = 2a + 2b
                 Perimeter = 2 × 3 + 2 × 8   ...times 'a' by 2 and 'b' by 2 and **then** add...
                 Perimeter = 6 + 16
                 Perimeter = 22 cm

Version 3:   Perimeter = 2(a + b)
                 Perimeter = 2 × (3 + 8)   ......add 3 to 8 first, **then** times by two...
                 Perimeter = 2 × 11
                 Perimeter = 22 cm

In versions 2 and 3, how do you know whether to: **add** first then **multiply**

or: **multiply** first then **add?**

ALGEBRA

To avoid any possible confusion, Mathematicians work to a **convention**. This means that everyone involved in using Maths will always interpret equations in the same way.

The agreed order is:

	Brackets	Always work out the brackets first.
Followed by...	**Powers**	Such as squaring or square rooting.
Followed by...	**Multiplication and Division**	These two have equal priority.
Followed by...	**Addition and Subtraction**	These two have equal priority.

ALGEBRA

EXAMPLE 1
Find the value of A, when $A = 4 \times 4 + 4$

There are no brackets and no powers, so first of all do the multiplication:	$A = 16 + 4$
Now do the addition:	$A = 16 + 4 = 20$

EXAMPLE 2
Find the value of A, when $A = (4 + 4) \div 4$

Evaluate the brackets first:	$A = 8 \div 4$
Now do the division:	$A = 8 \div 4 = 2$

EXAMPLE 3
$A = 16xy + 3(x + y) - 13$ Find the value of A when $x = 7$ and $y = 5$.

So, $A = 16 \times 7 \times 5 + 3(7 + 5) - 13$

Evaluate the bracket first:	$A = 16 \times 7 \times 5 + 3(7 + 5) - 13$
	$A = 16 \times 7 \times 5 + 3 \times 12 - 13$
Now do the multiplications: [There are no divisions]	$A = 560 + 36 - 13$
Lastly, do the addition and subtraction:	$A = 583$

EXAMPLE 4
Find the value of s, if $s = ut + \dfrac{at^2}{2}$ and $u = 7$, $t = 5$ and $a = 3$

So: $s = 7 \times 5 + \dfrac{3 \times 5^2}{2}$

There are no brackets, so first evaluate the power:	$s = 7 \times 5 + \dfrac{3 \times 5^2}{2}$
	$s = 7 \times 5 + \dfrac{3 \times 25}{2}$
Now do the multiplications:	$s = 35 + \dfrac{75}{2}$
And the division:	$s = 35 + 37.5$
And, lastly, do the addition	$s = 72.5$

QUESTIONS 2.2

If $a = 3$, $b = 7$ and $c = 8$, find the value of X for each of these formulae:

1. $X = 3a$

2. $X = 3a + 9$

3. $X = 3a - 7$

4. $X = 3a + 5b$

5. $X = 3a + 5b - 2c$

6. $X = 3ab$

7. $X = 3ab - 7$

8. $X = abc$

9. $X = 5abc + 3bc$

10. $X = ab + bc + ac$

If $a = -2$, $b = 5$ and $c = 0$, find the value of Y for each of these formulae:

11. $Y = 5(2a + b) + 3c$

12. $Y = ab + bc + ac$

13. $Y = 4c(a + b)$

14. $Y = c(34a + 76b)$

15. $Y = 3a^2 + 7b^2 + 5c^2$

16. $Y = 5(a + b)^2$

17. $Y = b^3 \div 2$

18. $Y = (2a)^2$

19. $Y = (2a + 5b)^2$

20. $Y = (2a + 5b + 3c)^2$

21. $Y = \dfrac{a + b + c}{3}$

22. $Y = \dfrac{5bc}{3a}$

23. $Y = \dfrac{3(2a + 5b - 7c)}{(a + b + c)}$

24. $Y = \dfrac{(3a)^2 + 7a - 9}{4}$

25. $Y = \dfrac{3a^2 + 7a - 9}{4}$

EXPANDING BRACKETS (MULTIPLYING OUT BRACKETS)

Start by working with some numbers first.

It will help to look at finding the area of this rectangle:

5 cm

8 cm

The area of a rectangle is width times length.

Area = width $\times$ length

Area = 5 cm $\times$ 8 cm

Area = 40 cm^2

Now, extend the length of the original rectangle:

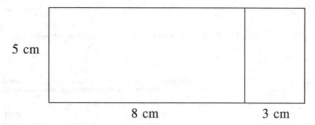

5 cm

8 cm   3 cm

So, to find the area of the new rectangle, use the same formula, with the new length, like this:

Area = width × length
Area = 5 cm × 11 cm
Area = 55 cm^2

But the length of 11 cm is made up of the original 8 cm plus the extension of 3 cm. So, it is still a correct statement to say that:

Area = 5 × (8 + 3)

When you want to remove the brackets, you can see that you must times **both** the 8 and the 3 by the 5, like this:

Area = 5 × 8 + 5 × 3
Area = 40 + 15
Area = old area + new area
Area = 55 cm^2

5 cm   A = 5 × 8 = 40   A = 5 × 8 = 15

8 cm   3 cm

You can see from the diagram that this is the correct answer.

Area = Old Area + New Area

Area = 40 + 15 = 55 cm^2

USING ALGEBRA

Now do the same again, but this time extend the rectangle by x cm.

So, the original rectangle still looks like this:

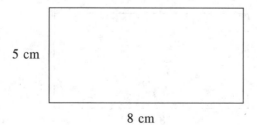

5 cm

8 cm

Now extend the length by x cm and the new rectangle looks like this:

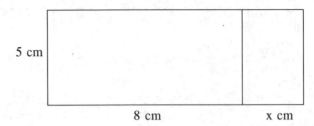

5 cm

8 cm   x cm

So, area = width × length
Area = 5 × (8 + x)
Area = 40 + 5x

Notice that we have multiplied **both** the 8 and the x by the 5, just as we did before. We cannot come up with a final answer this time, because we don't know the numerical value of the x. As soon as someone tells us the value of the x, we could evaluate the new area.

Suppose we are told that x = 2 cm, then:

	OR	
Area = width × length		Area = width × length
Area = 5 × (8 + x)		Area = 5 × (8 + x)
Area = 5 × 8 + 5x		Area = 5 × (8 + 2)
Area = 5 × 8 + 5 × 2		Area = 5 × 10
Area = 40 + 10		Area = 50 cm²
Area = 50 cm²		

Both ways of working give us the same answer.   Area = Old Area + New Area
Area = 40 + 10 = 50 cm²

So, we can see from the diagram that 50 cm² is the correct answer.

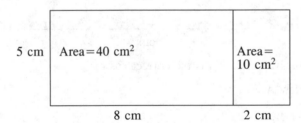

5 cm   Area=40 cm²   Area=
                          10 cm²

8 cm   2 cm

EXAMPLE 2
Suppose that instead of increasing the length of the rectangle, we decrease it. Suppose that the original rectangle is still the same as before:

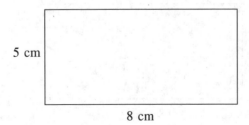

5 cm

8 cm

Now decrease the length by x cm:

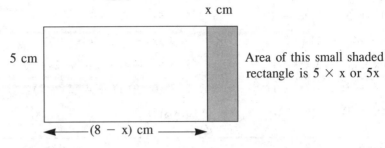

x cm

5 cm

Area of this small shaded
rectangle is 5 × x or 5x

◄─── (8 − x) cm ───►

So, the area of the new rectangle is:
Area = width × length
Area = 5 × (8 − x)
Area = 5 × 8 − 5x
Area = 40 − 5x
Area = Old area − New area

> You can see that, to remove brackets, you must
> multiply everything in the brackets by the
> number outside. This applies equally to
> positive and negative numbers.

QUESTIONS 2.3
Multiply out these brackets:

1. 5(4 + x)
2. 6(x + 8)
3. 7(x + 13)
4. 3(x − 8)
5. 3(4x − 9)

6. 5(4x + 7y +3)
7. 2(6x + 2 − y)
8. 3x(5x + 6)
9. 6x(5x − 5y + 3)
10. 4x(7x − 4y + 3)

EXAMPLE 3
Multiply out these brackets and simplify, collecting any like terms: 7(5x + 4) + 3(2x − 7)

7(5x + 4) = 35x + 28

3(2x − 7) =   6x − 21

now add $\overline{41x + 7}$

So, 7(5x + 4) + 3(2x − 7) = 41x + 7

EXAMPLE 4 (HARDER!)
Multiply out these brackets and simplify: 5(2x + 7) − 3(2x + 10)   [Notice the subtraction sign]

5(2x + 7) = 10x + 35

3(2x + 10) = 6x + 30

now subtract $\overline{4x + 5}$

So, 5(2x + 7) − 3(2x + 10) = 4x + 5

EXAMPLE 5 (HARDER STILL!)
Multiply out these brackets and simplify: 5(2x + 7) − 3(2x − 10)   [Notice the signs]

5(2x + 7) = 10x + 35

3(2x − 10) = 6x − 30

now subtract $\overline{4x + 65}$ [35 − (−30) = 35 + 30 = 65]

So, 5(2x + 7) − 3(2x − 10) = 4x + 65

ALGEBRA

QUESTIONS 2.4

Multiply out these brackets and simplify:

1. $7(4x + 5) + 3(2x - 4)$ 6. $5(5x - 3) - 6(x - 8)$

2. $4(x + 4) + 4(3 - 5x)$ 7. $9(3x - 7) - 5(4x - 7)$

3. $6(9x + 7) - 3(x + 7)$ 8. $3(5x + 4) - 7(6 - 2x)$

4. $2(3x + 7) - 4(2x - 1)$ 9. $3x(6x + 1) + 4x(5x - 2)$

5. $3(4x + 1) - 7(x - 2)$ 10. $6x(5x - 7) - 5x(7 - 2x)$

EXAMPLE 6

Multiply out these brackets: $(x + 5)(x + 2)$

Suppose we start with a square of side x, like this:

The area of the square is x^2.

Now extend one side to a new length of $(x + 5)$.

	x	5
x	x^2	5x

The new area is now $x^2 + 5x$

Now extend the other side to a new length of $(x + 2)$.

	x	5
x	x^2	5x
2	2x	10

The total area is now $x^2 + 5x + 2x + 10$.

We can simplify this to $x^2 + 7x + 10$

Notice that there are 4 parts to our answer:

$$x \times x = x^2$$

$$x \times 5 = 5x$$

$$2 \times x = 2x$$

$$2 \times 5 = 10$$

Both terms in the first bracket have been multiplied by both terms in the second bracket.

EXAMPLE 7

Multiply out these brackets: $(2x + 3)(x + 5)$

We don't need to draw out a rectangle which has the correct dimensions, but we still do need to find the 4 parts that will make up the answer. This grid will help:

	2x	+3
x	2x²	+3x
+5	+10x	+15

So, $(2x + 3)(x + 5)$ $= 2x^2 + 3x + 10x + 15$

$= 2x^2 + 13x + 15$

EXAMPLE 8

Multiply out these brackets: $(x + 8)(x - 3)$

Use the same grid as before. Notice that the minus sign stays in front of the 3, like this:

	x	+8
x	x²	+8x
-3	-3x	-24

So, $(x + 8)(x - 3)$ $= x^2 + 8x - 3x - 24$

$= x^2 + 5x - 24$

EXAMPLE 9

Multiply out these brackets: $(x - 7)(x - 2)$

Use the same grid as before. Notice that the minus signs stay with the 7 and the 2, like this:

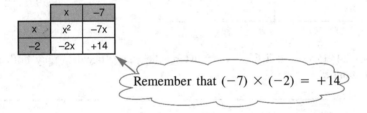

	x	-7
x	x²	-7x
-2	-2x	+14

Remember that $(-7) \times (-2) = +14$

So, $(x - 7)(x - 2)$ $= x^2 - 7x - 2x + 14$

$= x^2 - 9x + 14$

QUESTIONS 2.5

Use the same grid as in the examples to multiply out these brackets:

1. $(x + 4)(x + 3)$

2. $(x + 8)(x + 5)$

3. $(x + 7)(x - 2)$

4. $(x + 9)(x - 14)$

5. $(x - 3)(x + 4)$

6. $(x - 7)(x + 9)$

7. $(x - 7)(x - 8)$

8. $(2x + 3)(x - 7)$

9. $(3x - 5)(x + 1)$

10. $(x - 5)(x + 5)$

FACTORISING (PUTTING INTO BRACKETS)

Read the section on multiplying out brackets first! Factorising is the opposite of multiplying out brackets. Also, read the section on factors of numbers, because exactly the same ideas apply.

EXAMPLE 1

If you are asked for the factors of 24, you look for two numbers which multiply together to give you 24. So, you could have:

$$1 \times 24 = 24$$
$$2 \times 12 = 24$$
$$3 \times 8 = 24$$
$$4 \times 6 = 24$$

If you are working with an algebraic expression, you might be asked to factorise 24 + 4x. The factors of 4x are:

$$1 \times 4x = 4x$$
$$2 \times 2x = 4x$$
$$4 \times x = 4x$$

Now look at the factors for 24 and 4x. The number 4 appears in both lists.

So,   24 + 4x = 4 × 6 + 4 × x
        24 + 4x = 4 × (6 + x)
Or,   24 + 4x = 4(6 + x)

We can check this makes sense, by considering a rectangle with width = 4 and length = (6 + x), like this:

4	Area = 24	Area = 4x
	6	x

So, the algebraic expressions 24 + 4x and 4(6 + x) must be the same, because they both represent the total area of this rectangle.

EXAMPLE 2

Factorise the following algebraic expression: 40 + 6x

Look at the factors of 40:   Look at the factors of 6x:
1 × 40 = 40   1 × 6x = 6x
2 × 20 = 40   2 × 3x = 6x
4 × 10 = 40   3 × 2x = 6x
5 × 8 = 40   6 × x = 6x

The only common factor is 2. So, we can write 40 + 6x = 2(20 + 3x)

Check this is correct, by multiplying out the brackets and making sure it does give what we have started with. Or, we could draw out a rectangle again, to check the areas:

2	Area = 40	Area = 6x
	20	3x

Again, the area = 40 + 6x **and** 2(20 + 3x), so both of these algebraic expressions are the same.

EXAMPLE 3
Factorise $56-12x$

Look at the factors of 56:
$1 \times 56 = 56$
$2 \times 28 = 56$
$4 \times 14 = 56$
$7 \times 8 = 56$

Look at the factors of 12x:
$1 \times 12x = 12x$
$2 \times 6x = 12x$
$3 \times 4x = 12x$
$4 \times 3x = 12x$
$6 \times 2x = 12x$
$12 \times x = 12x$

The largest factor which is in both lists is 4, which is the Highest Common Factor (or HCF). [Look back at the section on Highest Common Factors if you need a reminder here!]

So, we can write: $56 - 12x = 4(14 - 3x)$

Check that this multiplies out to give what we started with. When you get more experience of finding factors, you will probably be able to do this part in your head.

EXAMPLE 4
Factorise $36x + 42xy +18$

Try to spot common factors!

Write 36x as $6 \times 6x$
Write 42xy as $6 \times 7xy$
Write 18 as 6×3

So, $36x + 42xy +18 = 6(6x + 7xy + 3)$

EXAMPLE 5
Factorise $20x^2 + 25xy$

Spotting common factors, again:

Write $20x^2$ as $5x \times 4x$
Write 25xy as $5x \times 5y$

So, $20x^2 + 25xy = 5x(4x + 5y)$

QUESTIONS 2.6
Factorise these algebraic expressions:

1. $5x + 10$
2. $12x - 30$
3. $36x + 42$
4. $20y + 16$
5. $28x - 70$
6. $27 - 36x$
7. $90 - 48x$
8. $45 + 19x$
9. $27x + 57$
10. $42x - 7y + 56$
11. $10x - 35y$
12. $10x^2 - 35xy$
13. $12x - 16y + 28$
14. $15xy - 3y^2 - 9y$
15. $24y - 72$
16. $42xy - 18y^2 + 30y$
17. $104x - 40xy - 56x^2$
18. $63y - 27xy - 45y^2$
19. $18xy - 12x^2y - 30xy^2$
20. $21x^2y - 35xy^2 - 28xy$

FACTORISING QUADRATIC EXPRESSIONS

EXAMPLE 1
Factorise the expression $x^2 + 7x + 10$. This means put $x^2 + 7x + 10$ into brackets.

Read the section on Multiplying Out Brackets first, examples 6 to 9.

In example 6 we took the expression $(x + 5)(x + 2)$ and multiplied out the brackets, like this:

	x	5
x	x^2	5x
2	2x	10

This told us that $(x + 5)(x + 2) = x^2 + 5x + 2x + 10$
$= x^2 + 7x + 10$

Now we are being asked to go the other way!

In other words, if we are given the expression $x^2 + 7x + 10$ we need to be able to write it as $(x + 5)(x + 2)$.

EXAMPLE 2

Now try an example where we don't know the answer already!

Factorise $x^2 + 7x + 12 \cdot$

Using the same grid as before, we can fill in some spaces straight away, like this:

	x	
x	x²	
		12

The two numbers which go into the shaded boxes must multiply together to give 12. So, we are looking for the factors of 12. The possibilities are:

$$1 \times 12 = 12$$
$$2 \times 6 = 12$$
$$3 \times 4 = 12$$

The grids for each of these possibilities looks like this:

	x	1
x	x²	x
12	12x	12

This grid shows that $(x + 1)(x + 12)$ $= x^2 + 12x + x + 12$
$= x^2 + 13x + 12$ ....Not what we wanted!

	x	2
x.	x²	2x
6	6x	12

This grid shows that $(x + 2)(x + 6) = x^2 + 2x + 6x + 12$
$= x^2 + 8x + 12$ ....Not what we wanted!

	x	3
x	x²	3x
4	4x	12

This grid shows that $(x + 3)(x + 4)$ $= x^2 + 3x + 4x + 12$
$= x^2 + 7x + 12$

You can see that this last grid is the one we want!

This shows that $x^2 + 7x + 12$ factorises to $(x + 3)(x + 4)$.

EXAMPLE 3

Factorise $x^2 - 2x - 15$

Some spaces on the grid can be filled in straight away, like this:

	x	
x	x²	
		−15

The two numbers which go into the shaded boxes multiply together to give -15 (minus 15). The possibilities are:

$-1 \times 15 \quad = -15$
$-3 \times 5 \quad = -15$
$1 \times -15 \ = -15$
$3 \times -5 \ = -15$

You can draw out the grids for all four possibilities, or you could start with the one in the list which you think looks more promising! When you have factorised more quadratic expression you will become much quicker at spotting the one which works! This time we need:

	x	−5
x	x²	−5x
+3	3x	−15

This grid shows that $(x - 5)(x + 3) \quad = x^2 - 5x + 3x - 15$
$$= x^2 - 2x - 15$$

This show that $x^2 - 2x - 15$ factorises to $(x - 5)(x + 3)$

EXAMPLE 4

Factorise $x^2 - 10x + 21$

Some spaces on the grid can be filled in straight away, like this:

	x	
x	x²	
		+21

The two numbers which go into the shaded boxes multiply together to give $+21$. Looking at the expression that we are trying to factorise, $x^2 - 10x + 21$, we can see that there is a minus sign in front of the 10x. We must therefore consider possibilities which include minus signs as well. The full list of possibilities is:

$1 \times 21 \quad = +21$
$-1 \times -21 \ = +21$
$3 \times 7 \quad\, = +21$
$-3 \times -7 \quad = +21$

So both factors must be positive, in order to multiply together to give $+21$, or, both factors must be negative to multiply together to give $+21$.

As we need to end up with "$-10x$", you can decide which of the possibilties on the list looks most promising to try:

	x	−7
x	x²	−7x
−3	−3x	+21

This grid shows that $(x - 7)(x - 3) = x^2 - 7x - 3x + 21$
$$= x^2 - 10x + 21$$

This show that $x^2 - 10x + 21$ factorises to $(x - 7)(x - 3)$

EXAMPLE 5

Factorise $3x^2 - 19x + 6$

Some spaces on the grid can be filled in straight away, like this:

	3x	
x	$3x^2$	
		+6

The two numbers which go into the shaded boxes multiply together to give $+6$. Looking at the expression that we are trying to factorise, $3x^2 - 19x + 6$, we can see that there is a minus sign in front of the 19x. We must therefore consider possibilities which include minus signs as well. The full list of possibilities is:

$$1 \times 6 = +6$$
$$-1 \times -6 = +6$$
$$2 \times 3 = +6$$
$$-2 \times -3 = +6$$

So both factors must be positive, in order to multiply together to give $+6$, or, both factors must be negative to multiply together to give $+6$.

As we need to end up with "$-19x$", you can decide which of the possibilties on the list looks most promising to try:

	3x	−1
x	$3x^2$	−x
−6	−18x	+6

This grid shows that $(3x - 1)(x - 6) = 3x^2 - x - 18x + 6$
$$= 3x^2 - 19x + 6$$

This show that $3x^2 - 19x + 6$ factorises to $(3x - 1)(x - 6)$

QUESTIONS 2.7

Factorise these quadratic expressions:

1. $x^2 + 5x + 6$
2. $x^2 + 9x + 20$
3. $x^2 + 12x + 35$
4. $x^2 + 8x + 12$
5. $x^2 + 8x + 7$
6. $x^2 - 5x - 24$
7. $x^2 + 6x - 16$
8. $x^2 - 5x + 6$
9. $x^2 - x - 20$
10. $x^2 - 8x + 15$
11. $x^2 + 4x - 5$
12. $x^2 - 11x + 28$
13. $x^2 + 3x - 10$
14. $2x^2 + 5x + 3$
15. $2x^2 + 9x + 4$
16. $2x^2 + 7x + 3$
17. $3x^2 + 13x + 4$
18. $2x^2 + 5x - 3$
19. $x^2 - 16$
20. $x^2 - 9$

SOLVING EQUATIONS

Find the value of x in this equation:

$x + 5 = 12$

You can probably see straight away that x can only be 7 to make this equation work.
Not all equations will be as easy to solve as this one!

So, we need to work towards a reliable method.

You can think of an equation as being similar to kitchen scale pans:

If you have some balanced scale pans, you will upset the balance if you add something to one side. But, if you add the same amount to the other side as well, then the scale pans will remain balanced. If you take out the same amount from both sides, you will also keep the balance.

> Our strategy for solving equations will be to do the **same thing to both sides of the equation** at each stage, so that we keep the balance.

With our first example:

$$x + 5 = 12$$

$$x + 5 - 5 = 12 - 5 \dots\dots\dots \text{I am going to subtract 5 from both sides.....}$$

$$\dots\dots\text{the } +5 \text{ and the } -5 \text{ cancel out, to leave just the x on the left hand side...}$$

$$x = 7$$

EXAMPLE 1

Find the value of x in this equation: $x - 17 = 39$

$$x - 17 = 39$$

$$x - 17 + 17 = 39 + 17 \dots\dots \text{ I am going to add 17 to both sides...}$$

$$\dots\text{ the } -17 \text{ and the } + 17 \text{ cancel out, to leave just the x on the}$$
$$x = 56 \qquad\qquad\qquad \text{left hand side}$$

EXAMPLE 2

Find the value of x in this equation: $x - 13 \cdot 27 = 18 \cdot 35$

$$x - 13 \cdot 27 = 18 \cdot 35$$

$$x - 13 \cdot 27 + 13 \cdot 27 = 18 \cdot 35 + 13 \cdot 27 \dots\dots \text{Add } 13 \cdot 27 \text{ to both sides..}$$

> Notice that it makes no difference that the numbers look harder! The $-13 \cdot 27$ still cancels with the $+13 \cdot 27$, to leave just the x on the left hand side.

$$x = 31 \cdot 62$$

EXAMPLE 3

Find the value of x in this equation: $3x + 5 = 17$

To make this equation, we must have started with x, then multiplied by 3, then added 5 and this equals 17. We could show this in a flow diagram, like this:

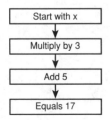

```
┌─────────────────┐
│  Start with x   │
└─────────────────┘
        ↓
┌─────────────────┐
│ Multiply by 3   │
└─────────────────┘
        ↓
┌─────────────────┐
│     Add 5       │
└─────────────────┘
        ↓
┌─────────────────┐
│   Equals 17     │
└─────────────────┘
```

So, to get back to the starting value of x, we must do the opposite of multiplying by 3 (which is dividing by 3) and the opposite of adding 5 (which is subtracting 5), and do them in the opposite order, like this:

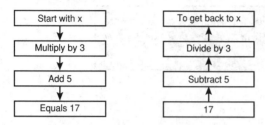

We can set out the working like this:

$$3x + 5 = 17$$

$$3x + 5 - 5 = 17 - 5 \quad \text{........ subtract 5 from both sides......}$$

$$3x = 12 \quad \text{........this has got '3x' on its own....}$$

$$\frac{3x}{3} = \frac{12}{3} \quad \text{........now divide both sides by 3....}$$

$$x = 4 \quad \text{Now check that x = 4 does work in the original equation!}$$

EXAMPLE 4

Find the value of x in this equation: $5x + 13 = -17$

$$5x + 13 = -17$$

$$5x + 13 - 13 = -17 - 13 \quad \text{.....I have subtracted 13 from both sides..}$$

$$5x = -30 \quad \text{.....this has got '5x' on its own.....}$$

$$\frac{5x}{5} = \frac{-30}{5} \quad \text{......now divide both sides by 5....}$$

$$x = -6$$

EXAMPLE 5

Find the value of x in this equation: $6(x + 7) = 120$

To make this equation, we must have started with x, then added 7 (the brackets tell us this was done first), then multiplied by 6 and this equals 120.

So, to get back to the starting value of x, we must reverse these operations, by dividing by 6, then subtracting 7, like this:

$$6(x + 7) = 120$$

$$\frac{6(x + 7)}{6} = \frac{120}{6} \quad \text{.......divide both sides by 6....}$$

$$(x + 7) = 20 \quad \text{.......this has got the (x + 7) on its own....}$$

$$x + 7 = 20 \quad \text{......I don't need the brackets now...}$$

$$x + 7 - 7 = 20 - 7 \quad \text{......subtract 7 from both sides...}$$

$$x = 13$$

EXAMPLE 6

Find the value of x in this equation: $4(5x - 7) = -138$

To make this equation, we must have started with x, then multiplied by 5, then subtracted 7, then multiplied by 4 and this equals -138.

So, to get back to the value of x, we must reverse these operations, by dividing by 4, then adding 7, then dividing by 5, like this:

$$4(5x - 7) = -138$$

$$\frac{4(5x - 7)}{4} = \frac{-138}{4} \qquad \text{....this time I must divide both sides by 4.....}$$

$$(5x - 7) = -34{\cdot}5 \qquad \text{....this has got the } (5x - 7) \text{ on its own...}$$

$$5x - 7 = -34{\cdot}5 \qquad \text{......I don't need the brackets now....}$$

$$5x - 7 + 7 = -34{\cdot}5 + 7 \qquad \text{....add 7 to both sides...}$$

$$\frac{5x}{5} = \frac{-27{\cdot}5}{5} \qquad \text{......divide both sides by 5....}$$

$$x = -5{\cdot}5$$

EXAMPLE 7

Find the value of x in this equation: $15 - 2x = 11$

> **CAUTION!**
>
> Notice that in this equation the 2x has a minus sign in front of it!
> Many pupils seem to ignore the minus sign, and of course they don't get the right answer in the end!

The best way forward is to add 2x to both sides, like this:

$$15 - 2x = 11$$

$$15 - 2x + 2x = 11 + 2x \qquad \text{......add 2x to both sides....}$$

$$15 = 11 + 2x \qquad \text{......the } -2x \text{ and the } + 2x \text{ cancel out, so that we have an equation with } +2x \text{ in it, and we can carry on as before....}$$

$$15 - 11 = 11 + 2x - 11 \qquad \text{......subtract 11 from both sides...}$$

$$4 = 2x$$

$$\frac{4}{2} = \frac{2x}{2} \qquad \text{......divide both sides by 2...}$$

$$2 = x$$

EXAMPLE 8

Find the value of x in this equation: $\dfrac{x}{2} = 7$

To make this equation, we must have started with x, then divided by 2 and this equals 7.

So, to get back to the value of x, we must reverse these operations, by multiplying by 2, like this:

$$\frac{x}{2} \times 2 = 7 \times 2 \dots \text{ multiply both sides by 2...}$$

$$x = 14$$

EXAMPLE 9

Find the value of x in this equation: $\dfrac{24}{x} = 8$

To make this equation, we must have started with 24, then divided by x and this equals 8.

So, we must multiply by x, like this:

$\dfrac{24}{x} \times x = 8 \times x$ ...... this will leave just the 24 on the left hand side ...

$24 = 8 \times x$ ....this brings the x we are trying to find to the top line, now we can continue as in earlier examples...

$\dfrac{24}{8} = \dfrac{8 \times x}{8}$ ......now divide both sides by 8.....

$3 = x$

EXAMPLE 10

Find the value of x in this equation: $\dfrac{(x + 7)}{2} = 5$

$\dfrac{(x + 7)}{2} \times 2 = 5 \times 2$ .....multiply both sides by 2...

$(x + 7) = 10$

$x + 7 = 10$ .....I don't need the brackets now....

$x + 7 - 7 = 10 - 7$ .....subtract 7 from both sides....

$x = 3$

EXAMPLE 11

Find the value of x in this equation: $\dfrac{(3x + 8)}{4} = 3 \cdot 65$

Don't worry that the numbers look 'difficult'. Go through the same processes as before.

$\dfrac{(3x + 8)}{4} \times 4 = 3 \cdot 65 \times 4$ ....multiply both sides by 4

$(3x + 8) = 14 \cdot 6$

$3x + 8 = 14 \cdot 6$ ....I don't need the brackets now....

$3x + 8 - 8 = 14 \cdot 6 - 8$ ....subtract 8 from both sides....

$3x = 6 \cdot 6$

$\dfrac{3x}{3} = \dfrac{6 \cdot 6}{3}$ .....divide both sides by 3...

$x = 2 \cdot 2$

ALGEBRA

EXAMPLE 12

Find the value of x in this equation: $5x - 13 = 2x + 5$

Notice that there are x's on both sides of the equation. We can subtract 2x from both sides, like this:

$5x - 13 - 2x = 2x + 5 - 2x$ .... subtracting 2x from both sides...

$3x - 13 = 5$ .....now we have the x's on only one side of the equation, so we can continue as before...

$3x - 13 + 13 = 5 + 13$ ....add 13 to both sides....

$3x = 18$

$\dfrac{3x}{3} = \dfrac{18}{3}$ .....divide both sides by 3....

$x = 6$

EXAMPLE 13

Find the value of x in this equation: $\dfrac{35}{x} + 17 = 24$

When solving equations, we want to get the x on its own. To start with we can get the $\dfrac{35}{x}$ term on its own, like this:

$\dfrac{35}{x} + 17 - 17 = 24 - 17$ ...subtracting 17 from both sides...

$\dfrac{35}{x} = 7$

$\dfrac{35}{x} \times x = 7 \times x$ ...multiplying both sides by x.....

$35 = 7 \times x$

$\dfrac{35}{7} = \dfrac{7 \times x}{7}$ ....dividing both sides by 7....

$5 = x$

Find the value of x in these equations. Substitute your answer back into the original equation, to check that it works!

QUESTIONS 2.8	QUESTIONS 2.9	QUESTIONS 2.10
1. $x + 27 = 34$	1. $3x + 7 = 19$	1. $7 + x = 12$
2. $x - 19 = 23$	2. $4x - 1 = 19$	2. $7 - x = 12$
3. $119 + x = 132$	3. $5x + 9 = 24$	3. $9 - x = 0$
4. $x + 7 = -10$	4. $3x + 2 = -19$	4. $9 - x = 1$
5. $x - 7 = -10$	5. $5(x + 4) = 40$	5. $9 - x = -2$
6. $x - 13 = -19$	6. $3(x + 8) = 15$	6. $9 - 2x = 3$
7. $x - 23 = -14$	7. $3(x - 2) = -18$	7. $17 - 2x = 25$
8. $x - 14 = 5 \cdot 26$	8. $3(x + 2) = 16 \cdot 5$	8. $4 - 3x = 19$
9. $x - 3 \cdot 2 = -7 \cdot 98$	9. $5(x + 1) = -7 \cdot 5$	9. $4 - 5x = -7 \cdot 5$
10. $x - 9 \cdot 7 = -16 \cdot 91$	10. $6x - 1 = -38 \cdot 2$	10. $3 - 6x = 7 \cdot 8$

ALGEBRA

QUESTIONS 2.11

1. $\dfrac{x}{4} = 6$

2. $\dfrac{x}{6} = -7$

3. $\dfrac{(x + 11)}{2} = 9$

4. $\dfrac{(2x - 1)}{5} = 1$

5. $\dfrac{(3x - 8)}{2} = -7$

6. $\dfrac{(2x - 7)}{4} = 3 \cdot 35$

7. $\dfrac{52}{x} = 13$

8. $\dfrac{60}{x} = -20$

9. $\dfrac{56}{x} - 3 = 5$

10. $\dfrac{51}{x} + 5 = -12$

QUESTIONS 2.12

1. $3x + 7 = 2x + 11$

2. $5x + 3 = 2x + 24$

3. $4x - 7 = 5x - 4$

4. $3x + 1 = 5x + 13$

5. $3x + 1 = 5x - 8$

6. $5x + 7 = 3x + 2 \cdot 6$

7. $6x - 1 = x + 2 \cdot 5$

8. $4x + 3 = x - 7 \cdot 2$

9. $6x + 7 = 3x + 8$

10. $3x + 5 = 7x + 6$

SOLVING QUADRATIC EQUATIONS

Read the section on Solving Quadratic Equations Graphically first!

There, we drew the graph of $y = x(x + 2)$, which looks like this:

We were asked to solve the equation $x(x + 2) = 0$

We have drawn the graph of $y = x(x + 2)$

Put these two equations together, to give $y = x(x + 2) = 0$

So, the solutions will be where $y = 0$, which is where the graph crosses the x-axis.

The co-ordinates of any point on the x-axis are (x = something, y = 0). To solve the equation, we need to find the value of x where the graph crosses the x-axis. So, looking at the graph, the solutions are **x = −2** and **x = 0**.

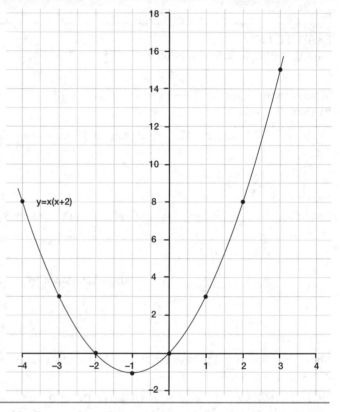

y=x(x+2)

In the section on Solving Quadratic Graphically, we drew these graphs and found these solutions:

Equation	Solutions (where the graph crosses the x-axis)
1. $y = x^2 + 3 = 0$	no solutions
2. $y = x^2 - 1 = 0$	$x = +1$ and $x = -1$
3. $y = x(x + 3) = 0$	$x = 0$ and $x = -3$
4. $y = x(x + 1) = 0$	$x = 0$ and $x = -1$
5. $y = (x + 2)(x - 2) = 0$	$x = -2$ and $x = +2$
6. $y = (x + 2)(x - 3) = 0$	$x = -2$ and $x = +3$
7. $y = x^2 + x - 2 = 0$	$x = -2$ and $x = +1$
8. $y = x^2 + x - 6 = 0$	$x = -3$ and $x = +2$
9. $y = x^2 + x - 7 = 0$	$x = 2 \cdot 2$ and $x = -3 \cdot 2$
10. $y = x^2 - 2x - 6 = 0$	$x = 3 \cdot 7$ and $x = -1 \cdot 7$

} Approximately, reading from the graph

EXAMPLE 1

So, you can see from the table that $y = x^2 + 3 = 0$ has no solutions, because the graph doesn't cross the x-axis at all.

EXAMPLE 2

The graphs of equations 9 and 10 do not cross the x-axis at nice, tidy whole numbers. We cannot be that accurate by reading off the x-axis. Read the section on Trial and Improvement if you want to know how to find a more accurate solution.

EXAMPLE 3

Consider the graph of equation 6:

$y = (x + 2)(x - 3)$

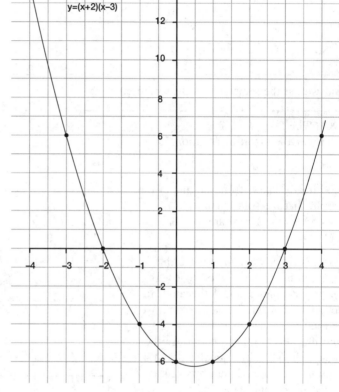

We already know from looking at the graph, that the solutions to
$y = (x + 2)(x - 3) = 0$
are $x = -2$ and $x = 3$.

We can work out the solutions using algebra, instead of having to draw a graph each time. We want to find the values of x which make $(x + 2)$ multiplied by $(x - 3)$ equal zero, like this:

$(x + 2) \times (x - 3) = 0$

$\square \times \square = 0$

> When we have two numbers and they multiply together to give zero, then one of those numbers must itself be zero!

So, either:

| (x + 2) = 0 |
| So, x = -2 |

or

| (x – 3) = 0 |
| x = 3 |

and we get the same solutions as before.

EXAMPLE 4

Consider equation 3: $y = x(x + 3)$

We already know, from looking at the graph, that the solutions to $y = x(x + 3) = 0$
are $x = 0$ and $x = -3$.

Again, using algebra, we want to find the values of x which make x multiplied by (x + 3) equal zero, like this:

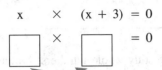

$$x \quad \times \quad (x + 3) = 0$$

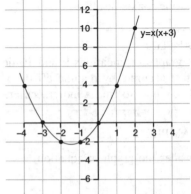

$$\boxed{} \times \boxed{} = 0$$

> Again, we are looking for two numbers which multiply together to give zero. So one of those numbers must itself be zero!

So, either:

So, x = 0		or	(x + 3) = 0
			x = −3

and we get the same solutions as before.

EXAMPLE 5

Consider the graph of equation 7:

$$y = x^2 + x - 2$$

We already know, from looking at the graph, that the solutions to
$y = x^2 + x - 2 = 0$ are $x = +1$
and $x = -2$.

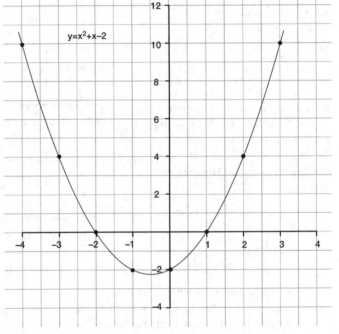

But this time, we cannot solve this equation using the method that we did in examples 3 and 4, because the equation is not in the same form. We can put the equation $y = x^2 + x - 2$ into brackets, so that we can use the same method as in examples 3 and 4. Putting $x^2 + x - 2$ into brackets is called factorising. (Re-read the section on Factorising Quadratic Expressions if you need a reminder here.)

To factorise, we used a grid, like this:

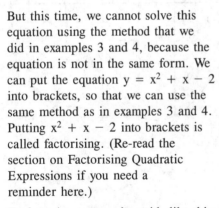

The two numbers which go into the shaded boxes must multiply together to give −2.

So, the possibilities are: $1 \times -2 = -2$ and $-1 \times 2 = -2$

Try the one that looks most promising:

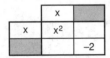

This shows you that $(x - 1)(x + 2) = x^2 - x + 2x - 2$
$$= x^2 + x - 2 \quad \ldots\ldots\text{So, this is the one we want!}$$

Now we have shown that $y = x^2 + x - 2$ is the same as $y = (x - 1)(x + 2)$ we can use the same method as before, like this:

$(x - 1) \times (x + 2) = 0$

So, either:

$(x - 1) = 0$
So, $x = 1$

or

$(x + 2) = 0$
$x = -2$

and we get the same solutions as before.

EXAMPLE 6

Consider the graph of equation 9:

$y = x^2 + x - 7$

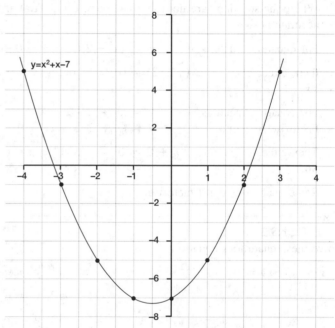

We already know, from looking at the graph, that the solutions to $y = x^2 + x - 7 = 0$ are approximately $x = 2 \cdot 2$ and $x = -3 \cdot 2$

Try to factorise $x^2 + x - 7$, using a grid, like this:

	x	
x	x^2	
		−7

The two numbers which go into the shaded boxes must multiply together to give $-7 \cdot$

So, the possibilities are: $1 \times -7 = -7$ and $-1 \times 7 = -7$

Try these 2 grids:

	x	+1
x	x^2	+x
−7	−7x	−7

This shows you that $(x + 1)(x - 7) = x^2 + x - 7x - 7$
$\qquad\qquad\qquad\qquad\quad = x^2 - 6x - 7 \quad$ ...not what we want.

	x	−1
x	x^2	−x
+7	+7x	−7

This shows you that $(x - 1)(x + 7) = x^2 - x + 7x - 7$
$\qquad\qquad\qquad\qquad\quad = x^2 + 6x - 7 \quad$ ....not what we want, either.

ALGEBRA

So, **neither** of these two possibilities actually gives us the answer we are looking for! We have considered the only two possibilities and they don't work! So, $x^2 + 6x - 7$ doesn't factorise. We cannot use algebra and the same method as the last few examples to solve quadratic equations that don't factorise. We *can* use a combination of drawing a graph and using a trial and improvement method, to solve this type of quadratic.

SOLVING QUADRATIC EQUATIONS: SUMMARY

- Drawing a graph of the equation will help you to see what the solutions are. The solutions to equations such as $y = ax^2 + bx + c = 0$ are found by looking at where the graph crosses the x-axis.

- Where the solutions are not exact numbers, use a Trial and Improvement method to get a more accurate answer.

- For equations such as $\qquad y = (x + 2)(x - 3) = 0$

  then, either $\qquad (x + 2) = 0 \qquad$ or $\qquad x - 3 = 0$
  so, $\qquad\qquad\qquad x = -2 \qquad$ or $\qquad\quad x = 3$

- For equations such as $\qquad y = x^2 + x - 2 = 0$
  Factorise first into $\qquad\quad y = (x + 2)(x - 1) = 0$

  Then either $\qquad x + 2 = 0 \qquad$ or $\qquad x - 1 = 0$
  So, $\qquad\qquad\quad x = -2 \qquad$ or $\qquad\quad x = 1$

- Some quadratics don't factorise!

QUESTIONS 2.13
Solve these quadratics equations:

1. $y = x^2 - 4 = 0$
2. $y = x^2 + 4 = 0$
3. $y = x(x + 4) = 0$
4. $y = (x + 3)(x - 4) = 0$
5. $y = x(x - 5) = 0$
6. $y = x^2 - 5x - 7 = 0$
7. $y = x^2 + 7x + 12 = 0$
8. $y = x^2 + 10x + 25 = 0$
9. $y = (x + 1)(x - 6) = 0$
10. $y = x^2 - 11x + 18 = 0$

11. $y = x^2 + 4x + 2 = 0$
12. $y = x^2 + 6x = 0$
13. $y = x^2 - 4x = 0$
14. $y = (2x - 1)(x - 3) = 0$
15. $y = x^2 - 25 = 0$
16. $y = x^2 + 25 = 0$
17. $y = (2x + 1)(x + 4) = 0$
18. $y = x^2 - 2x - 24 = 0$
19. $y = x^2 - 2x - 15 = 0$
20. $y = x^2 + 2x - 24 = 0$

SOLVING EQUATIONS BY TRIAL AND IMPROVEMENT

What are the solutions of $x^2 - 4x + 2 = 0$?

First of all let's draw a graph of $y = x^2 - 4x + 2$, so we can see where the solutions occur. Fill in a table of values, like this:

x	0	1	2	3	4	5
y	2	−1	−2	−1	2	7

The solutions of y = x² − 4x + 2 = 0 happen where y = 0. This is where the graph crosses the x-axis.

The co-ordinates of any point on the x-axis are (x = something, y = 0). To solve the equation, we need to find the value of x, where the graph crosses the x-axis.

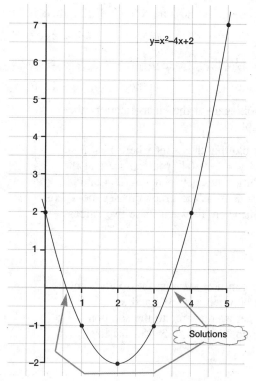

The graph crosses the x-axis between 0 and 1 and again between 3 and 4. So there are two solutions. One solution is between 0 and 1, and the other solution is between 3 and 4. The solutions are clearly not nice, tidy whole numbers. One way to find the solutions is to use a trial and error method. This is probably better called a 'trial and improvement' method. We can try a value of x in the equation x² − 4x + 2 = 0, then decide whether this value of x is too big or too small to be the solution. Then we can try another value of x, based on what we have just found out.

Let's see how this will work for this example.

Let's try to find the solution that is between 3 and 4.

We could start by trying x = 3·5

	x²	−4x	+ 2	= y
x = 3·5	12·25	−14	+ 2	= 0·25

Look at this enlargement of the graph. You can see that x = 3·5 is too large.

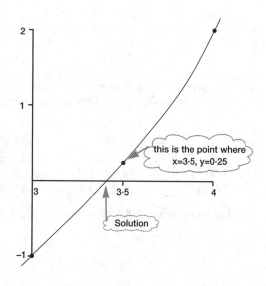

So, we could now try x = 3·4, like this:

	x^2	– 4x	+ 2	= y	
x = 3·5	12·25	– 14	+ 2	= 0·25	too large
x = 3·4	11·56	– 13·6	+ 2	= – 0·04	

Look again at the enlargement of the graph.

By plotting the point where x = 3·4 and y = −0·04, you can see that the solution lies between x = 3·4 and x = 3·5, as the graph crosses the x-axis somewhere between these two values.

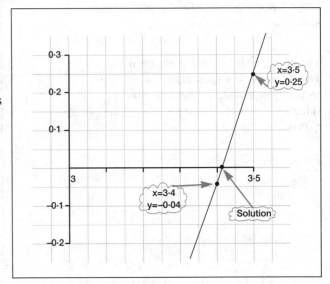

We can now see that the solution must lie between x = 3·4 and x = 3·5, so to get even nearer to the solution we could try x = 3·45, like this:

	x^2	– 4x	+ 2		
x = 3·5	12·25	– 14	+ 2	= 0·25	too large
x = 3·4	11·56	– 13·6	+ 2	= −0·04	too small
x = 3·45	11·9025	– 13·8	+ 2	= 0·1025	

So now continue this processs. You will be able to see that x = 3·45 is too large.
We could try x = 3·44, like this:

	x^2	– 4x	+ 2		
x = 3·4	11·56	– 13·6	+ 2	= −0·04	too small
x = 3·45	11·9025	– 13·8	+ 2	= 0·1025	too large
x = 3·44	11·8336	– 13·76	+ 2	= 0·0736	too large

So, carry on, trying different values of x, like this:

	x^2	– 4x	+ 2		
x = 3·44	11·8336	– 13·76	+ 2	= 0·0736	too large
x = 3·43	11·7649	– 13·72	+ 2	= 0·0449	too large
x = 3·42	11·6964	– 13·68	+ 2	= 0·0164	too large
x = 3·41	11·6281	– 13·64	+ 2	= −0·0119	too small

The last two entries in the table show that the solution must lie between x = 3·41 and x = 3·42. So, to get even closer to the solution, we could try x = 3·415 and continue as before, like this:

	x^2	−4x	+ 2		
x = 3·42	11·6964	– 13·68	+ 2	= 0·0164	too large
x = 3·41	11·6281	– 13·64	+ 2	= −0·0119	too small
x = 3·415	11·662225	– 13·66	+ 2	= 0·002225	too large
x = 3·414	11·655396	– 13·656	+ 2	= −0·000604	too small

The last two entries in the table show that the solution must lie between x = 3·414 and x = 3·415

We could continue this process of trial and improvement, to get even closer to the solution. We are already pretty close to the solution, because we wanted to find a value of x which made $x^2 - 4x + 2$ equal zero. We have found that x = 3·414 makes $x^2 - 4x + 2$ equal $-0·000604$ (where the first non-zero entry is not until the 4th place of decimals.) So we are about 6 ten thousandths too small, which is probably close enough for most purposes!

We can now say that the solution is x = 3·414......... We could continue our trial and improvement method if we wanted to obtain this solution to even more decimal places.

EXAMPLE 2

The equation $x^2 - 4x = 6$ has a solution between 5 and 6. Find this solution correct to 3 decimal places.

The question itself has told us where to look, so, we could begin by trying x = 5·5, like this:

	x^2	$- 4x$	= ?	
x = 5·5	30·25	$- 22$	= 8·25	too large

Clearly, this is too large. Try other values of x, like this:

	x^2	$- 4x$	= ?	
x = 5·5	30·25	$- 22$	= 8·25	too large
x = 5·4	29·16	$- 21·6$	= 7·56	too large
x = 5·3	28·09	$- 21·2$	= 6·89	too large
x = 5·2	27·04	$- 20·8$	= 6·24	too large
x = 5·1	26·01	$- 20·4$	= 5·61	too small

The last two entries in the table show that the solution lies between 5·1 and 5·2. So, we could try x = 5·15, and continue the process, like this:

	x^2	$- 4x$	= ?	
x = 5·2	27·04	$- 20·8$	= 6·24	too large
x = 5·1	26·01	$- 20·4$	= 5·61	too small
x = 5·15	26·5225	$- 20·6$	= 5·9225	too small
x = 5·16	26·6256	$- 20·64$	= 5·9856	too small
x = 5·17	26·7289	$- 20·68$	= 6·0489	too large

The last two entries in the table show that the solution lies between x = 5·16 and x = 5·17, so we could now try x = 5·165, and continue the process, like this:

	x^2	$- 4x$	= ?	
x = 5·16	26·6256	$- 20·64$	= 5·9856	too small
x = 5·17	26·7289	$- 20·68$	= 6·0489	too large
x = 5·165	26·677225	$- 20·66$	= 6·017225	too large
x = 5·164	26·666896	$- 20·656$	= 6·010896	too large
x = 5·163	26·656569	$- 20·652$	= 6·004569	too large
x = 5·162	26·646244	$- 20·648$	= 5·998244	too small

The last two entries in the table show that the solution lies between x = 5·162 and x = 5·163, so we could try x = 5·1625 and continue the process, like this:

	x^2	$- 4x$	= ?	
x = 5·163	26·656569	$- 20·652$	= 6·004569	too large
x = 5·162	26·646244	$- 20·648$	= 5·998244	too small
x = 5·1625	26·65140625	$- 20·65$	= 6·00140625	too large
x = 5·1624	26·65037376	$- 20·6496$	= 6·00077376	too large
x = 5·1623	26·64934129	$- 20·6492$	= 6·00014412	too large
x = 5·1622	26·64830884	$- 20·6488$	= 5·99950884	too small

The last two entries in the table show that the solution must lie between x = 5·1622 and x = 5·1623

We can see that the required solution is x = 5·1622......... We could continue the process of trial and improvement if we wanted to get even closer to the solution. The solution is x = 5·162 (correct to 3 decimal places).

QUESTIONS 2.14

1. The equation $x^2 + 3x = 20$ has a solution between $x = 3$ and $x = 4$. Find this solution to 3 decimal places.

2. The equation $x^2 + 4x = 80$ has a solution between $x = 7$ and $x = 8$. Find this solution to 3 decimal places.

3. Draw a graph of $y = x^2 - 8x + 9$. Use your graph to help you find both solutions of $x^2 - 8x + 9 = 0$ to 3 decimal places.

4. Draw a graph of $y = x^2 + x - 15$. Use your graph to help you find both solutions of $x^2 + x - 15 = 0$ to 3 decimal places.

SIMULTANEOUS EQUATIONS

Person A thinks of a number x and doesn't tell me what it is! Person B thinks of a number y and doesn't tell me what it is either! Instead they give me clues, so I can try to work out the numbers they have thought of!

Clue 1: $x + y = 12$

So, I have written a list of possible values of x and y, like this:

x	y
0	12
1	11
2	10
3	9
4	8
5	7
6	6
7	5
8	4
9	3
10	2
11	1
12	0

In fact, there is an infinite number of possible answers! I could, for example, start to use negative numbers, like this:

x	y
13	−1
14	−2
15	−3

Or, I could start to use decimals, like this:

x	y
8·5	3·5
9·5	2·5
11·9	0·1

My friends A and B have decided that they will give me another clue, to put me out of my misery!

Clue 2: $x - y = 8$

Now, if I look at my list of possible values, I can now see that only $x = 10$ and $y = 2$ work in both equations.

So, this is the solution:

Person A thought of the number 10, so x = 10

Person B thought of the number 2, so y = 2

x + y = 12
x − y = 8

> These equations are called **simultaneous equations**. They are both true at the **same time**. This is what simultaneous means.

EXAMPLE 2

This time, clue 1 is: 2x + y = 14

So, some of the possible values of x and y are:

x	y
0	14
1	12
2	10
3	8
4	6
5	4
6	2
7	0
8	−2
9	−4
10	−6

My friends A and B now give me another clue: x − y = 4

Now, if I look at my list of possible values, I can now see that only x = 6 and y = 2 work in both equations.

So, this is the solution:
Person A thought of the number 6, so x = 6
Person B thought of the number 2, so y = 2

EXAMPLE I AGAIN

Clearly, we need to find a method to solve simultaneous equations, rather than this trial and error approach.

The two equations for example 1 are: x + y = 12

x − y = 8

Now, if I add the two equations together, like this:

x + y = 12

x − y = 8 +

2x   = 20

> The reason I have added the two equations together is because the "+y" and the "−y" have cancelled out, leaving an equation with just x's in it, which I can solve to find the value of x.

So, x = 10 as we found before.

Now substitute this back into the first equation x + y = 12, to give:
10 + y = 12
So, y = 2, again, as before.

So the solution is: x = 10 and y = 2

It is always a good idea to check your answers in the other equation as well! So, substitute in x = 10 and y = 2 into:

x − y = 8
10 − 2 = 8

So, these solutions do work in the second equation as well. It is particularly important in an exam to substitute your answers into the second equation to check. You should know if you have the correct answer or not.

EXAMPLE 2 AGAIN

The two equations for example 2 are:
$$2x + y = 14$$
$$x - y = 4$$

Now, if I add the two equations together, like this:

$$2x + y = 14$$
$$\underline{x - y = 4} +$$
$$3x = 18$$

Again, adding the two equations together is useful, because the "+y" and the "− y" have again cancelled out, leaving an equation with just x's in it, which I can solve to find the value of x.

So, x = 6 as we found before.

Now substitute this back into the first equation 2x + y = 14, to give:

12 + y = 14
So, y = 2, again, as before.

So the solution is: x = 6 and y = 2

Now check that these values of x and y do work in the original equations.

EXAMPLE 3

Solve:
$$5x + y = 38$$
$$3x + y = 24$$

This time, if I add the two equations together, I get:

$$5x + y = 38$$
$$\underline{3x + y = 24} +$$
$$8x + 2y = 62$$

This is no use at all! I now have only one equation, but I still have x's and y's in it!

This time, I must subtract, like this:

$$5x + y = 38$$
$$\underline{3x + y = 24} -$$
$$2x = 14$$

So, x = 7. Substitute this back into either one of the equations. I use the first one, like this:

$$35 + y = 38$$
So, $$y = 3$$

So, the solution is x = 7 and y = 3

Now check that these values of x and y do work in the original equations.

EXAMPLE 4

Solve: $\quad 5x + 2y = 30$
$\qquad\quad x - y = -1$

This time, if I add the two equations together, I get:

$$5x + 2y = 30$$
$$\underline{x - y = -1} \; +$$
$$6x + y = 29$$

Again, this is no use at all! I have only one equation, and I still have x's and y's in the equation, so I cannot solve it.

Let's try subtracting:

$$5x + 2y = 30$$
$$\underline{x - y = -1} \; -$$
$$4x + 3y = 31$$

Remember: $2y - (-y) = 2y + y = 3y$
And: $30 - (-1) = 31$

Again, this is no use at all! I have only one equation, and I still have x's and y's in the equation, so I cannot solve it.

So, this time I decide to leave the first equation alone, and to multiply the second equation by two, like this:

$$5x + 2y = 30 \longrightarrow 5x + 2y = 30$$
$$x - y = -1 \xrightarrow{\;\times 2\;} 2x - 2y = -2 \qquad \text{Now add....}$$
$$\overline{7x \qquad\quad = 28}$$

$$\frac{7x}{7} = \frac{28}{7}$$
$$x = 4$$

By multiplying the second equation by two, I have arranged for there to be "$-2y$" in the second equation. There was a "$+2y$" in the first equation already. So, when I add the two equations the $+2y$ and the $-2y$ cancel out. This leaves me with an equation with just x's in, which I can solve.

Now, substitute $x = 4$ into the first equation, like this:

$$5x + 2y = 30$$
$$20 + 2y = 30$$
$$2y = 10$$
$$y = 5$$

So, the solution is: $x = 4$ and $y = 5$

EXAMPLE 5

Solve: $\quad 2x + 5y = 4$
$\qquad\quad 3x + 4y = 13$

I multiply the first equation by 3 and the second equation by 2, like this:

$$2x + 5y = 4 \xrightarrow{\;\times 3\;} 6x + 15y = 12$$
$$3x + 4y = 13 \xrightarrow{\;\times 2\;} 6x + 8y = 26$$

So, I have arranged that there is a "$+6x$" in both equations. So, now I can subtract, so the x's cancel out, like this:

$$6x + 15y = 12$$
$$\underline{6x + 8y = 26} \; -$$
$$7y = -14$$

$$y = -2$$

Now substitute y = −2 into the first equation, like this:

$$2x + 5y = 4$$
$$2x − 10 = 4$$
$$2x = 14$$
$$x = 7$$

So, the solution is: x = 7 and y = −2

QUESTIONS 2.15
Solve these simultaneous equations:

1. $2x + y = 12$
   $3x − y = 13$

2. $3x + 2y = 23$
   $5x − 2y = 33$

3. $3x − y = 9$
   $−3x + 5y = 3$

4. $3x + 5y = 31$
   $2x + 5y = 29$

5. $3x + y = 32$
   $5x + 2y = 55$

6. $2x + y = −5$
   $5x + 3y = −11$

7. $2x + 3y = 20$
   $5x − 2y = 31$

8. $5x + 3y = −19$
   $4x − 5y = −30$

9. $2x − 3y = 10$
   $−5x + 7y = −23$

10. $3x − 5y = 0$
    $−4x + 3y = 11$

CHANGING THE SUBJECT OF A FORMULA

Every time someone writes down a piece of Mathematical information using numbers, there is at least one other way of expressing the same information!

EXAMPLE I
I am sure you will agree that: 5 + 7 = 12

I can also write that: 5 = 12 − 7

and also: 7 = 12 − 5

So, these three statements are all correct and are equivalent to each other:

5 + 7 = 12	5 = 12 − 7	7 = 12 − 5

To go from the first statement to the second, it might be useful to put in a line of working, like this:

$$5 + 7 = 12$$
$$5 + 7 − 7 = 12 − 7 \quad ......\text{I have subtracted 7 from both sides...}$$
$$5 = 12 − 7$$

Now consider the same ideas using algebra. If I know that:

$$a + b = c \quad ....\text{I can subtract b from both sides } .....$$
$$a + b − b = c − b \quad .....\text{like this.....}$$
$$\text{So, } a = c − b$$

Re-arranging in this way to give 'a = something' is called **making 'a' the subject of the formula.**

To make b the subject of the formula, we could subtract 'a' from both sides, like this:

$$a + b = c$$
$$a − a + b = c − a \quad ....\text{subtracting 'a' from both sides.....}$$
$$\text{So, } b = c − a$$

So, these three expressions are all equivalent:

a + b = c	a = c − b	b = c − a

In fact, our strategy for changing the subject of a formula will be exactly the same as when we solved equations!

> At each stage, do the **same thing to both sides of the equation**, so that we keep the balance.

EXAMPLE 2
Using numbers: $\qquad 2 \times 6 = 12$

To re-arrange this statement to read '2 = something', I need to divide both sides by 6, like this:

$$\frac{2 \times 6}{6} = \frac{12}{6} \qquad \text{..... dividing both sides by 6...}$$

multiplying by 6 and dividing by 6 cancel out to give...

$$2 = \frac{12}{6}$$

Or, I could re-arrange this statement to read '6 = something', then I need to divide both sides by 2, like this:

$$\frac{2 \times 6}{2} = \frac{12}{2} \quad \text{..... dividing both sides by 2...}$$

$$6 = \frac{12}{2}$$

So, these three expressions are all equivalent:

2 × 6 = 12	$2 = \dfrac{12}{6}$	$6 = \dfrac{12}{2}$

Using Algebra: $b \times c = a$

To re-arrange this statement to read 'b = something', then I need to divide both sides by c, like this:

$$\frac{b \times c}{c} = \frac{a}{c} \qquad \text{.... dividing both sides by c...}$$

.....multiplying by c and dividing by c cancel out to give...

$$b = \frac{a}{c}$$

Or, I could re-arrange this statement to read 'c = something', then I need to divide both sides by b, like this:

$$\frac{b \times c}{b} = \frac{a}{b} \quad \text{..... dividing both sides by b, so the b's will cancel...}$$

$$c = \frac{a}{b}$$

So, these different expressions are equivalent:

b × c = a	$b = \dfrac{a}{c}$	$c = \dfrac{a}{b}$
Or, bc = a	Or, b = a ÷ c	Or, c = a ÷ b

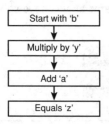

ALGEBRA

EXAMPLE 3

Make 'b' the subject of this formula: $a + by = z$

To make this equation, start with 'b', multiply by 'y', then add 'a' and this equals 'z'.

We could this use a flow diagram, like this:

| Start with 'b' |
| Multiply by 'y' |
| Add 'a' |
| Equals 'z' |

So, to get back to 'b', we must do the opposite of multiplying by 'y' (which is dividing by 'y') and the opposite of adding 'a' (which is subtracting 'a'), and do them in the oppopsite order, like this:

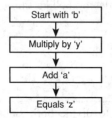
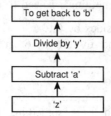

We can set the working out like this:

$$a + by = z$$
$$a - a + by = z - a \;\dots\dots\text{subtract 'a' from both sides}\dots$$
$$\frac{by}{y} = \frac{z - a}{y} \;\dots\dots\text{divide both sides by 'y'}$$
$$b = \frac{z - a}{y}$$

You can check with some numbers that this equation is equivalent to the original equation. If you put $a = 7$, $b = 2$, and $y = 5$ into the original equation, you get:

$a + by = z$
$7 + 2 \times 5 = 17$
So $z = 17$

Now put $z = 17$, $a = 7$, and $y = 5$ into our new equation:

$$b = \frac{z - a}{y}$$

$$b = \frac{17 - 7}{5}$$

$$b = 2$$

So, this is consistent with our first equation!

QUESTIONS 2.16

1. Make 'a' the subject of this formula: $a + b + c = x$

2. Make 'd' the subject of this formula: $de = y$

3. Make 'x' the subject of this formula: $ax + b = z$

4. Make 'x' the subject of this formula: $a - x = b$
   [Hint: Add x to both sides first, to make x positive]

5. Make 'x' the subject of this formula: $2a - x = b$
   [Hint: Add x to both sides first, to make x positive]

6. Make 'x' the subject of this formula: $2a - x = b + y$
   [Hint: Add x to both sides first, to make x positive]

7. Make 'a' the subject of this formula: $ab + x = y$

8. Make 'a' the subject of this formula: $ab + 2x = 3y$

9. Make 'a' the subject of this formula: $ab - 2x = 3y$

10. Make 'x' the subject of this formula: $ab - 2x = 3y$
    [Hint: Add 2x to both sides to make 2x positive]

▲ *USING ALGEBRA* ▼

USING EQUATIONS TO SOLVE PROBLEMS

You can use algebra to solve problems!

PROBLEM

> If you multiply my age by 4 then add 9 you
> get 157. How old am I?

Let my age be x. Now, if we write an equation for the above statement, we can then solve it to find out how old I am.

Start with x standing for my age in years, then multiply by 4, then add 9 and this equals 157.

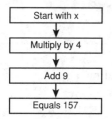

So, the equation is $4x + 9 = 157$

Now, we can solve this equation to find the value of x, which is my age.

So, to get back to the starting value of x, we must do the opposite of multiplying by 4 (which is dividing by 4) and the opposite of adding 9 (which is subtracting 9), and do them in the opposite order, like this:

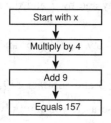 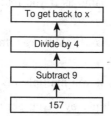

We can set out the working like this:

$$4x + 9 = 157$$
$$4x + 9 - 9 = 157 - 9 \quad \ldots\ldots\text{subtract 9 from both sides}\ldots$$
$$4x = 148$$
$$\frac{4x}{4} = \frac{148}{4} \quad \ldots\ldots\text{.divide both sides by 4}\ldots$$
$$x = 37$$

So, my age is 37!

EXAMPLE 2

PROBLEM

> If you multiply my age by 3 and then add 17, you get the same as if you multiply by 5 and then subtract 19.
> How old am I?

Let my age be x in years. Using the same ideas as before, the equation is:

$$3x + 17 = 5x - 19$$
$$3x + 17 - 3x = 5x - 19 - 3x \quad \ldots \text{ subtract 3x from both sides}..$$
$$17 = 2x - 19 \quad \ldots.. \text{ this means we only have x's on one side of the equation}$$
$$17 + 19 = 2x - 19 + 19 \quad \ldots. \text{ add 19 to both sides}\ldots$$
$$36 = 2x$$
$$\frac{36}{2} = \frac{2x}{2} \quad \ldots. \text{ divide both sides by 2}\ldots$$
$$18 = x$$

So, my age is 18!

QUESTIONS 2.17

Call my age x. Write an equation for each statement. Solve your equation to find my age.

1. If you multiply my age by 3 and subtract 7 you get 89.

2. If you multiply my age by 13 and add 5 you get 226.

3. If you subtract 11 from my age and then multiply by 3 you get 138.

4. If you double my age, add 15 then multiply by 7 you get 511.

5. If you subtract my age from 27 and then multiply by 7 you get 56.

6. If you divide my age by 9 then add 5 you get 14.

7. If you multiply my age by 5 and add 9 you get the same as if you multiply my age by 7 and then subtract 135.

8. If you double my age and add 7 you get the same as if you multiply my age by 5 and subtract 98.

9. If you subtract my age from 19 you get the same as if you multiply my age by 3 and subtract 149.

10. If you divide my age by three and add 7 then multiply by 4 you get the same as if you multiply my age by 5 and subtract 71.

USING FORMULAE

When you are asked to solve an *equation*, such as $3x + 7 = 19$, you are trying to find the *one* value of x which makes this equation a true statement. The only value of x which works in this equation is x = 4.

When you are using a *formula*, such as:

> Area of a rectangle = length × width

This formula gives you the area for *all* rectangles.

12 cm

5 cm

So, the area of this rectangle is 12 cm × 5 cm = 60 cm²

8·7 cm

4·1 cm

The area of this rectangle is 8·7 cm × 4·1 cm = 35·67 cm²

The formula gives the area of a rectangle, no matter how 'difficult' the numbers for the length and width.

EXAMPLE 2

The volume of a can of vegetable soup is 380 cm³. The soup weighs 290 g. What is the density of the soup?

The formula for density is:

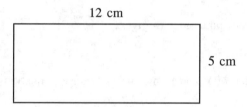

$$\text{Density} = \frac{\text{Mass}}{\text{Volume}}$$

So, Density = $\frac{\text{Mass}}{\text{Volume}}$ = $\frac{290 \text{ g}}{380 \text{ cm}^3}$ = 0·763 g/cm³

Mass is measured in grams (or kilograms for larger objects).

Volume is measured in cm³ (or m³ for larger objects).

So, you can work out the units for Density, by considering the formula, like this:

Density = $\frac{\text{Mass}}{\text{Volume}}$ = $\frac{\text{grams}}{\text{cm}^3}$ or $\frac{\text{kg}}{\text{m}^3}$

So, density is measured in grams per cm³ (or kg per m³).

This is also often written as g/cm³ (or kg/m³).

EXAMPLE 3

Find the radius of a cylinder, if the height of the cylinder is 17 cm and the volume 850 cm^3.

The formula for the volume of a cylinder is:

$$V = \pi r^2 h$$

For this example, I must re-arrange the formula so that it has 'r' as the subject of the formula. [See the section on Changing the Subject of a Formula if you need a reminder here.]

$V \quad = \quad \pi r^2 h$

Divide both sides by πh to give.....

$\dfrac{V}{\pi h} = \dfrac{\pi r^2 h}{\pi h}$

The right hand side simplifies to give ...

$\dfrac{V}{\pi h} = r^2$

Square root both sides to give...

$\sqrt{\dfrac{V}{\pi h}} = r$

So, now I can substitute the value of V and h into the re-arranged equation, like this:

$r = \sqrt{\dfrac{V}{\pi h}}$

$r = \sqrt{\dfrac{850}{\pi \times 17}}$

$r = \sqrt{15 \cdot 9}$

$r = 3 \cdot 98$

$r = 4 \cdot 0$ cm (to 1 decimal place)

QUESTIONS 2.18

Select from these formulae to answer the questions below:

Speed = $\dfrac{\text{Distance}}{\text{Time}}$	Acceleration = $\dfrac{\text{Speed}}{\text{Time}}$
Density = $\dfrac{\text{Mass}}{\text{Volume}}$	Area of a rectangle = Length $\times$ Width
$C = \pi d$	$A = \pi r^2$
The surface area of a sphere: $S = 4\pi r^2$	The volume of a cone: $V = \dfrac{\pi r^2 h}{3}$
The volume of a cylinder: $V = \pi r^2 h$	The formula to change °C to °F $F = \dfrac{9C}{5} + 32$

1. A container of UHT milk has a volume of 500 cm^3. The milk weighs 575 grams. Find the density of the milk.

2. A motorist has driven 152 miles and taken 3 hour 20 minutes. What is his average speed? [Think very carefully about the 20 minutes! Look back at the section Time for a reminder.]

3. A gardener has a circular pond. She measures the circumference to be 7 metres 54 centimetres. What is the diameter? She needs to know the area of her pond. What is it?

4. My cookery book gives the temperature to cook a dish as 200°C. What is this in °F?

5. Find the surface area of a sphere of diameter 12 cm.

6. Find the radius of a sphere whose surface area is 800 cm^2.

7. A tin can for a supermarket's own brand baked beans is to have a volume of 500 cm^3. (a) If the radius is fixed at 4 cm, what should the height of the can be? (b) If the height is fixed at 12 cm, what should the radius be?

8. The distance between London and Cardiff is 152 miles. A driver calculates that her average speed is 48 miles per hour. How long must the journey have taken her? Give your answer in hours and minutes.

9. The volume of a metal component for a car is 247 cm^3. The mass of the metal used is 2240 grams. What is the density of the metal component?

10. My cookery book gives a formula for roasting lamb. To calculate the length of the cooking time, the formula says to cook the meat for 27 minutes per pound plus an extra 27 minutes. How long should I cook a leg of lamb which weighs 4 lbs 6 oz? [Think very carefully about the 6 oz here! There are 16 oz in a pound.] Give your answer in hours and minutes.

GROWING PATTERNS (Straight Line Graphs)

EXAMPLE 1 SQUARES:
Use matches to build these patterns:

Pattern 1:   Pattern 2:   Pattern 3:    Pattern 4: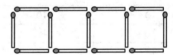

Continue building until you have made the tenth pattern. Now complete this table:

Number of Squares	Number of Matches
1	4
2	7
3	10
4	
5	
6	
7	
8	
9	
10	

You will be able to see that the "Number of Matches" column goes up three each time. You can relate this to the diagrams, as you need to use three extra matches each time.

This rule is easy to spot! It takes you down the page, because, if you know that 10 squares need 31 matches, you will be able to say that 11 squares will need 31 + 3 = 34 matches.

How many matches will you need to build 12 squares?

How many matches will you need to build 17 squares?

How many matches will you need to build 19 squares?

To answer these questions, you could make the patterns with matches and count how many you have used. Or, you could continue the table of results:

Number of Squares	Number of Matches
1	4
2	7
3	10
4	13
5	16
6	18
7	22
8	25
9	28
10	31
11	34
12	37
13	40
14	43
15	46
16	49
17	52
18	55
19	58

What if someone asked you how many matches will be needed to build 100 squares? If you actually built 100 squares, it would be difficult to count all the matches without making a mistake! Carrying the table on would become very tedious, as well as prone to error. So, we need to look for a new approach.

What we need is a quick way of finding the number of matches, when we know how many squares we want to build. The clue is that the number of matches goes up 3 each time we add another square. We could put in a "difference" column, which would show this clearly.

Number of Squares	Number of Matches	Difference Column
1	4	
		> 3
2	7	
		> 3
3	10	
		> 3
4	13	
		> 3
5	16	
		> 3
6	19	
		> 3
7	22	
		> 3
8	25	
		> 3
9	28	
		> 3
10	31	

We can see from the way each pattern of matches is formed that, for each square you want to build, you need three matches plus the extra match needed to complete the first square.

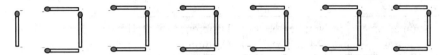

So, the Number of Matches is always **THREE** times the Number of Squares plus one more.

If we use algebra, we can express this last sentence more simply:

Call the number of squares S

Call the number of matches M

So, M = 3 × S + 1

> You will remember that mathematicians write this equation without the multiplication sign, as M = 3S + 1

We can now use our formula to find the number of matches needed to build the 100th pattern:

M = 3S + 1

S = 100, so, M = 3 × 100 + 1

so, M = 301

We would need 301 matches.

The M = 3S + 1 rule is a more sophisticated rule than the "add 3" rule. I can now work out the number of matches for the following table, with complete confidence that my answers will be correct, but without needing to do any more drawing.

Number of Squares	Number of Matches
10	3 × 10 + 1 = 31
20	3 × 20 + 1 = 61
25	3 × 25 + 1 = 76
50	3 × 50 + 1 = 151
100	3 × 100 + 1 = 301
1000	3 × 1000 + 1 = 3001
578	3 × 578 + 1 = 1735

CAUTION!

A COMMON MISCONCEPTION

Number of Squares	Numbers of Matches
10	31
20	How many matches needed?

> If we need 31 matches for 10 sqaures, how many do we heed for 20 squares?

There is a temptation to say: "We've doubled the number of squares, so we must double the number of matches that are needed."

But we can see from our previous working, that this isn't sound reasoning. We actually need 61 matches, not 62.

We must apply the formula, which reflects the structure of the problem. So we must continue to "multiply by three and add one", which will give 61 matches.

ALGEBRA

DRAWING THE GRAPH OF M = 3S + 1

Plot the points from our results table:

Number of Squares	Number of Matches	Difference Column
1	4	
		> 3
2	7	
		> 3
3	10	
		> 3
4	13	
		> 3
5	16	
		> 3
6	19	
		> 3
7	22	
		> 3
8	25	
		> 3
9	28	
		> 3
10	31	

Draw a horizontal axis for the number of squares, and a vertical axis for the number of matches.

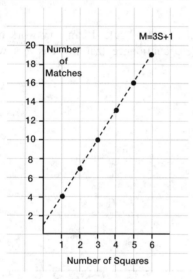

Drawing a graph of your table of results is always a good way of looking at your results. Notice that I have joined the points with a dotted line only, not a solid line. This is because, in this example, it is not possible to give meaning to the points which are half way between the ones we have plotted. What would two and a half squares look like? As this does not make any sense, we can put a dotted line in to give an indication of the direction of the line.

You can see that we have got a straight line. The line goes up three matches for every extra square.

Notice also that the straight line cuts the y-axis at y = 1

QUESTIONS 2.19
1. TRIANGLES:

(a) Use matches to make these patterns:

Pattern 1:   Pattern 2:   Pattern 3:   Pattern 4:

   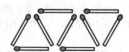

(b) Continue building or drawing the first ten diagrams for these patterns.

Fill your results into the table:

Number of Triangles	Number of Matches	Difference Column
1	3	
2	5	
3	7	
4		
5		
6		
7		
8		
9		
10		
T	M	

(c) Find the difference and use this to help you express the rule using algebra and using words.

Using words: The number of matches is always ☐ times the number of triangles plus ☐.

Using algebra: M = T × ☐ + ☐

(d) Use your formula to complete this table:

Number of Triangles	Number of Matches
10	
20	
25	
50	
100	
1000	
381	

(e) Draw the graph with the number of triangles going across the page and the number of matches going up the page. You should have a straight line. Where does the straight line cross the y-axis?

2. HEXAGONS

(a) Continue to draw more patterns in this sequence:

Pattern 1:   Pattern 2:   Pattern 3:

          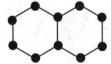   

Pattern 4:

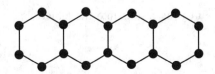

(b) Continue to draw the first ten diagrams for these patterns. Fill your results into the table:

Number of Hexagons	Number of Dots	Difference Column
1		
2		
3		
4		
5		
6		
7		
8		
9		
10		
H	D	

(c) Find the difference and use this to help you express the rule using algebra and using words.

Using words: The number of dots is always ☐ times the number of hexagons plus ☐ .

Using algebra: D = H × ☐ + ☐

(d) Use your formula to complete this table:

Number of Hexagons	Number of Dots
10	
20	
25	
50	
100	
1000	
372	

(e) Draw the graph with the number of hexagons going across the page and the number of dots going up the page. You should have a straight line. Where does the straight line cross the y-axis?

---

3. HOUSES

(a) Use matches to build more patterns in this sequence:

   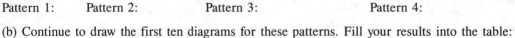

Pattern 1:   Pattern 2:   Pattern 3:   Pattern 4:

(b) Continue to draw the first ten diagrams for these patterns. Fill your results into the table:

Number of Houses	Number of Matches	Difference Column
1		
2		
3		
4		
5		
6		
7		
8		
9		
10		
H	M	

(c) Find the difference and use this to help you express the rule using algebra and using words.

Using words: The number of matches is always ☐ times the number of houses plus ☐.

Using algebra: M = H × ☐ + ☐

(d) Use your formula to complete this table:

Numbers of Houses	Number of Matches
10	
20	
25	
50	
100	
1000	
739	

(e) Draw the graph with the number of houses going across the page and the number of matches going up the page. You should have a straight line. Where does the straight line cross the y-axis?

USING DIFFERENCES TO FIND EQUATIONS

Read the previous section on Growing Patterns first!

In that section, there was a worked example called Squares and three examples called Triangles, Hexagons and Houses. These are the tables of results and the equations that go with them:

Number of Squares	Number of Matches	Difference Column
1	4	
		> 3
2	7	
		> 3
3	10	
		> 3
4	13	
		> 3
5	16	
		> 3
6	19	
		> 3
7	22	
		> 3
8	25	
		> 3
9	28	
		> 3
10	31	
		> 3
S	M	

$$M = 3S + 1$$

Number of Triangles	Number of Matches	Difference Column
1	3	
		> 2
2	5	
		> 2
3	7	
		> 2
4	9	
		> 2
5	11	
		> 2
6	13	
		> 2
7	15	
		> 2
8	17	
		> 2
9	19	
		> 2
10	21	
T	M	

$$M = 2T + 1$$

Number of Hexagons	Number of Dots	Difference Column
1	6	
		> 4
2	10	
		> 4
3	14	
		> 4
4	18	
		> 4
5	22	
		> 4
6	26	
		> 4
7	30	
		> 4
8	34	
		> 4
9	38	
		> 4
10	42	
H	D	

$$D = 4H + 2$$

Number of Houses	Number of Matches	Difference Column
1	5	
		>4
2	9	
		>4
3	13	
		>4
4	17	
		>4
5	21	
		>4
6	25	
		>4
7	29	
		>4
8	33	
		>4
9	37	
		>4
10	41	
H	M	

$$M = 4H + 1$$

You can see that whatever the number in the difference column, it always appears in the equation as the number to multiply by. Then add or subtract the number which gives the right answer for each entry in the table.

QUESTIONS 2.20

Add a difference column to these tables of results and use it to find the equation.

Draw the graph for each table of results. Put the x values along the horizontal axis and the y values along the vertical axis. Can you find a connection between the equation and the graph?

1.

x	y
1	7
2	10
3	13
4	16
5	19
6	22
7	25
8	28

2.

x	y
1	10
2	13
3	16
4	19
5	22
6	25
7	28
8	31

3.

x	y
1	3
2	7
3	11
4	15
5	19
6	23
7	27
8	31

4.

x	y
1	2.5
2	3
3	3.5
4	4
5	4.5
6	5
7	5.5
8	6

EXAMPLE 2 (SLIGHTLY HARDER!)

Find the equation for this table of results:

x	y
1	13
2	11
3	9
4	7
5	5
6	3
7	1
8	−1

Put in the difference column as before:

x	y	Difference
1	13	
		>−2
2	11	
		>−2
3	9	
		>−2
4	7	
		>−2
5	5	
		>−2
6	3	
		>−2
7	1	
8	−1	

Notice that this time the values are going down, so the difference is **minus 2**.

Fortunately, though, the equation is found just as before! Multiply the x by minus 2 and then add or subtract a number as appropriate.

So, the equation will be: $y = -2x + 15$

Check that this works for all entries in the table, which it does!

For example, when x = 8 $y = -2x + 15$

$$y = -2 \times 8 + 15$$

$$y = -16 + 15$$

$$y = -1 \ldots\text{.which is correct!}$$

QUESTIONS 2.21

Add a difference column to these tables of results and use it to find the equation.
Draw the graph for each table of results. Put the x values along the horizontal axis and the y values along the vertical axis. Can you find a connection between the equation and the graph?

1.

x	y
1	8
2	7
3	6
4	5
5	4
6	3
7	2
8	1

2.

x	y
1	7
2	5
3	3
4	1
5	-1
6	-3
7	-5
8	-7

3.

x	y
1	11
2	8
3	5
4	2
5	-1
6	-4
7	-7
8	-10

4.

x	y
1	5
2	3
3	1
4	-1
5	-3
6	-5
7	-7
8	-9

USING GROWING PATTERNS TO SOLVE PROBLEMS

We can use the ideas of growing patterns to solve some types of problems.
Try to solve this problem, called Garden Designs, before you read any further.

GARDEN DESIGNS

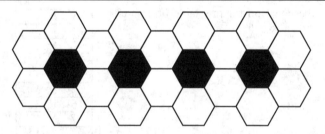

A landscape gardener, Mr Rose, is designing a garden to go in front of a new office block. He wants to create 100 flower beds and surround them with hexagonal paving slabs according to the pattern shown in the picture. (In this arrangement 18 slabs surround 4 flower beds.) How many paving slabs will he need to order?

 = Flower Bed   = Paving Slab

We could draw 100 flower beds and surround them with slabs and then count the slabs. This would be a very long, slow process and we might make a mistake counting up at the end! We need a new approach and a good method is to start with small numbers of flower beds to see the underlying structure of the problem.

With one flower bed, you need 6 paving slabs.

With two flower beds, you need 10 paving slabs.

Continue to draw out successive patterns. Put your results into a table and carry on until you can see what is happening:

Number of Flower Beds	Number of Paving Slabs	Difference Column
1	6	
		> 4
2	10	
		> 4
3	14	
		> 4
4	18	
		> 4
5	22	
		> 4
6	26	
		> 4
7	30	
		> 4
8	34	
F	S	

You can see from the difference column that the number of paving slabs we need increases by 4 each time. We can relate this to the structure of the problem:

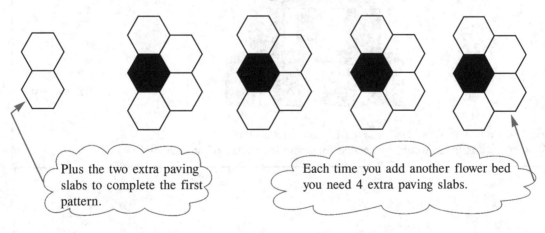

Plus the two extra paving slabs to complete the first pattern.

Each time you add another flower bed you need 4 extra paving slabs.

Call the number of flower beds F   The formula is: $S = 4 \times F + 2$
Call the number of slabs S $S = 4F + 2$

So, when the landscape gardener creates 100 flower beds, F = 100

So the number of paving slabs he needs will be:

$$S = 4 \times F + 2$$
$$S = 4 \times 100 + 2$$
$$S = 402$$

So, Mr Rose will need 402 paving slabs, which must be the right answer, when you consider the structure of the problem.

QUESTION 2.22

A rival landscape gardener, Mrs Flowers, has put in a plan for a different design in front of the office block.

She would like to put a row of hexagonal ponds in front of the office block, each pond with a fountain in the middle and 12 small conifers round the outside, like this:

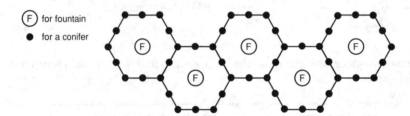

F for fountain
● for a conifer

Mrs. Flowers calculates that her design will need 46 hexagonal ponds in the line. How many conifers will she have to order?

GROWING PATTERNS 2 (Curved Graphs)

Try to solve the problem below, called House of Dominoes, by using the ideas of growing patterns before you read any further.

HOUSE OF DOMINOES

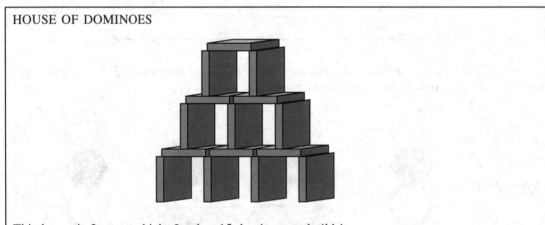

This house is 3 storeys high. It takes 15 dominoes to build it
How many dominoes would be needed for a similar house, 65 storeys high?

Starting with small numbers can be very effective when trying to solve a problem. It can help you to understand the structure of the problem and get a feel for what is going on!

Look at a house of dominoes only one storey high:

Next, look at a house two storeys high:

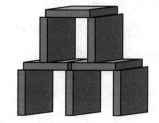

We need only 3 dominoes to build this house.

We need 8 dominoes to build this house.

We already know that three storeys takes 15 dominoes. Build bigger houses and complete the table of results below:

Number of Storeys	Number of Dominoes
1	3
2	8
3	15
4	
5	
6	
7	
8	

Plot a graph of your results, to look at the shape of the graph. Can you find the equation which links the number of storeys to the number of dominoes used?

Your table of results should look like this, with the difference column added:

Number of Storeys	Number of Dominoes	Difference
1	3	
		> 5
2	8	
		> 7
3	15	
		> 9
4	24	
		> 11
5	35	
		> 13
6	48	
		> 15
7	63	
		> 17
8	80	
x	y	

This time you can see that the difference column changes each time. When we plot the graph of the results we do not get a straight line, but a curved graph.

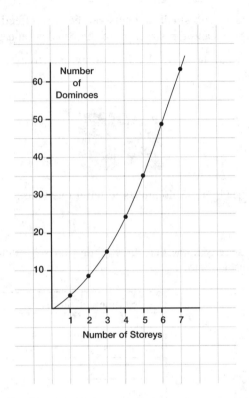

How can we find the equation for this example?

Add in another column, which gives you the difference of the difference, like this:

Number of Storeys	Number of Dominoes	Difference Column	Difference of the Difference
1	3		
		> 5	> 2
2	8		
		> 7	> 2
3	15		
		> 9	> 2
4	24		
		> 11	> 2
5	35		
		> 13	> 2
6	48		
		> 15	> 2
7	63		
		> 17	> 2
8	80		
x	y		

The difference of the difference is also called the **second difference**.

You can see that the difference of the difference is always 2.

When you have to go to the difference of the difference column, before you keep getting the same number, this tells you that you have a quadratic to deal with. This means that your graph is a curve, not a straight line and that you have an x squared in the equation.

Number of Storeys	Numbers of Dominoes
1	$1 \times 3 = 3$
2	$2 \times 4 = 8$
3	$3 \times 5 = 15$
4	$4 \times 6 = 24$
5	$5 \times 7 = 35$
6	$6 \times 8 = 48$
7	$7 \times 9 = 63$
8	$8 \times 10 = 80$
x	$x \times (x + 2) = y$

You may have spotted the equation already, by noticing that you can find the y value by multiplying x by (x + 2), for each entry in the table.

So, the equation is $y = x(x + 2)$
or $y = x^2 + 2x$

QUESTIONS 2.23

1. Complete these tables of values for the given equations. Add in the difference column, then the difference of the difference column. Write down a conclusion about what you notice. Some entries are started for you.

(a) $y = x^2$

x	y	difference column	diff of diff
1			
2			
3			
4			
5			
6			
7			
8			
9			
10			

(b) $y = 2x^2$

x	y	difference column	diff of diff
1	2		
2	8		
3	18		
4	32		
5			
6			
7			
8			
9			
10			

(c) $y = 3x^2$

x	y	difference column	diff of diff
1	3		
2	12		
3			
4			
5			
6			
7			
8			
9			
10			

(d) $y = 4x^2$

x	y	difference column	diff of diff
1	4		
2	16		
3			
4			
5			
6			
7			
8			
9			
10			

(e) $y = 0 \cdot 5x^2$

x	y	difference column	diff of diff
1	0.5		
2	2		
3			
4			
5			
6			
7			
8			
9			
10			

(f) $y = 1 \cdot 5x^2$

x	y	difference column	diff of diff
1			
2			
3			
4			
5			
6			
7			
8			
9			
10			

2. Use what you have found out in question 1 to find the equations for these tables of results:

(a)

x	y	difference column	diff of diff
1	2		
2	6		
3	12		
4	20		
5	30		
6	42		
7	56		
8	72		
9	90		
10	110		

(b)

x	y	difference column	diff of diff
1	0		
2	2		
3	6		
4	12		
5	20		
6	30		
7	42		
8	56		
9	72		
10	90		

(c)

x	y	difference column	diff of diff
1	4		
2	14		
3	30		
4	52		
5	80		
6	114		
7	154		
8	200		
9	252		
10	310		

(d)

x	y	difference column	diff of diff
1	2.5		
2	8		
3	16.5		
4	28		
5	42.5		
6	60		
7	80.5		
8	104		
9	130.5		
10	160		

3. HOUSE OF CARDS

This house of cards is 3 storeys high. I need 15 cards to make this house.

How many cards would be needed to make a house of cards 20 storeys high? If the world record is a house of cards that is 61 storeys high, how many cards would be needed to equal the world record?

How many cards would be needed to break the world record and build a house that is 62 storeys high?

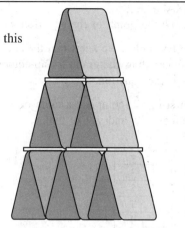

▲ GRAPHS ▼

DRAWING STRAIGHT LINE GRAPHS

Look back to and re-read the whole section on Growing Patterns! The ideas covered there will help you to understand this section more fully. In Growing Patterns we generated this table of results and we drew the graph, like this:

Number of Squares	Number of Matches
1	4
2	7
3	10
4	13
5	16
6	19
7	22
8	25
9	28
10	31
S	M

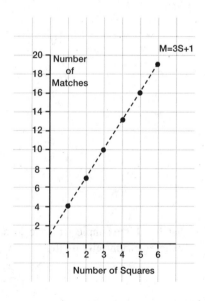

Notice that we have put the Number of Squares along the x-axis and the Number of Matches along the y-axis. Whenever you draw a graph, you should label the line with the equation, which we found to be: $M = 3S + 1$

For this situation we can have only whole numbers of squares. It makes no sense to have $S = 2 \cdot 5$ as we cannot have two and a half squares. So we have drawn the straight line in as a dotted line.

EXAMPLE 2

Draw the graph of the equation $y = 2x + 3$.

In Example 1 we knew that the equation came from a growing pattern of squares made from matches. We can draw the graph for an equation, even if we don't know the particular situation that has generated the equation.

First of all, complete a table of values of x and y, like this:

The graph will look like this:

x	y
0	3
1	5
2	7
3	9
4	11
5	13
6	15
7	17
8	19
9	21
10	23

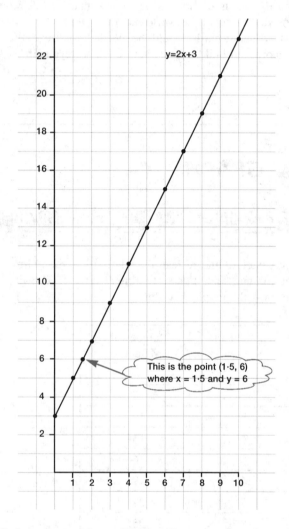

This is the point (1·5, 6) where x = 1·5 and y = 6

Notice that for this example we have joined all the points with a solid line. For example, when $x = 1 \cdot 5$ the equation tells us that:

$$y = 2x + 3$$
$$y = 2 \times 1 \cdot 5 + 3$$
$$y = 3 + 3 = 6$$

You can see that the point (1·5, 6) does lie on the straight line.

EXAMPLE 3

Draw the graph of $y = 3x - 5$ for values of x between -4 and $+4$. This time, write the table of results going horizontally. It makes no difference to the points plotted, but will save some space!

Be careful with the minus signs! It is often easier to complete the table of results by starting with the positive values of x first. This is the table of results:

x	−4	−3	−2	−1	0	1	2	3	4
y	−17	−14	−11	−8	−5	−2	1	4	7

Make sure that you can fill in the table
of results correctly:

When   x = −4, for example, check that:
        y = 3x − 5
        y = 3 × (−4) − 5
        y = −12 − 5
        y = −17

The graph will look like this:

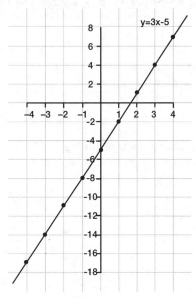

EXAMPLE 4

Draw the graph of y = 8 − x for values of x between −4 and +4.

This is the table of results:

x	−4	−3	−2	−1	0	1	2	3	4
y	12	11	10	9	8	7	6	5	4

When x = −4, check that:
y = 8 − x
y = 8 − (−4)
y = 8 + 4

so, y = 12

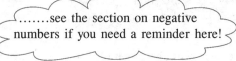

.......see the section on negative
numbers if you need a reminder here!

The graph will look like this:

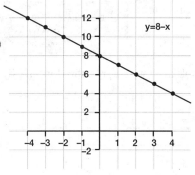

QUESTIONS 2.24

Draw the graphs of these equations, for values of x between −4 and +4.

1. y = x + 5
2. y = 2x + 5
3. y = 3x + 2
4. y = 2 + 3x
5. y = 2x − 3
6. y = 4x − 2

7.   y = 7 − x
8.   y = 9 − 2x
9.   y = 4x + 7
10. y = 7 − 3x
11. y = −3 − 3x
12. y = $\frac{1}{2}$ x + 2

13. y = 7 + 3x
14. y = $\frac{1}{2}$x + 5
15. y = $\frac{1}{2}$x − 3

ALGEBRA

THE GRADIENT OF A STRAIGHT LINE

Look at the graphs for questions 1 and 2 that you have just drawn. Your graphs should look like this:

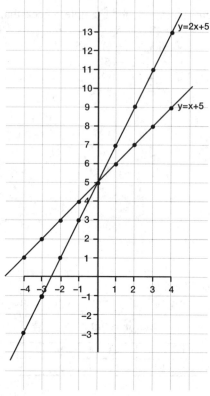

You can see that both graphs go through the point (0,5), but the line $y = 2x + 5$ is steeper than the line $y = x + 5$.

We use the word **gradient** to describe how steep a line is.

Definition:

$$\text{Gradient} = \frac{\text{Increase in the y direction}}{\text{Increase in the x direction}}$$

Look at how to apply this formula by considering the graph of $y = x + 5$ on its own.

This is the table of results for $y = x + 5$

x	−4	−3	−2	−1	0	1	2	3	4
y	1	2	3	4	5	6	7	8	9

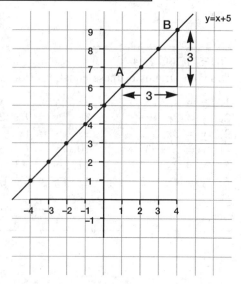

Choose two points on the line:
A(1, 6) [where x = 1 and y = 6], and
B(4, 9) [where x = 4 and y = 9].

Draw in a triangle on the graph between the two points A and B.

Now, apply the formula:

$$\text{Gradient} = \frac{\text{Increase in the y direction}}{\text{Increase in the x direction}} = \frac{3}{3} = 1$$

So, the gradient of the line $y = x + 5$ is 1.

Now find the gradient of the line y = 2x + 5, in the same way.

This is the table of results for y = 2x + 5

x	−4	−3	−2	−1	0	1	2	3	4
y	−3	−1	1	3	5	7	9	11	13

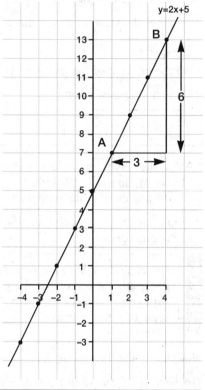

Choose two points on the line:
A(1, 7) [where x = 1 and y = 7], and B(4, 13)
[where x = 4 and y = 13].

Draw in a triangle on the graph between the two
points A and B.

Now, apply the formula:

Gradient = $\dfrac{\text{Increase in the y direction}}{\text{Increase in the x direction}}$ = $\dfrac{6}{3}$ = 2

So, the gradient of the line y = 2x + 5 is 2.

What if we had chosen two different points?
Would the gradient be different?

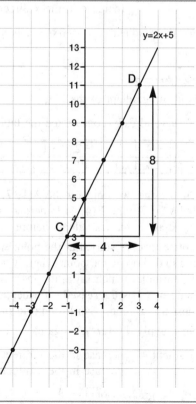

Choose the points C(−1, 3)
[where x = −1 and y = 3] and
D(3, 11) [where x = 3 and y = 11].

Now, apply the formula again:

Gradient = $\dfrac{\text{Increase in the y direction}}{\text{Increase in the x direction}}$ = $\dfrac{8}{4}$ = 2

So, we still get the gradient of the line y = 2x + 5
to equal 2.

For the graph of $y = 2x + 5$, take the points E(-3, -1) [where $x = -3$ and $y = -1$], and F(2, 9) [$x = 2$ and $y = 9$]. Draw in the triangle, apply the formula and show that you **still** get the gradient to equal 2!

We have found that the gradient of the line $y = x + 5$ is 1.

And the gradient of the line $y = 2x + 5$ is 2.

The larger the value of the gradient, the steeper the straight line!

EXAMPLE 2
Find the gradient of the line $y = 3x - 2$.

This is the table of results:

x	−4	−3	−2	−1	0	1	2	3	4
y	−14	−11	−8	−5	−2	1	4	7	10

Choose the two points A(2, 4) [where $x = 2$ and $y = 4$], and B(4, 10) [where $x = 4$ and $y = 10$] and draw in the triangle as before.

A pupil has drawn the graph quite correctly like the one opposite:

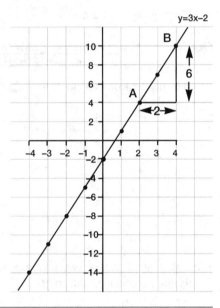

CAUTION!

> Notice that we have not counted 3 **squares** going up, but 6 **units** up the y-axis. We started with $y = 4$ and got to where $y = 10$. So, the value of y has increased by 6.

Now, apply the formula again:

Gradient $= \dfrac{\text{Increase in the y direction}}{\text{Increase in the x direction}} = \dfrac{6}{2} = 3$

So, the gradient of $y = 3x - 2$ is 3.

EXAMPLE 3
Find the gradient of the line $y = 8 - x$.

We have already constructed the table of results:

x	−4	−3	−2	−1	0	1	2	3	4
y	12	11	10	9	8	7	6	5	4

Choose the two points to be A(1, 7) [where $x = 1$ and $y = 7$], and B(4, 4) [where $x = 4$ and $y = 4$] and draw in the triangle as before.

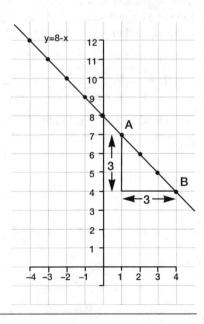

Notice that we started at the point where $y = 7$ and ended up at the point where $y = 4$. Look at the formula, which says "the increase in y". The value of y has **decreased**, not increased! So, I must use a minus sign to indicate this.

Now, apply the formula again:

Gradient $= \dfrac{\text{Increase in the y direction}}{\text{Increase in the x direction}} = \dfrac{-3}{3} = -1$

So, the gradient of $y = 8 - x$ is -1 (minus one).

POSITIVE GRADIENT

All graphs which slope this way will have a gradient which is a positive value.

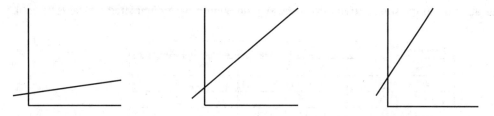

NEGATIVE GRADIENT

All graphs which slope this way will have a gradient which is a negative value.

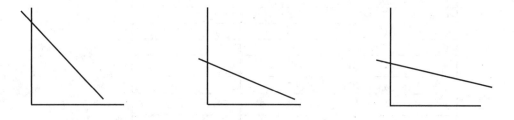

QUESTIONS 2.25

1. For each of the questions below, draw a separate diagram. Use your diagram to find the gradient of the line joining these points:

(a)   A(1, 3) to B(4, 6)   (d)   G(2, 11) to H(5, 2)
(b)   C(2, 5) to D(8, 17)   (e)   J(4, 5) to K(17, 8)
(c)   E(−2, 5) to F(6, 9)   (f)   L(−2, 7) to M(5, 5)

2. Go back to the graphs which you drew earlier. Draw in a triangle which will enable go to find the gradient of each graph. Write down also where the graph cuts the y-axis. Fill your results into this table:

Equation	Gradient	Cuts y-axis
$y = x + 5$		
$y = 2x + 5$		
$y = 3x + 2$		
$y = 2 + 3x$		
$y = 2x - 3$		
$y = 4x - 2$		
$y = 7 - x$		
$y = 9 - 2x$		
$y = 4x + 7$		
$y = 7 - 3x$		
$y = -3 - 3x$		
$y = \frac{1}{2}x + 2$		
$y = 7 + 3x$		
$y = \frac{1}{2}x + 5$		
$y = \frac{1}{2}x - 3$		

THE y = mx + c FORMULA FOR A STRAIGHT LINE

Look at your answers to question 2 (Questions 2.25). You should have completed the table to look like this:

Equation	Gradient	Cuts y-axis
$y = x + 5$	1	5
$y = 2x + 5$	2	5
$y = 3x + 2$	3	2
$y = 2 + 3x$	3	2
$y = 2x - 3$	2	−3
$y = 4x - 2$	4	−2
$y = 7 - x$	−1	7
$y = 9 - 2x$	−2	9
$y = 4x + 7$	4	7
$y = 7 - 3x$	−3	7
$y = -3 - 3x$	−3	−3
$y = \frac{1}{2}x + 2$	$\frac{1}{2}$	2
$y = 7 + 3x$	3	7
$y = \frac{1}{2}x + 5$	$\frac{1}{2}$	5
$y = \frac{1}{2}x - 3$	$\frac{1}{2}$	−3

Look carefully at each of the entries in the table.

The gradient of each line is always the number in front of the x in the equation. (The number in front of the x in the equation is called the **coefficient** of x.)

The place where each line cuts the y-axis is always the other number in the equation – the one which does not involve x. (This number is independent of the value of x and is called the **constant**.)

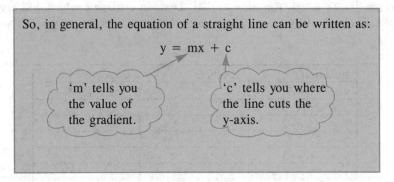

So, in general, the equation of a straight line can be written as:

$$y = mx + c$$

'm' tells you the value of the gradient.

'c' tells you where the line cuts the y-axis.

CAUTION!

What is the gradient of the straight line y = 8 − 5x ?

Many pupils wrongly give the answer to this question as "8".

Pupils who fall into this trap probably think y = mx + c tells them that the gradient is the **first** number in the equation. This is not a useful way of remembering the y = mx + c equation. The gradient is always the **coefficient** of x (which in this case is −5), not the first number in the equation.

So, for the equation y = 8 − 5x , the gradient is −5 and the line cuts the y-axis at 8.

ALGEBRA

TWO SPECIAL CASES!

What is the equation of this line?

You can see that the gradient of this line is zero, and the line cuts the y-axis at y = 3.

So, applying the y = mx + c formula:

y = 0x + 3. .... This simplifies to y = 3.

So, the equation of this line is y = 3.

You can see from the co-ordinates marked that each y co-ordinate is always 3, but the x co-ordinate can take any value.

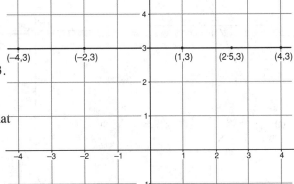

What is the equation of this line?

This time, you can see that the gradient of this line is actually infinity! And the line does not cut the y-axis at all!

So, we cannot apply the formula as before. But you can see from the co-ordinates marked on the line, that each x co-ordinate is always 4, but the y co-ordinate can take any value.

So, the equation of this line is x = 4

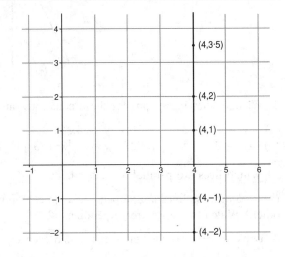

QUESTIONS 2.26

1. Plot these points (1, 8), (3, 14), (4, 17), (6, 23), (9, 32) and join them with a straight line. Find the equation of the line you have drawn.

2. Write down the equations of these lines.

(a)

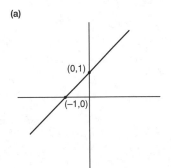

(b)

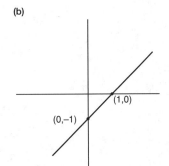

(c)

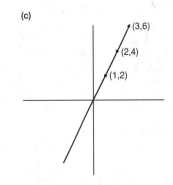

ALGEBRA

ALGEBRA

(d)

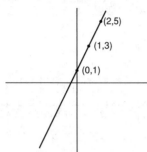

(e)

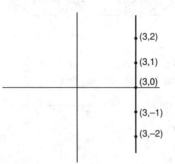

(f)

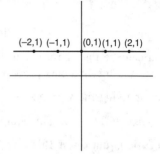

(g)

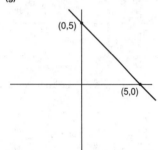

(h)

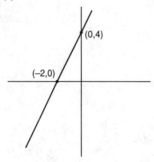

(i)

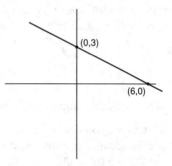

3. **Without** drawing graphs for these equations, answer the following questions:

(a) $y = 2x + 3$	(c) $y = 4x + 3$	(e) $y = 5 + 2x$
(b) $y = 3x - 5$	(d) $y = -\frac{1}{4}x + 3$	(f) $y = 3x + 4$

(i) Which lines are parallel to each other?

(ii) Two of these lines are perpendicular to each other. (Perpendicular means at right angles to each other.) Which two lines are perpendicular?

4. Look at these graphs below and match each equation with a graph:

Equation	Graph
$y = x$	
$y = 2x$	
$y = 2x - 3$	
$y = 7 - x$	
$y = -5$	
$y = -2x + 7$	
$y = \frac{1}{2}x + 4$	
$y = -\frac{1}{2}x + 1$	

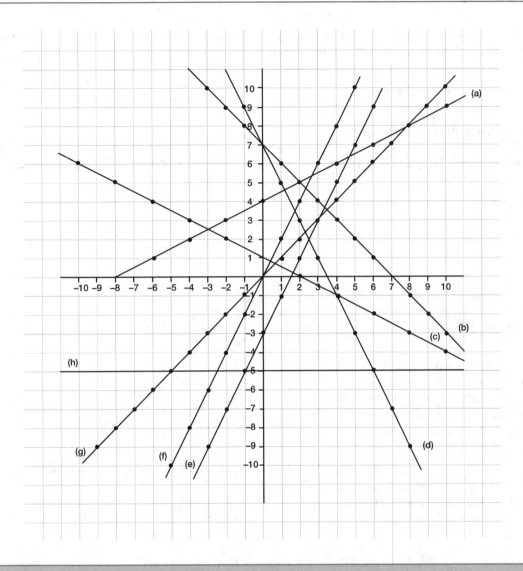

THE ax + by = c FORMULA FOR A STRAIGHT LINE

The equation of a straight line is not always in the y = mx + c form!

Draw the graph of 2x + 3y = 6 for values of x between −4 and +4.

Can you fill in this table of results for this equation?

x	−4	−3	−2	−1	0	1	2	3	4
y									

Substitute x = 4 into the equation
$$2x + 3y = 6$$
$$8 + 3y = 6$$
$$3y = -2 \quad \text{......subtracting 8 from both sides}$$
$$y = -\tfrac{2}{3} \quad \text{...dividing both sides by 3}$$

We can proceed in this way, substituting the different values of x into the equation in turn.

Or, we can take a short cut! Look at the equation 2x + 3y = 6. It must represent a straight line as it does not include x-squared or y-squared terms. To draw a straight line we only need to find two points which we know are on the straight line, then use a ruler to join these two points together.

To find two points, choose x = 0 first of all. (I've chosen x = 0 because it makes the calculation nice and easy!) Substitute x = 0 into the equation:

$$2x + 3y = 6$$
to give: $0 + 3y = 6$
so $y = 2$

So, the point (0, 2) lies on our line.

Now choose y = 0 (again this makes the calculation nice and easy). Substitute this into the equation

$$2x + 3y = 6$$
to give $2x + 0 = 6$
so $2x = 6$
so $x = 3$

So, the point (3, 0) lies on our line.

To draw the straight line 2x + 3y = 6, plot these two points and join them together, like this:

You could argue that we should find three points which lie on our straight line, to check that all three points do actually lie on the line. This will show us that we haven't made a mistake.

We have already found that $(4, -\frac{2}{3})$ lies on the straight line and you can see from the graph that the straight line does indeed go through this point.

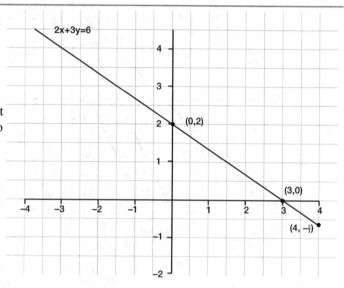

What is the gradient of our straight line?

Choose the points A(0, 2) and B(3, 0). Draw in the triangle as before.

Now, apply the formula again:

$$\text{Gradient} = \frac{\text{Increase in the y direction}}{\text{Increase in the x direction}} = \frac{-2}{3}$$

So the gradient of the line 2x + 3y = 6 is $-\frac{2}{3}$.

Where does the straight line 2x + 3y = 6 cross the y-axis?

At the point y = 2.

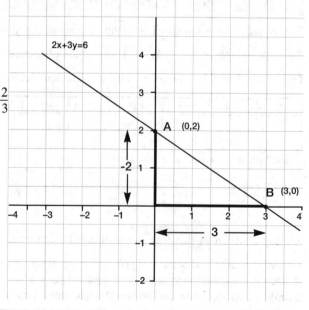

Put these two pieces of information together in the y = mx + c formula.

So, our line 2x + 3y = 6 must be the same as $y = -\frac{2}{3}x + 2$ when written in the y = mx + c form.

We can practice our algebra skills to show that this must be the case!

Start with $\qquad$ 2x + 3y $\quad$ = 6

$$2x + 3y - 2x = 6 - 2x \quad ....\text{subtract 2x from both sides...}$$
$$3y = 6 - 2x$$

$$\frac{3y}{3} = \frac{6}{3} - \frac{2x}{3} \quad .....\text{ divide both sides by 3....}$$

$$y = 2 - \frac{2}{3}x$$

This is can be written as $y = -\frac{2}{3}x + 2$ as before.

QUESTIONS 2.27

Draw the following graphs. Choose x = 0 and find y. Then choose y = 0 and find x. This will give you two points which lie on the straight line. Find a third point which lies on the straight line to check that you are correct.

Find the gradient and where the line crosses the y-axis.

Fill your results into this table of results.

Use algebra to show that your last column is correct!

	ax + by = c form of the equation	Gradient	Cuts y-axis	y = mx + c form of the equation
1.	3x + 4y = 12			
2.	x + 5y = 10			
3.	2x − 3y = 12			
4.	−3x + 5y = 15			
5.	4x + 5y = 10			

THE DIFFERENCE COLUMN AND THE GRADIENT!

Look back at the section Using Differences to Find Equations. There we found that:

Number of Squares	Number of Matches	Difference Column	
1	4		
		> 3	
2	7		
		> 3	
3	10		
		> 3	
4	13		
		> 3	M = 3S + 1
5	16		
		> 3	
6	19		
		> 3	
7	22		
		> 3	
8	25		
		> 3	
9	28		
		> 3	
10	31		
S	M		

The Difference Column is 3 and the Gradient of the line M = 3S + 1 is also 3!

The Difference Column and the Gradient will always be the same!

The Gradient tells you how much you go up (or down) each time you go along one in the x direction. This is exactly what the Difference Column tells you!

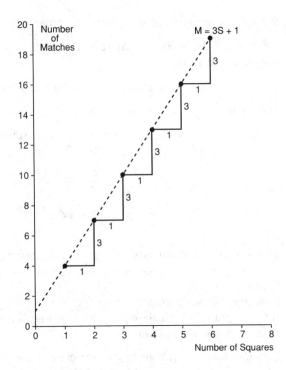

SIMULTANEOUS EQUATIONS SOLVED GRAPHICALLY

See also the section on Solving Simultaneous Equations Using Algebra.

Solve the simultaneous equations: $y = 8 - x$
$y = 2x + 5$

We have already met these two graphs before. Plot them on the same axes, like this:

The solution to the simultaneous equations is the value of x and of y which satisfies both equations. This is where the graphs cross.

So, the solution is x = 1 and y = 7.

You can check that these values work in both equations:

For $y = 8 - x$
Substitute in x = 1, like this:
So, y = 8 − 1 = 7
So, y does indeed equal 7·

For $y = 2x + 5$
Substitute in x = 1, like this:
So, y = 2 + 5 = 7
So, y does indeed equal 7.

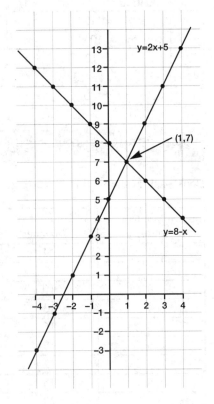

QUESTIONS 2.28

Solve these simultaneous equations graphically:

1. $x + y = 6$
    $x - y = 2$

2. $x - 3y = 6$
    $x + y = 10$

3. $2x + y = 5$
    $x - y = 4$

4. $y = 4x - 5$
    $3x - y = 1$

5. $2x + y = 7$
    $3x + 2y = 12$

6. $2x + y = 8$
    $y = 4x - 7$

7. $3x - 4y = 5$
    $y = 4x + 2$

8. $3x + 8y = -5$
    $-5x + 2y = 16$

9. $x + 4y = 6$
    $3x + 8y = 19$

10. $3x - 4y = 9$
    $y = 6x - 4$

DRAWING QUADRATIC GRAPHS

Draw the graph of $y = x^2$ for values of x between -4 and $+4$.

Fill in a table of results, like this:

x	-4	-3	-2	-1	0	1	2	3	4
y	$+16$	$+9$	$+4$	$+1$	0	1	4	9	16

Remember that when $x = -4$,

$y = x^2$
$y = (-4) \times (-4)$
$y = +16$

.....look back at the section on negative numbers, if you need a reminder here!

Plotting the graph looks like this:

So, you can see that the graph is a nice smooth, u-shaped curve.

Equations with an x^2 term in them are called **quadratic equations**.

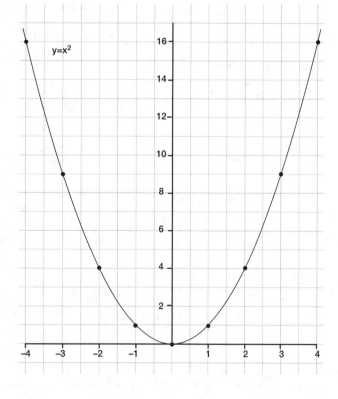

$y=x^2$

EXAMPLE 2

Draw the graph of $y = x^2 - 5$ for values of x between -4 and $+4$.

Fill in a table of results, like this:

x	−4	−3	−2	−1	0	1	2	3	4
y	11	4	−1	−4	−5	−4	−1	4	11

If you need to do some working out, to help you fill in values in the table, you could set your work out like this:

	x^2	−5	=	y
x = 4	16	−5	=	11
x = 3	9	−5	=	4
x = 2	4	−5	=	−1
x = 1	1	−5	=	−4
x = 0	0	−5	=	−5
x = −1	1	−5	=	−4
x = −2	4	−5	=	−1
x = −3	9	−5	=	4
x = −4	16	−5	=	11

Plot the graph, which looks like this:

Again, you can see that the graph is a nice smooth, u-shaped curve.

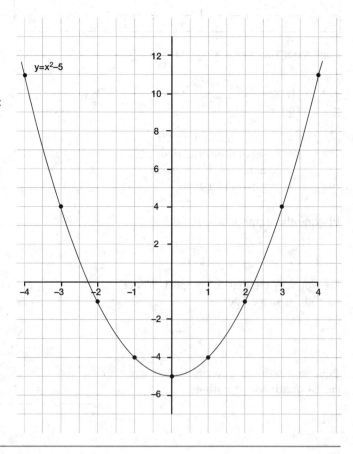

ALGEBRA

EXAMPLE 3

Draw the graph of y = x(x + 2) for values of x between −4 and +4.

Fill in a table of results, like this:

x	−4	−3	−2	−1	0	1	2	3	4
y	8	3	0	−1	0	3	8	15	24

To help fill in the table, set the working out like this:

	x	×	(x + 2)	=	y
x = 4	4	×	6	=	24
x = 3	3	×	5	=	15
x = 2	2	×	4	=	8
x = 1	1	×	3	=	3
x = 0	0	×	2	=	0
x = −1	−1	×	1	= −1	
x = −2	−2	×	0	=	0
x = −3	−3	×	−1	=	3
x = −4	−4	×	−2	=	8

Remember that: "a minus times a plus is a minus"

Remember that: "a minus times a minus is a plus"

Plot the graph, which looks like this:

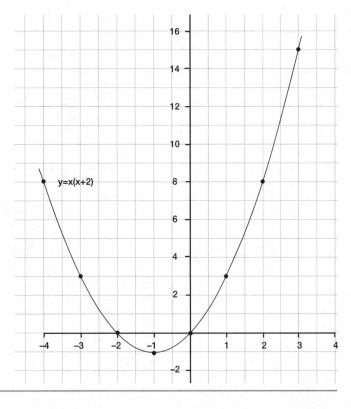

y=x(x+2)

EXAMPLE 4

Draw the graph of y = (x + 3)(x − 2) for values of x between −4 and +4.

Fill in a table of results, like this:

x	−4	−3	−2	−1	0	1	2	3	4
y	6	0	−4	−6	−6	−4	0	6	14

To help fill in the table, set the working out like this:

	(x+3)	×	(x−2)	=	y
x = 4	7	×	2	=	14
x = 3	6	×	1	=	6
x = 2	5	×	0	=	0
x = 1	4	×	−1	=	−4
x = 0	3	×	−2	=	−6
x = −1	2	×	−3	=	−6
x = −2	1	×	−4	=	−4
x = −3	0	×	−5	=	0
x = −4	−1	×	−6	=	6

Plot the graph, which looks like this:

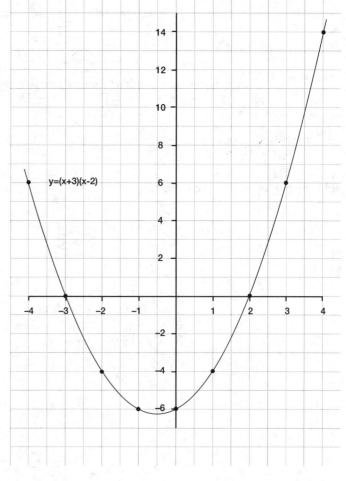

y=(x+3)(x−2)

EXAMPLE 5

Draw the graph of $y = x^2 + 2x - 7$ for values of x between -4 and $+4$.

Fill in a table of results, like this:

x	−4	−3	−2	−1	0	1	2	3	4
y	1	−4	−7	−8	−7	−4	1	8	17

To help fill in the table, set the working out like this:

	x^2	+	2x	−	7	=	y
x = 4	16	+	8	−	7	=	17
x = 3	9	+	6	−	7	=	8
x = 2	4	+	4	−	7	=	1
x = 1	1	+	2	−	7	=	−4
x = 0	0	+	0	−	7	=	−7
x = −1	1	+	−2	−	7	=	−8
x = −2	4	+	−4	−	7	=	−7
x = −3	9	+	−6	−	7	=	−4
x = −4	16	+	−8	−	7	=	1

Plot the graph, which looks like this:

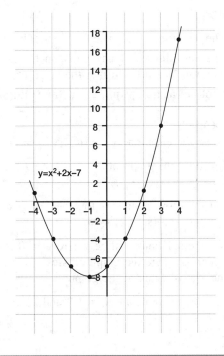

ALGEBRA

QUESTIONS 2.29

Draw these quadratic graphs for values of x between $+4$ and -4.

1. $y = x^2 + 3$
2. $y = x^2 - 1$
3. $y = x(x + 3)$
4. $y = x(x + 1)$
5. $y = (x + 2)(x - 2)$
6. $y = (x + 2)(x - 3)$
7. $y = x^2 + x - 2$
8. $y = x^2 + x - 6$
9. $y = x^2 + x - 7$
10. $y = x^2 - 2x - 6$

SOLVING QUADRATIC EQUATIONS GRAPHICALLY

Solve the equation x(x + 2) = 0

We have already drawn the graph of
y = x(x + 2) and it looks like this:

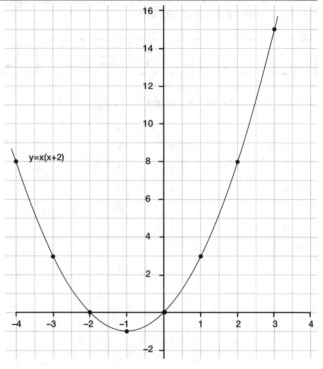

We have been asked to find the solutions
of the equation x(x + 2) = 0.
The graph we have drawn is
y = x(x + 2) and we want
x(x + 2) = 0.

Put these two equations together,
to give y = x(x + 2) = 0.

The solutions occur where y = 0. This is where the graph crosses the x-axis.

The co-ordinates of any point on the x-axis are (x = something, y = 0). To solve the equation, therefore, we need to find the value of x, where the graph crosses the x-axis.

Looking at the graph, then, the solutions are x = −2 and x = 0.

EXAMPLE 2
Solve the equation (x + 3)(x − 2) = 0.

Consider the graph of
y = (x + 3) (x − 2).

Put these two equations together, to give
y = (x + 3)(x − 2) = 0.

So, the solutions will be where y = 0,
which is where the graph crosses
the x-axis. Look at the graph:

So, the solutions are x = −3 and
x = 2

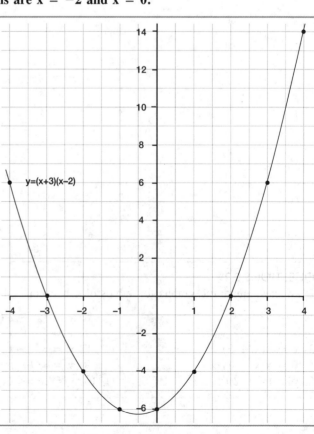

EXAMPLE 3

Solve the equation $x^2 + 2x - 7 = 0$.

Consider the graph of $y = x^2 + 2x - 7$.

Put these two equations together, to give
$y = x^2 + 2x - 7 = 0$.

So, the solutions will be where $y = 0$, which is where the graph crosses the x-axis. Look at the graph:

So, reading from the graph, the solutions are approximately $x = -3 \cdot 8$ and $x = 1 \cdot 8$

Notice that the solutions to quadratic equations don't have to be nice, tidy whole numbers! If you need to know these solutions more accurately, read the section on Trial and Improvement!

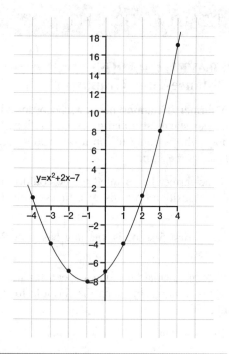

$y = x^2 + 2x - 7$

QUESTIONS 2.30

Use the graphs you have drawn in the previous section to find the solutions to these equations:

Equation	Solutions (where the graph crosses the x-axis)
1. $y = x^2 + 3 = 0$	
2. $y = x^2 - 1 = 0$	
3. $y = x(x + 3) = 0$	
4. $y = x(x + 1) = 0$	
5. $y = (x + 2)(x - 2) = 0$	
6. $y = (x + 2)(x - 3) = 0$	
7. $y = x^2 + x - 2 = 0$	
8. $y = x^2 + x - 6 = 0$	
9. $y = x^2 + x - 7 = 0$	
10. $y = x^2 - 2x - 6 = 0$	

Can you see any connection between the solutions and the equations?

11. Draw the graph of $y = x^2 - x - 2$ for values of x between $+4$ and -4.
(a) Use your graph to find the solutions of $x^2 - x - 2 = 0$
(b) On the same axes, draw the graph of $y = 5$.
Use your graph to find the solutions to the equation $x^2 - x - 2 = 5$
[Hint: Find the co-ordinates of where the two graphs cross.]

12. Draw the graph of $y = x^2 - 2x - 3$ for values of x between $+4$ and -4.
(a) Use your graph to find the solutions of $x^2 - 2x - 3 = 0$
(b) On the same axes, draw the graph of $y = 4$.
Use your graph to find the solutions to the equation $x^2 - 2x - 3 = 4$

REAL LIFE GRAPHS

TRAVEL GRAPHS:
Distance-Time Graphs

A farmer is training his new sheep dog. The farmer stands still and gives instructions to the dog, who is going to run down a long, straight lane on the farm.

If the farmer had a mind to, he could plot the dog's position on a distance-time graph, like this:

In the first 5 seconds, the dog has gone 20 metres.

We can calculate the dog's speed for this part of his training, by using the formula for speed, like this:

Speed = $\dfrac{\text{Distance}}{\text{Time}}$

Speed = $\dfrac{20 \text{ metres}}{5 \text{ seconds}}$ = 4 m/s

Notice that the gradient of the graph tells us the same information. Using the formula for gradient, we can see that:

Gradient = $\dfrac{\text{Increase in the y-direction}}{\text{Increase in the x-direction}}$

Take two points P and Q on the graph, so:

Gradient = $\dfrac{12 \text{ metres}}{3 \text{ seconds}}$ = 4 m/s ..... as before!

Remember that it doesn't matter which two points you choose on the straight line, you still get the same gradient.

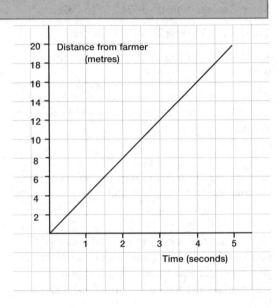

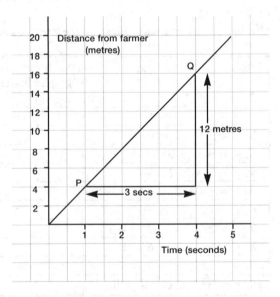

The gradient of a distance-time graph gives you the speed.

Speed = $\dfrac{\text{Distance}}{\text{Time}}$

ALGEBRA

Now the farmer whistles the dog to stand absolutely still for ten seconds. So, the distance between the dog and the farmer remains at 20 metres for the next 10 seconds.

The graph now looks like this:

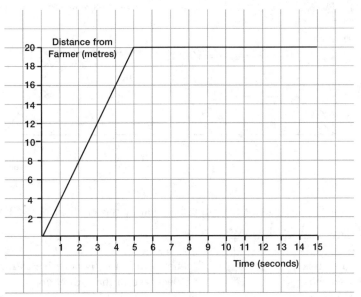

Notice that I have changed the scale on the time axis to get this new information on the graph.

Then the farmer whistles the dog to carry on down the lane. The dog moves more quickly than before and the graph now looks like this:

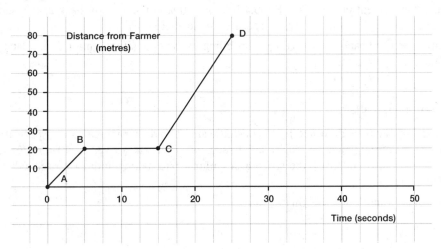

Notice that I have changed the scale on both axes to get this new information on the graph.

The dog's speed is given by the gradient of the line CD. Notice that the line CD is steeper than the line AB.

Gradient = $\dfrac{\text{Increase in the y-direction}}{\text{Increase in the x-direction}}$

Gradient = $\dfrac{60 \text{ metres}}{10 \text{ seconds}}$ = 6 m/s

This confirms that the dog is moving more quickly than before, when the speed was 4 m/s.

The farmer now whistles the dog to stand absolutely still for 5 seconds, before instructing the dog to return to the farmer as quickly as possible, to get a reward!

The completed graph looks like this:

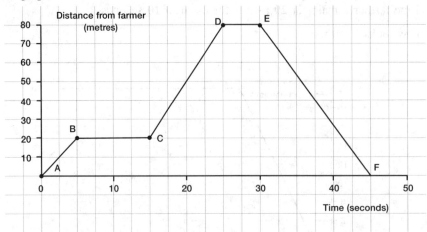

The dog's speed for the last part of the graph is given by the gradient of the line EF.

Gradient = $\dfrac{\text{Increase in the y-direction}}{\text{Increase in the x-direction}}$

Gradient = $-\dfrac{80 \text{ metres}}{12 \text{ seconds}}$ ← notice that this is negative as there has been a **decrease** in the y-direction.

Gradient = $-6 \cdot 66666....$

Gradient = $-6 \cdot 7$ m/s (to one decimal place)

So, the dog's speed is $6 \cdot 7$ m/s to one decimal place.

Notice that the gradient of the line EF must be a negative number (look back at the section on the gradient of a straight line graph if you need a reminder here.)

The negative sign indicates that the dog is travelling in the opposite direction in the lane than at the start of his training session!

Speed-Time Graphs

A new model of car is being tested by the design team. The driver increases the speed from nothing to 40 m/s at a constant rate for the first 10 seconds. Then she drives at 40 m/s for the next 20 seconds, then brakes to decrease the speed at a uniform rate, taking another 15 seconds to bring the car back to rest.

The speed-time graph looks like this:

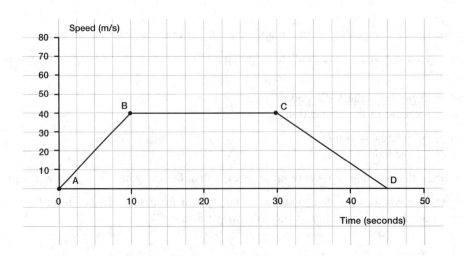

What is the gradient of the line AB?

Gradient = $\dfrac{\text{Increase in the y-direction}}{\text{Increase in the x-direction}}$

Gradient = $\dfrac{40 \text{ m/s}}{10 \text{ secs}} = \dfrac{\text{(Speed)}}{\text{(Time)}}$

Gradient = 4 m/s²   Notice that the units are read as: "metres per second squared".

The gradient is found from $\dfrac{\text{Speed}}{\text{Time}}$ This is the same formula as acceleration!

> The gradient of a speed-distance graph gives you acceleration.
>
> $$\text{Acceleration} = \dfrac{\text{Speed}}{\text{Time}}$$

So, in the first 10 seconds of the motion, the acceleration is 4 m/s². This means that the car's speed increases at a uniform rate of 4 m/s every second.

So, after 1 second the car is travelling at 4 m/s
After 2 seconds the car is travelling at 8 m/s
After 3 seconds the car is travelling at 12 m/s .....and so on.

What is the gradient of the line BC?

The gradient is zero
Therefore the acceleration is zero
This is correct because the car is travelling at a constant speed of 40 m/s between t = 10 seconds and t = 30 seconds.

What is the gradient of the line CD?

Gradient = $\dfrac{\text{Increase in the y-direction}}{\text{Increase in the x-direction}}$

Gradient = $\dfrac{-40 \text{ m/s}}{15 \text{ sec}}$ ◄———— note the minus sign, because this is actually a decrease!

Gradient = $-2\cdot666666$ m/s²

Gradient = $-2\cdot7$ m/s² (to one decimal place)

So, acceleration = $-2\cdot7$ m/s²

The minus sign tells us that the car is slowing down, or **decelerating**.

ALGEBRA

QUESTIONS 2.31
1. A group of venture scouts go on a lengthy walk, starting from their base camp.

They walk to a waterfall and back again, stopping for refreshments during the morning and lunch whilst at the waterfall. This is the distance-time graph for their walk:

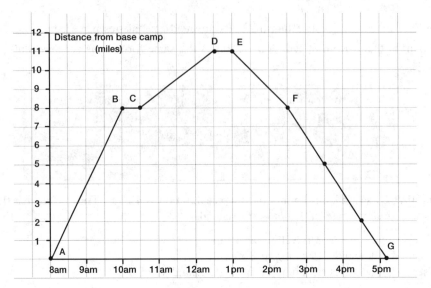

What is the speed of the walkers:

(a) between A and B?   (c) between C and D?   (e) between E and F?
(b) between B and C?   (d) between D and E?   (f) between F and G?

Why do you think the speed of the walkers might vary in each section?

2. Two friends, Aaron and Beattie, live in two villages 10 miles apart. Aaron thinks they have agreed to meet at Beattie's house and starts cycling towards her house. Beattie thinks they have agreed to meet at Aaron's house and starts cycling towards his house.

This is the distance-time graph for their two journeys:

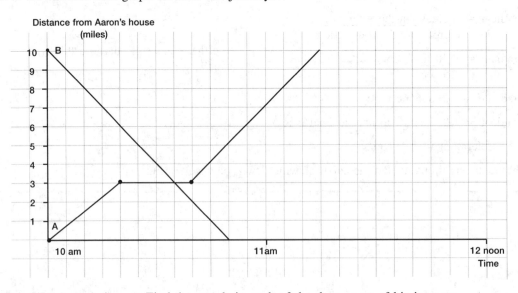

(a) Describe Aaron's jouney. Find the speeds in each of the three parts of his journey.
(b) Describe Beattie's jouney. Find the speed at which she cycles.
(c) At what time might they have met each other on the way? Why didn't they, do you think?

3. Car designers put a car on a test run, which produces this speed-time graph:

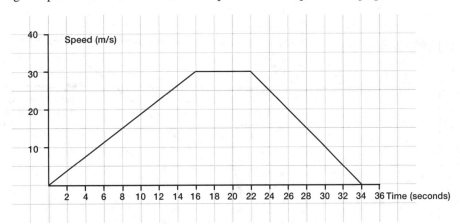

(a) When was its speed greatest?
(b) When is the car travelling at 15 m/s?
(c) What is the acceleration for the first 16 seconds?
(d) What is the deceleration for the last 12 seconds?

CONVERSION GRAPHS

I am going to take my car to the continent, where all road distances are given in kilometres. I want an easy way to convert miles to kilometres and kilometres to miles.

I know that: 1 mile is approximately equal to 1·6 km

So,

1 mile ≈ 1·6 km

So, multiplying both sides by 5 (this is the same idea of retaining the balance, just like we did in the section on solving equations).

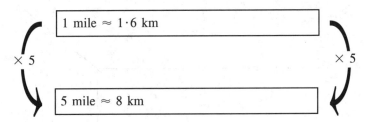

Also, I can find another equivalent statement, like this:

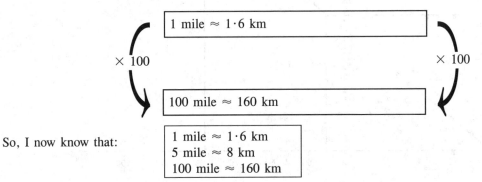

So, I now know that:

1 mile ≈ 1·6 km
5 mile ≈ 8 km
100 mile ≈ 160 km

I can use these to plot a conversion graph, like this:

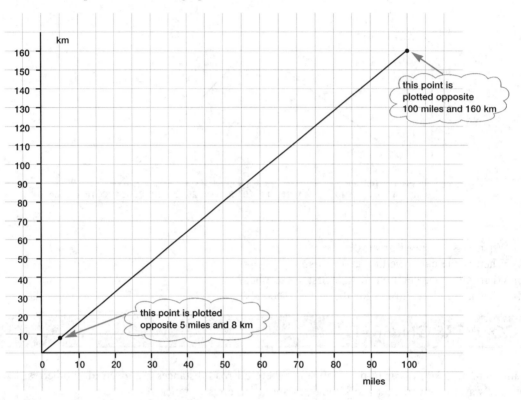

You can use the graph to convert from miles to kilometres, and from kilometres to miles.

(a) What is 45 miles in km?
(b) What is 125 km in miles?

Add some lines to the graph to help you answer these questions.

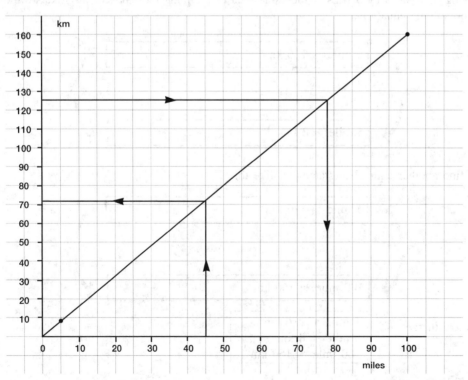

ALGEBRA

(a) Find 45 miles on the horizontal axis. Follow the arrow up to the line, then across to the vertical scale and read off 72 km.

So, 45 miles ≈ 72 km

(b) Find 125 km on the vertical axis. Follow the arrow across to the line, then down to the horizontal scale and read off 78 miles.

So, 125 km ≈ 78 miles

We could, of course, have answered these questions by doing some calculations.

(a) Start with :

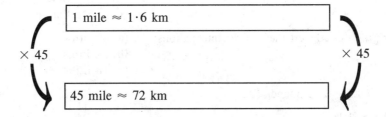

As we have already found from the graph.

(b) Start with:

1 mile ≈ 1·6 km

Now find what 1 km is in miles by dividing both sides by 1·6 km, like this:

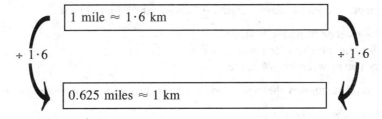

Now multiply both sides by 125, like this:

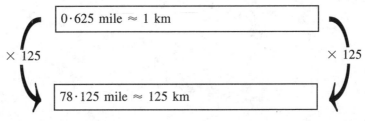

Notice that when I read off the graph I found that 125 km was equivalent to 78 miles. This is accurate enough information for me to plan my car journeys. So, reading off the graph is quicker and easier than doing the calculations, and gives accurate enough information for my purposes.

QUESTIONS 2.32

1. Use the miles-kilometres conversion graph to convert these mileages into kilometres:

(a) 92 miles   (c) 65 miles
(b) 30 miles   (d) 52 miles

2. Use the miles-kilometres conversion graph to convert these kilometres into miles:

(a) 150 km

(b) 35 km

(c) 115 km

(d) 65 km

3. I know that 1 gallon ≈ 4·5 litres

So: 10 gallons ≈ _____ litres

Fill in the space above! Use this information to draw a graph which converts gallons to litres.
[Hint: Put gallons on the horizontal axis and go from 0 to 10. Put litres on the vertical axis and go from 0 to 50.]

(i) Use your graph to convert these gallons into litres:

(a) 8 gallons

(b) 3·5 gallons

(c) 5·5 gallons

(ii) Use your graph to convert these litres into gallons:

(a) 40 litres

(b) 32 litres

(c) 18 litres

4. I know that 1 kg ≈ 2·2 pounds (lb)

So, _____ kg ≈ 1 lb

So, _____ kg ≈ 14 lb = 1 stone

So, _____ kg ≈ 10 stone

Fill in the spaces above! Use the information to draw a graph which converts pounds and stones into kilogrammes.
[Hint: Put stones across the horizontal axis and go from 0 to 15. Put kilogrammes on the vertical axis and go from 0 to 100.]

(i) Use your graph to convert these weights in stones into kilogrammes:

(a) a Maths teacher weighing 9 stone.

(b) a small child weighing 2·5 stone.

(c) a rugby player weighing 14 stone.

(ii) Use your graph to convert these weights in kilogrammes into stones and pounds:

(a) a hockey player weighing 68 kg.

(b) a teenager weighing 48 kg.

(c) a child weighing 32 kg.

SHAPE AND SPACE

▲ ANGLES ▼

What do we mean by the term angle? The word angle is used to describe the amount of **turn**.

We use a **protractor** to measure angles and the units we use are **degrees**.

There are **360°** in a complete circle. If you stand up, face a particular wall and turn all the way round so that you are facing that same wall again, you will have turned through 360°.

Why should a complete turn be 360°? Why not 100°? Choosing 360° rather than 100° (or indeed any other number) is an example of a Mathematical **convention**. All Mathematicians agree to use 360° in a complete circle, so that we all know that we are talking the same language! We could have chosen a different number, but we have all got used to 360° – probably because the Ancient Babylonians were fond of their number system, which was based on 60's. So, 360 (which is 6 lots of 60) is what we are still using to this day!

We use conventions in other walks of life as well as Mathematics. For instance, we all agree to drive on the left in Britain, but we know that other countries have made a decision to drive on the right! It doesn't matter, so long as you know which country you are in and therefore which convention to use!

SPECIAL ANGLES

A **complete turn** is 360°

A **half turn** is 180°

A **quarter turn** is 90°
This is called a **right angle**.

This shows a 90° turn going **clockwise** (this means turning the same way as the hands on the clock).

This shows a 90° turn going **anti-clockwise**.

A **three-quarter** turn is 270°
This shows a 270° turn going **anti-clockwise**.

ACUTE ANGLES

These are all acute angles. They are any angle which is less than a right angle. So, all these angles are between 0° and 90°.

OBTUSE ANGLES

These are all obtuse angles. They are any angle which is bigger than a right angle but smaller than a half turn. So, all these angles are between 90° and 180°.

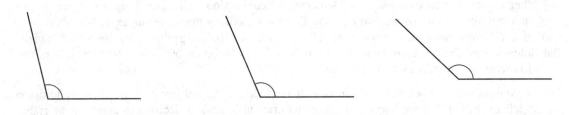

REFLEX ANGLES

These are all reflex angles. They are any angle which is bigger than a half turn but smaller than a complete turn. So, all these angles are between 180° and 360°.

▲ TRIANGLES ▼

Triangles are shapes with three straight sides. You probably already know that the angles of a triangle add to 180°. Do you know why? We can demonstrate that this is the case, by drawing a large triangle on a piece of card. Any triangle will do!

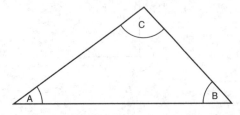

Mark in the angles as A, B and C. Shade them in to make your labelling even more prominent.

Now, carefully tear off the three angles A, B and C. You will find that whatever triangle you began with, you will be able to arrange those three angles to fit along a straight edge like this:

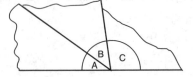

Without having to measure the angles of the particular triangle which I chose to draw, I have shown that the sum of these angles is 180°, because I have been able to fit them along a straight edge. So, the angles of a triangle must add to 180° whatever the angles chosen in the starting triangle. It works for all triangles. Try some other triangles yourself!

TYPES OF TRIANGLE

EQUILATERAL TRIANGLE

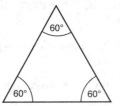

All angles are the same, so they must all be 60°
All sides are the same length.
This is the only **regular** triangle.

ISOSCELES TRIANGLE

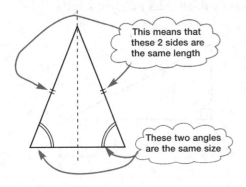

This means that these 2 sides are the same length

These two angles are the same size

Two sides are the same length.
Two angles are the same.
There is one line of symmetry, shown by a dotted line.

EXAMPLE I
Fill in the missing two angles:

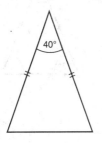

This triangle is an isoceles triangle, as it has two equal sides.
The angles of a triangle add to 180°, so take away the angle we already know:
180° − 40° = 140°
The two missing angles are both the same, so
140° ÷ 2 = 70°
Both missing angles are 70°

Check this works: 70° + 70° + 40° = 180°

EXAMPLE 2
Fill in the missing angles:

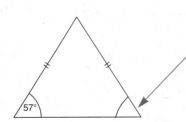

As this is an isosceles triangle, this angle must be 57° as well.

The angles of a triangle add to 180°, so:
57° + 57° = 114°
180° − 114° = 66°

The third angle must be 66°. Check this works:
57° + 57° + 66° = 180°

SCALENE TRIANGLES

Scalene triangles are ones which have all their three sides a different length. All three angles will also be different from each other.

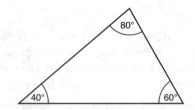

RIGHT-ANGLED TRIANGLES

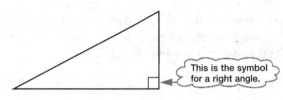

These are triangles which have a right angle as one of their angles. The other two angles must therefore add to 90°.

The longest side of a right-angled triangle is called the **hypotenuse**.

The hypotenuse is always opposite the right angle.

A right-angled triangle can be an isosceles triangle (with the two shorter sides of equal length), like this:

Or a right-angled triangle can be a scalene triangle (with all sides different lengths), like this:

QUESTIONS 3.1

Find the angles marked with a letter in these diagrams:

1.
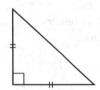

2.
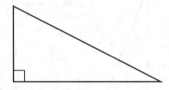

3.

4.
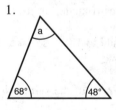

5.
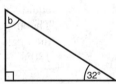

6.
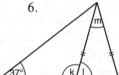

7.
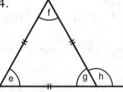

8.
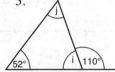

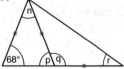

▲ *QUADRILATERALS* ▼

Quadrilaterals are shapes with four straight sides.

Label each of the following diagrams with the correct name. Choose from the list: kite, rhombus, square, parallelogram, rectangle and trapezium.

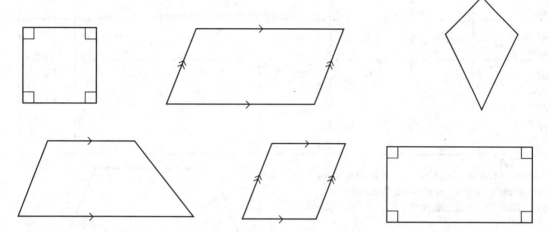

Fill in yes or no in this table:

	Square	Rectangle	Rhombus	Parallelogram	Trapezium	Kite
Are all four sides the same length?						
Are all the angles 90°?						
Are opposite sides the same length?						

Your answers should look like this:

	Square	Rectangle	Rhombus	Parallelogram	Trapezium	Kite
Are all four sides the same length?	Yes	No	Yes	No	No	No
Are all the angles 90°?	Yes	Yes	No	No	No	No
Are opposite sides the same length?	Yes	Yes	Yes	Yes	No*	No

* No, not necessarily, although the two sides which **aren't** parallel might be the same length, like this trapezium:

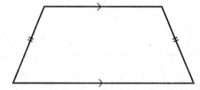

How many of the above quadrilaterals are regular? Which ones? Try to answer these questions before reading on!

Every time I ask a class full of pupils to name as many regular quadrilaterals as they can, they usually list (eventually) all the quadrilaterals which appear in our table above. This is not the correct answer! The square is the **only** regular quadrilateral! Remember that the word regular means that all angles are the same **and** all sides are the same length. Clearly, the only regular quadrilateral is the square. All the others in our table have special properties and have therefore been given special names – but they are not regular!

PROPERTIES OF QUADRILATERALS

Squares and Rectangles:
Look at the entries in the table. Look down the columns for square and rectangle. The only difference between the square and the rectangle is that **all** the sides on a square are the same length. The square is said to be a special kind of rectangle. It has all the properties of the rectangle, plus one more extra property.

Squares and Rhombuses:
Look down the columns for square and rhombus. The only difference between the square and the rhombus is that **all** the angles in a square are right-angles. The square is said to be a special kind of rhombus. It has all the properties of the rhombus, plus one more extra property.

Rectangles and Parallelograms:
Look down the columns for rectangle and parallelogram. The only difference between the rectangle and parallelogram is that **all** the angles in a rectangle are right-angles. The rectangle is said to be a special kind of parallelogram. It has all the properties of the parallelogram, plus one more extra property.

Rhombuses and Parallelograms:
Look down the columns for rhombus and parallelogram. The only difference between the rhombus and parallelogram is that **all** the sides in a rhombus are the same length. The rhombus is said to be a special kind of parallelogram. It has all the properties of the parallelogram, plus one more extra property.

So, to re-cap:

The square is the only regular quadrilateral.

Rectangles, rhombuses, parallelograms, trapezia (this is the plural for trapezium) and kites are quadrilaterals with special properties, but, nevertheless, they are irregular.

These are also irregular quadrilaterals:

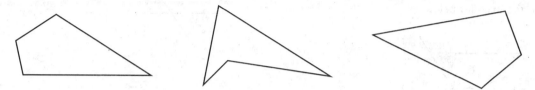

ANGLES IN QUADRILATERALS

How many degrees are there in a quadrilateral?

If we add another line to this diagram, we can see that it is made up of two triangles.

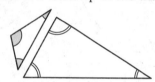

We already know that the angles of a triangle add to 180°. Here we have two triangles, so the angles of any quadrilateral must add to two times 180° that is 360°.

> The angles of any quadrilateral must add to 360°.

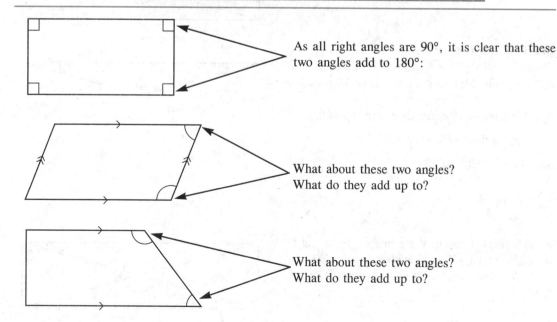

As all right angles are 90°, it is clear that these two angles add to 180°:

What about these two angles?
What do they add up to?

What about these two angles?
What do they add up to?

Draw some parallelograms and some trapezia and measure the angles. What do you conclude and why ?

Now consider the diagram opposite where one straight line crosses two parallel lines.

The diagram tells us one angle is 55°. So, all the other marked angles must also be 55°, as in the diagram below:

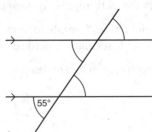

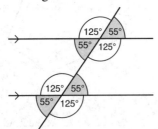

As we know one angle is 55°, then the angle next to it must be 125°, because they are on a straight line and therefore must add to 180°. So, once you know one angle here, you can work out all the others.

So, if we have a parallelogram, with one angle marked, like this:

Then we can use the above to fill in all the other angles, like this:

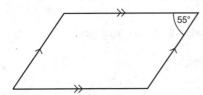

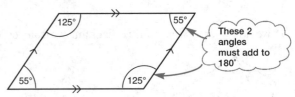

These 2 angles must add to 180°

Notice that the sum of the angles is 360°, as we know it should be.

EXAMPLE I
Fill in all the angles marked with a letter in this diagram of a rectangle:

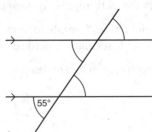

Consider this triangle:

These two sides must be the same length.

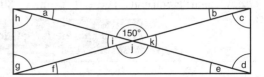

So, this triangle must be an isosceles triangle.

So, angle a must equal angle b.

So, 180° − 150° = 30°
30° ÷ 2 = 15°

So a = 15°
b = 15°

By symmetry, I can now see that angles e and f must also equal 15°, and angle j must equal 150°. Put these angles into the diagram, like this:

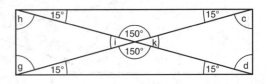

Angle c must be 75°, because:
angle b + angle c = 90° .... to make
the right angle of the rectangle.

So, by symmetry, the angles d, g and h must
also equal 75°.

Add these angles to the diagram, like this:

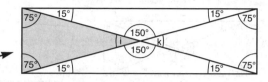

Consider this triangle: ─────

Angle i must equal 30°, as the angles of a triangle add to 180°.
By symmetry, angle k must also equal 30°. The completed solution is therefore:

a = 15°	d = 75°	g = 75°	j = 150°
b = 15°	e = 15°	h = 75°	k = 30°
c = 75°	f = 15°	i = 30°	

EXAMPLE 2

Fill in all the angles marked with a letter in
this diagram of a parallelogram.

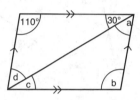

By symmetry, angle b must also equal 110°.
Fill this into the diagram, like this:

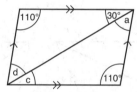

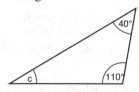

These two shaded angles must add to 180°.

So, angle a + 30° + 110° = 180°

So angle a must equal 40°.

Consider this triangle:

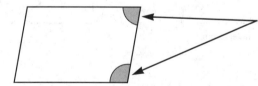

The angles of this triangle must add to 180°.
So, angle c must equal 30°.

Using the same reasoning, angle d must be
equal to 40°.

The completed solution is therefore:

a = 40°
b = 110°
c = 30°
d = 40°

The parallelogram looks like this:

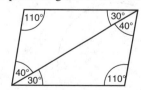

QUESTIONS 3.2

Now fill in the missing angles from these diagrams. Work them out by thinking about them! Don't measure them with a protractor, because the diagrams are not necessarily drawn accurately!

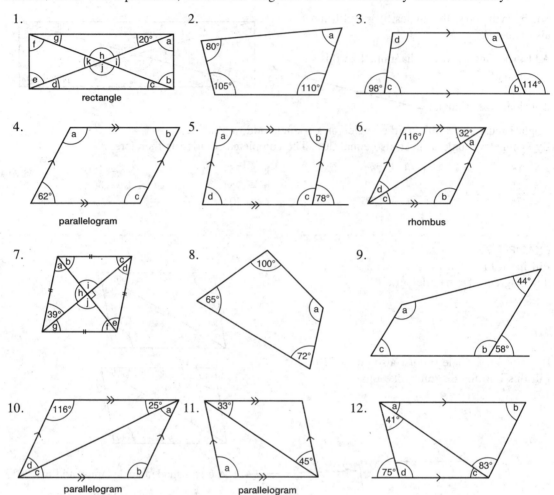

1. rectangle

2.

3.

4. parallelogram

5.

6. rhombus

7.

8.

9.

10. parallelogram

11. parallelogram

12.

▲ **INSCRIBED POLYGONS** ▼

Drawing a regular pentagon is not an easy task! Remember that a pentagon has five straight sides and **regular** means that all *sides* must be the same length and all *angles* must be the same. One way to make the task much simpler is to draw your pentagon inside a circle. Drawing a shape inside a circle is called **inscribing**.

Draw a circle which has a radius of 5 cm:

Draw in a spoke, which goes from the centre of the circle to the circumference:

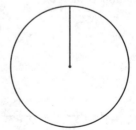

In order to draw a regular pentagon, I need to space five spokes equally around my circle. I need to find the angle between each spoke. I can find the angle I need by taking 360° (which is the complete turn) and dividing by five (which is the number of sides).

$360° \div 5 = 72°$

So, I need to space out my spokes with 72° between each one. Draw in the next spoke and the diagram looks like this:

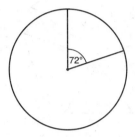

Draw in the next spoke and your diagram looks like this:

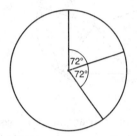

Measure each angle of 72° very carefully. When you have drawn in your last spoke, check that the last angle actually *is* 72°. This will tell you how accurately you have worked. Your diagram should now look like this:

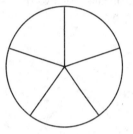

Each point where a spoke touches the circle is the **vertex** of a regular pentagon.

Vertex is the mathematical name for a corner of a shape. The plural of vertex is **vertices**. Now join up these points to make the pentagon:

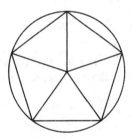

QUESTIONS 3.3

Draw your own inscribed polygons and record the angle needed at the centre for the polygons in the following table:

Polygon	Number of Sides	Angle at the Centre
Equilateral Triangle	3	
Square	4	
Pentagon	5	72°
Hexagon	6	
Heptagon	7	
Octagon	8	
Nonagon	9	
Decagon	10	
11-sided polygon	11	
Dodecagon	12	
N-Sided Polygon	N	

INTERIOR ANGLE OF A REGULAR POLYGON

Look again at the inscribed pentagon:

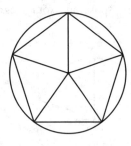

We can look at the triangles which make up the shape like this:

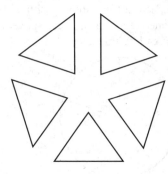

Each one of these triangles is an **isosceles** triangle. This means that two of its sides are the same length.

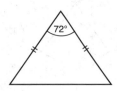

Also, we can see that each triangle has a line of symmetry:

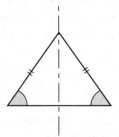

The two shaded angles must be the same. We already know that the third angle is 72°. We can calculate the missing angles because we know that the angles of a triangle add up to 180°.

180° − 72° = 108°

108° ÷ 2° = 54°

So these are the angles of the isosceles triangle:

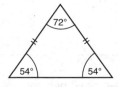

These are all the isosceles triangles in the inscribed pentagon:

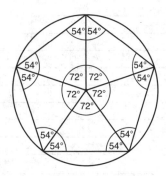

The shaded angle here is called the **interior angle** of our pentagon and you can see that it must be equal to 108°. The word interior is another word for 'inside'

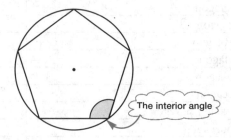

The interior angle

SHAPE AND SPACE

QUESTIONS 3.4

1. Use the same type of reasoning to calculate the interior angles of the following list of polygons and add your results to the table:

Polygon	Angle at the Centre	Interior Angle
Equilateral Triangle		
Square		
Pentagon	72°	108°
Hexagon		
Heptagon		
Octagon		
Nonagon		
Decagon		
11-sided Polygon		
Dodecagon		
N-Sided Polygon		

EXTERIOR ANGLE OF A REGULAR POLYGON

Look at our regular pentagon:

If we continue one of the sides, like this:

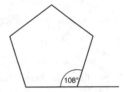

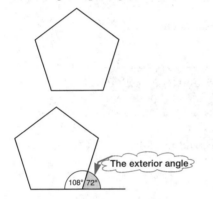

The exterior angle

The marked angle is called the **exterior** angle. The word exterior is another word for 'outside'.

We know that the interior angle is 108°, so the size of the exterior angle must be 72°, because these two angles must add up to 180° as they are on a straight line.

Interior angle + Exterior angle = 180°

QUESTIONS 3.5

1. Use similar reasoning to calculate the exterior angles of your regular polygons and write your answers in the table below:

Polygon	Angle at the Centre	Interior Angle	Exterior Angle
Equilateral Triangle			
Square			
Pentagon	72°	108°	72°
Hexagon			
Heptagon			
Octagon			
Nonagon			
Decagon			
11-sided Polygon			
Dodecagon			
N-Sided Polygon			

You should now have a set of regular polygons and a table filled in correctly, like this:

Polygon	Angle at the Centre	Interior Angle	Exterior Angle
Equilateral Triangle	120°	60°	120°
Square	90°	90°	90°
Pentagon	72°	108°	72°
Hexagon	60°	120°	60°
Heptagon	51·4°	128·6°	51·4°
Octagon	45°	135°	45°
Nonagon	40°	140°	40°
Decagon	36°	144°	36°
11-sided Polygon	32·7°	147·3°	32·7°
Dodecagon	30°	150°	30°
N-Sided Polygon	$\dfrac{360°}{N}$	$180 - \dfrac{360°}{N}$	$\dfrac{360°}{N}$

You can see that the angle at the centre, which we calculated to help us separate the spokes, is always the same as the exterior angle. For an N-sided polygon the angle at the centre will be:

$360 \div N$ or $\dfrac{360}{N}$ which are mathematically equivalent.

$$\text{Angle at the Centre} = \text{Exterior Angle} = 360 \div N = \dfrac{360}{N}$$

The exterior angle and the interior angle must, of course, add to 180°.

Interior angle + Exterior angle = 180°

So, re-arranging this equation gives:

Interior angle = 180° − Exterior angle

So, Interior angle $= 180 - \dfrac{360}{N}$

$$\text{Interior angle} = 180 - \dfrac{360°}{N}$$

INTERIOR ANGLE SUM OF A REGULAR POLYGON

We have already calculated the interior angle of our regular pentagon as 108°. If we fill in all the interior angles, we can see that there are five of them all at 108°.

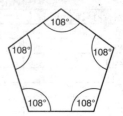

The **interior angle sum** of a regular pentagon must be 108° × 5 = 540°.

The **Interior Angle Sum** is the name given to the total of all the interior angles added together.

QUESTIONS 3.6

1. Use similar reasoning to calculate the interior angle sum of the other regular polygons and record your results in the following table:

Polygon	Interior Angle	Calculation	Interior Angle Sum
Equilateral Triangle	60°		
Square	90°		
Pentagon	108°	108° × 5	540°
Hexagon	120°		
Heptagon	128·6°		
Octagon	135°		
Nonagon	140°		
Decagon	144°		
11-sides Polygon	147·3°		
Dodecagon	150°		
N-sided Polygon	$180 - \dfrac{360°}{N}$		

INTERIOR ANGLE SUM OF AN IRREGULAR POLYGON

What do the interior angles of an irregular pentagon add up to?
An irregular pentagon still has five straight sides, but these can be any length you like and the angles can be any angle you like. Nothing has to be the same as anything else any more!
This is an irregular pentagon:

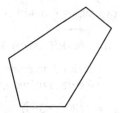

Measure each of the angles as accurately as you can and add them all together. What do you think the answer should be, if you were able to measure extremely accurately? Draw some more irregular pentagons of your own, measure their interior angles and add them altogether. What conclusion are you coming to?

Incredibly, no matter how we draw our irregular pentagon, the angle sum will turn out to be 540°, just the same as when we drew a regular pentagon!

Can you think how you would prove that this is true for all irregular pentagons?

Add two lines to our diagram like this and you can see that we have created three triangles:

Now, the angles of each triangle add up to 180°.

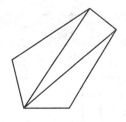

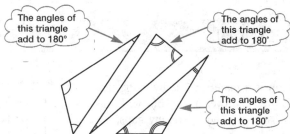

There are 3 triangles whose angles all add to 180°. So, whatever the angles of our irregular pentagon, altogether its angles must add to 3 × 180° = 540°.

This shows that the interior angle sum of a pentagon is the same whether it is regular or irregular!

SHAPE AND SPACE

QUESTIONS 3.7

1. Use similar diagrams to calculate the interior angle sum of our other polygons.

Polygon	Diagram	Calculation	Interior Angle Sum
Equilateral Triangle			
Square			
Pentagon	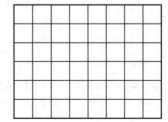	180° × 3	540°
Hexagon			
Heptagon			
Octagon			
Nonagon			
Decagon			
11-sided Polygon			
Dodecagon			
N-sided Polygon			

Your last two tables should have given you the same results, by two different methods!

Finding the Angle Sum for REGULAR Polygons:

We took the Interior Angle and multiplied by the number of angles (which is the same as the number of sides). In algebra, this works out as:

Angle Sum $= (180 - \dfrac{360}{N}) \times N = 180N - 360$

Finding the Angle Sum for IRREGULAR Polygons:

We found out how many triangles could be made in each polygon and then multiplied that number by 180°. There are always two less triangles possible in each polygon than there are sides altogether.

So, to find the Angle Sum we must multiply 180° by (N − 2) which is the number of triangles for an N-sided polygon.

Angle Sum $= 180 \times (N - 2) = 180N - 360$

So, you can see that the algebra shows us that it was no accident that we got the same answer, whichever method we employed. This is why algebra is so powerful and Maths is so wonderful!

TESSELLATIONS

A **tessellation** is a pattern made by using the same shape over and over again, but with the added rule that I must not leave any gaps.

Imagine that I am going to tile my bathroom wall. What shape tiles shall I choose? I know that I could use square tiles (most people do!).

I can see that I would have no difficulty filling a complete wall with square tiles, leaving no gaps. Notice that I am also choosing to fit the square tiles together edge to edge, so that all the corners (or vertices) of the squares meet at a point, which is called a **node**.

I can see from the work we did in the previous section that the interior angle of a square is 90° and that four squares are meeting at each node. As 4 × 90° = 360° this confirms that squares do tessellate and leave no gaps.

EXAMPLE 2

This tessellation uses squares and one other shape. What is the name of the second shape? Find all the angles in the second shape.

The second shape is a parallelogram. Look at the angles around the node marked with the letter X.

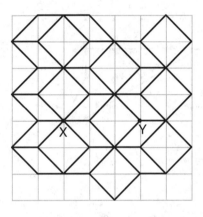

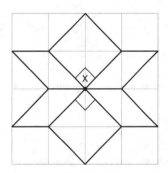

There are 2 squares and also 4 equal angles meeting at X. The angles at a node add to 360°. The 2 squares have already accounted for 180°, so the remaining angles must also make 180°. So, each angle must be 45°.

Look at the angles around the node marked with the letter Y.

At the node Y there is one right angle (90°) and also two equal angles meeting at Y. The angles at a node add to 360°. The square has already accounted for 90°, so the remaining angles must make 270°. So, each angle must be 135°.

So, the angles of the parallelogram are:

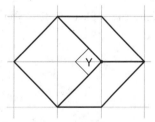

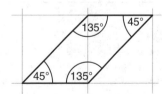

SHAPE AND SPACE

QUESTIONS 3.8

1. Use dotted paper to construct tessellations for these shapes. Draw at least 20 of the given shapes to show how they tessellate.

(a)

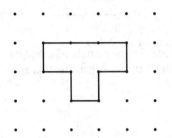

(b)

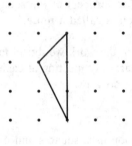

(c)

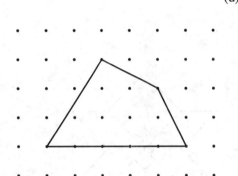

(d)

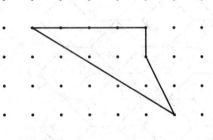

2. The diagram shows part of a floor design which uses two types of tile. One is a regular pentagon.

(a) What is the name of the other shape?

(b) Find the angles labelled x and y.

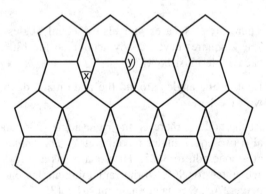

SHAPE AND SPACE

▲ *Symmetry* ▼

There are two types of symmetry, **line symmetry** and **rotational symmetry** in 2-D shapes.

LINE SYMMETRY

The shapes below have line symmetry:

One line of symmetry

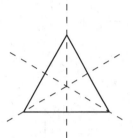

Three lines of symmetry

Trace these shapes and the lines of symmetry. Fold your tracing along each line of symmetry. As you make the fold, you can see that the two halves of the shape match up perfectly. This is what is meant by line symmetry.

QUESTIONS 3.9

1. Copy these shapes and draw in **all** the lines of symmetry for each shape.

(a)

(b)

(c)
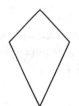

(d)

(e)

(f)
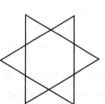

2. How many lines of symmetry are there in these shapes?

(a)

(b)

(c)

(d)

3. Copy and complete these drawings, so that each dotted line is a line of symmetry. Using tracing paper may help!

(a)

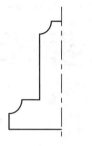

(b)

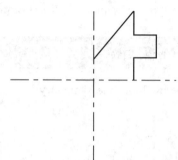

(c)

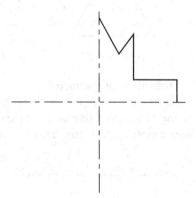

(d)

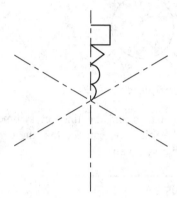

For the rectangle, when asked to draw in the lines of symmetry, many pupils draw in lines like this:

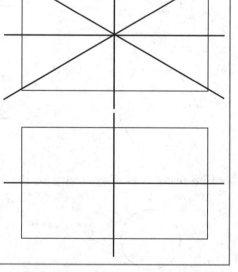

Be careful! This may look like a good pattern, but not all of these lines are lines of symmetry. If you cut out a rectangle from a piece of paper, and fold along the diagonals, the two halves do not match up at all! The only lines of symmetry are like this:

ROTATIONAL SYMMETRY

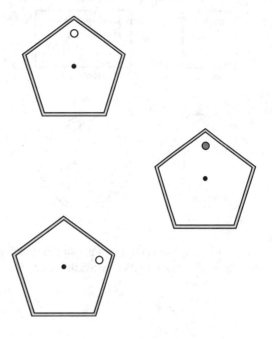

I have a pentagonal beer mat. (You can make one yourself – see the chapter on inscribed polygons). I have used a hole-punch to put a hole in one corner of the beer mat. I now draw round the outside of the pentagon using a nice fat felt pen. It now looks like this:

I now colour in the hole. So this marks my starting position. It now looks like this:

I am going to rotate the pentagon clockwise about its centre and stop every time the pentagon fits into the outline shape that I've drawn. The first time this happens the pentagon now looks like this:

I continue to turn the pentagon and again stop every time the pentagon fits the outline shape. The complete equence looks like this:

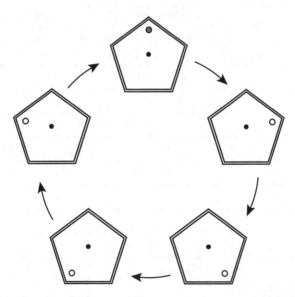

You can see that I get back to where I started, as I can see the coloured dot again. I have made **5 turns** of the pentagon. A regular pentagon is said to have **rotational symmetry of order** 5.

QUESTIONS 3.10

1. Trace each of these shapes to help you find the order of rotational symmetry for each of them.

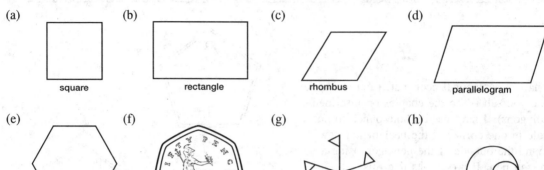

(a)   (b)   (c)   (d)

square   rectangle   rhombus   parallelogram

(e)   (f)   (g)   (h)

hexagon

2. Copy and complete each diagram, so that the finished shape has rotational symmetry of the given order, about the centre marked with the letter O.

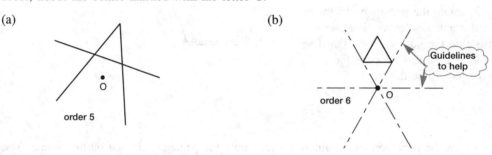

(a)   (b)

O

order 5   order 6   Guidelines to help

3. Copy and complete this table:

NAME OF SHAPE	LINE SYMMETRY		ROTATIONAL SYMMETRY	
	Yes/No	Number of Lines	Yes/No	Order
Equilateral Triangle				
Isosceles Triangle				
Scalene Triangle				
Square				
Rhombus				
Parallelogram				
Kite				
Trapezium				

▲ CIRCLES ▼

TECHNICAL TERMS

Circles occur so often in every day life, that there is a specialised vocabulary of technical terms associated with them.

Circumference: This is the name of the distance right round the outside of the circle.
(The distance round the outside of any other shape is called the perimeter.)

Arc: This is part of the way around a circle, so it is a curved line.

Radius: This is the straight line from the centre to the circumference of the circle. So, when you set your compasses, the distance between the point of the compasses and your pencil is the radius of the circle you are about to draw. (The plural of radius is radii.)

Diameter: This is the straight line which passes through the centre of the circle from opposite points on the circumference.
So, the diameter is twice the radius.
D = 2 × R

Chord: Any straight line which cuts a circle into two parts.

So, a diameter is a special type of chord.

Segment: A piece of the circle cut off by a chord.

We call the smaller piece the minor segment.

We call the larger piece the major segment.

Sector: A wedge of the circle made by two radii.
This is the sort of cut you make into a cake!

SHAPE AND SPACE

THE CIRCUMFERENCE AND THE DIAMETER

I asked a class to find some circular objects at home for their homework. Having assembled their collection of circular objects, I asked them to measure the diameter and the circumference carefully by using a tape measure. These are the results which some of them have collected:

Object	Diameter (cm)	Circumference (cm)
Bread bin	29·5	93
Tin of cat food	7·5	23·5
Small saucepan	17·5	55
Medium saucepan	19·5	61
Large saucepan	21·5	67·5
Fruit bowl	21	66
Plant pot	16	50
Saucer	14	44

I have used my calculator to complete the last column in this new table, by multiplying the diameter by three.

Object	Diameter (cm)	Circumference (cm)	3 × Diameter
Bread bin	29·5	93	88·5
Tin of cat food	7·5	23·5	22·5
Small saucepan	17·5	55	52·5
Medium saucepan	19·5	61	58·5
Large saucepan	21·5	67·5	64·5
Fruit bowl	21	66	63
Plant pot	16	50	48
Saucer	14	44	42

For all of these circular objects, no matter how big or small, you can see that the circumference is always about three times the diameter.

So, Circumference ≈ 3 × Diameter
C ≈ 3 × D

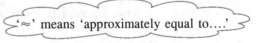

'≈' means 'approximately equal to....'

For thousands of years, Mathematicians have been intrigued by the equation C ≈ 3 × D

They have looked for the number which you multiply the diameter by to give you the circumference. This number is called Pi and is written as π (which is a Greek letter).

Pi turns out to be: $\pi = 3\cdot141592653589793238462643383279502884197169399375\ldots\ldots$

and still we are unable to pin it down exactly! In fact, Mathematicians have shown that you will never be able to calculate Pi exactly!

We are normally content to use the equation C ≈ 3 × D if we are happy with a rough and ready answer. If we need a more accurate answer, we could use:

C = 3·1 × D

or:

C = 3·14 × D

or:

C = 3·142 × D

Taking Pi to three decimal places is usually more than accurate enough for most situations.

The general formula is:

$$\text{Circumference} = \pi \times \text{Diameter}$$

Or:

$$C = \pi \times D$$

EXAMPLE 1

My garden pond has a diameter of 150 cm. What is its circumference?

If I choose to use the formula
then,

$C = 3 \times D$
$C = 3 \times 150$
$C = 450$ cm

If I choose to use the formula
then,

$C = 3 \cdot 1 \times D$
$C = 3 \cdot 1 \times 150$
$C = 465$ cm

If I choose to use the formula
then,

$C = 3 \cdot 14 \times D$
$C = 3 \cdot 14 \times 150$
$C = 471$ cm

If I choose to use the formula
then,

$C = 3 \cdot 142 \times D$
$C = 3 \cdot 142 \times 150$
$C = 471 \cdot 3$ cm

So, you can see that the more decimal places you take for the value of π, the more accurate your answer. You must decide from the situation, just how accurate your answer needs to be and therefore which approximation for π is best for you to use.

EXAMPLE 2

My bicycle wheel has a radius of 35 cm. What is the circumference of the wheel?

We know the radius and we want to know the circumference. We know the formula:

$$C = \pi \times D$$

but,

$$D = 2 \times R$$

so,

$$C = 2 \times \pi \times R$$

If I choose to use the approximation $\pi \approx 3 \cdot 142$, then the formula becomes:
$C = 2 \times 3 \cdot 142 \times R$
$C = 2 \times 3 \cdot 142 \times 35$
$C = 219 \cdot 94$ cm

EXAMPLE 3

My next door neighbour, who is nine, has a smaller bike than I do! She has measured the wheel and tells me that the circumference of her wheel is 125 cm. What is the radius of her bicycle wheel?

This time I know the circumference and I have been asked to work out the radius. Use this formula, $C = 2 \times \pi \times R$, taking π to be $3 \cdot 14$ and substitute in the known values, like this:

$$C = 2 \times \pi \times R$$
$$125 = 2 \times 3 \cdot 14 \times R$$
$$125 = 6 \cdot 28 \times R \qquad \ldots\ldots\text{divide both sides by } 6 \cdot 28 \ldots$$

So,
$$R = 125 \div 6 \cdot 28$$
$$R = 19 \cdot 9 \text{ cm} \qquad \ldots\ldots\text{to one decimal place.}$$

QUESTIONS 3.11

Take π to be $3 \cdot 14$ throughout this exercise and give your answers to one decimal place.

1. Find the circumference of a circle with:

(a) radius 4 cm
(b) radius 8·5 cm
(c) radius 2·4 m
(d) diameter 34 cm

(e) diameter 78 cm
(f) radius 3·5 m
(g) diameter 22·8 cm
(h) diameter 140 cm

2. Find the radius of a circle whose circumference is:

(a) 312 cm
(b) 86 cm
(c) 15·7 cm
(d) 855 cm

(e) 4·75 m
(f) 677 cm
(g) 345 cm
(h) 218 cm

3. The diameter of a circular cycle track is 154 m. Find the length of its circumference.

4. A quadrant (one quarter) of a circle of radius 4 cm is cut away from a square piece of card of side 20 cm. Find the perimeter of the resulting shape.

5. A goat is tethered by a rope 5 m long to the corner of a square field of side 25 m. Find the perimeter of the grassy area from which the goat may eat.

6. A circular table cloth is to be made for a circular table of radius 65 cm. If the overhang is to be 15 cm all the way round, find the length of ribbon needed to go all the way round the edge of the table cloth.

7. The diagram shows a circular cycle track of inside radius 120 m and width 6 m.

How much further does a cyclist go if he keeps to the outside edge of the track rather than the inside edge for each lap?

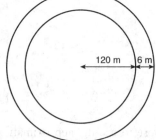

8. A surveyor uses a trundle wheel to measure out distances. Each complete turn is 1 m of ground covered. What is the radius of the trundle wheel?

9. What is the length of ribbon needed to decorate the rim of a circular table lamp if the diameter is 55 cm?

10. Find the perimeter of these shapes, assuming that they are made from quarters and halves of circles:

(a)

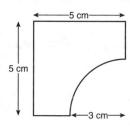

(b)

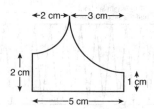

(c)

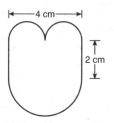

(d)

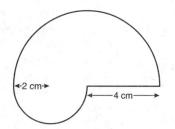

(e)

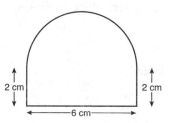

(f)

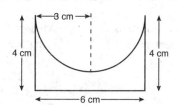

FINDING THE AREA OF A CIRCLE

Draw three circles of radius 5 cm onto card, then cut them out. Take your first circle and cut it into eight eighths. Arrange those eight pieces like this:

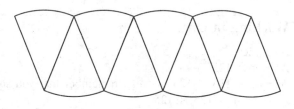

Take your second circle and cut it into sixteen sixteenths. Arrange the pieces 'head to tail' like this:

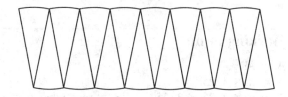

Take your third circle and cut it into thirty-two thirty-secondths. Arrange the pieces 'head to tail' like this:

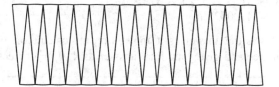

I haven't changed the area of the circles by cutting them up. But as I cut the circles into more and more pieces, and arrange them head to tail, you can see that the resulting shape becomes more and more like a rectangle.

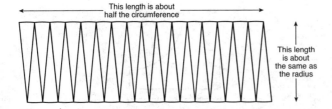

If I was to continue this process of cutting the circle into smaller and smaller sectors and arranging them 'head to tail', I can calculate the area of the circle by finding the area of the equivalent rectangle, like this:

So, the area of circle is $\approx$ Area of the rectangle

Area of the rectangle = Length $\times$ Width

= Half of the circumference $\times$ Radius

= $\frac{1}{2} \times 2 \times \pi \times R \times R$

$A = \pi \times R \times R$

$A = \pi R^2$

So, the formula for the area of a circle is given by:

$$\text{Area} = \pi \times \text{Radius} \times \text{Radius}$$

Also written as:

$$A = \pi R^2$$

EXAMPLE I

Find the area of a circular garden pond of radius 125 cm. Take π to be $3 \cdot 14$. Decide whether you should give your answer in cm^2 or in m^2.

Use the formula:

$$A = \pi R^2$$

Working in cm:

$A = \pi R^2$

$A = \pi \times 125^2$

$A = \pi \times 125 \times 125$ ....remember that you square the 125 only, not the π

$A = 3 \cdot 14 \times 125 \times 125$

$A = 49062 \cdot 5$ cm^2 ...as the answer appears on my calculator...

Working in m:

$A = \pi R^2$

$A = \pi \times 1 \cdot 25^2$

$A = \pi \times 1 \cdot 25 \times 1 \cdot 25$ ..remember that you square the $1 \cdot 25$ only, not the π

$A = 3 \cdot 14 \times 1 \cdot 25 \times 1 \cdot 25$

$A = 4 \cdot 90625$ m^2

This is the answer as it appears on my calculator. For this example it is probably better to work in metres and give your final answer as $4 \cdot 9$ m^2 correct to one decimal place.

EXAMPLE 2

What would be the radius of a circle whose area was 100 cm^2 ? Take π to be 3·14.

Use the formula:

$$A = \pi R^2$$

Substitute in the values we know, like this:

$\quad$ A $\quad = \pi R^2$
$\quad\quad$ 100 $\quad = 3\cdot14 \times R^2$ $\quad$ ....divide both sides by 3·14...
$\quad$ 31·847 .... $= R^2$ $\quad\quad\quad$ ....square root both sides...
$\quad$ 5·6433 ... $= R$

So, the radius would be 5·6 cm to one decimal place.

QUESTIONS 3·12

Take π to be 3·14 throughout this exercise and give your answers to one decimal place.

1. Find the area of a circle with:

(a) radius 7 cm

(b) radius 5·5 cm

(c) radius 3·2 m

(d) diameter 68 cm

(e) diameter 124 cm

(f) radius 4·8 m

(g) diameter 36·8 cm

(h) diameter 245 cm

2. Find the radius of a circle whose area is:

(a) 480 cm^2

(b) 775 cm^2

(c) 225 cm^2

(d) 1200 cm^2

3. Find the diameter of a circle whose area is:

(a) 8·6 m^2

(b) 950 cm^2

(c) 680 cm^2

(d) 550 cm^2

4. A circle of radius 4·5 cm is cut from a square piece of paper of side 15 cm. Find the area remaining.

5. The area of a circle is 870 cm^2. What is its circumference?

6. From a thin square metal plate of side 25 cm, four quadrants of a circle, each of radius 6 cm, are cut away at the corners. Find (a) the area cut away (b) the area remaining.

7. The outside diameter of a metal washer is 25 mm. The inside diameter is 10 mm. What is the cross-sectional area of the washer?

8. A cake of radius 10 cm is shared equally between 8 people. (a) What is the angle of the sector formed by each portion? (b) The cake has icing on the top (not the sides!) Find the area of icing for each portion of the cake.

9. A cake of radius 12 cm is shared equally between 10 people. (a) What is the angle of the sector formed by each portion? (b) The cake has icing on the top (not the sides!) Find the area of icing for each portion of the cake.

10. Find the shaded area in each of these diagrams, assuming that they are made from quarters and halves of circles.

(a)

8 cm

5 cm   5 cm

2 cm   ←4 cm→   2 cm

(b)

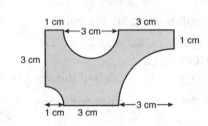

4 cm   4 cm

4 cm

(c)

7 cm

3 cm   3 cm

←4 cm→ ←3 cm→

(d)

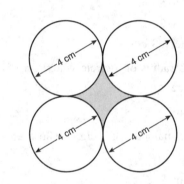

1 cm   ←3 cm→   3 cm

1 cm

3 cm

1 cm   3 cm   ←3 cm→

(e)

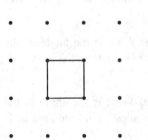

←5 cm→
←3 cm→←2 cm→

(f)

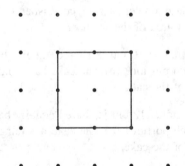

4 cm   4 cm

4 cm   4 cm

▲ SQUARES AND TRIANGLES ON DOTTED PAPER ▼

The dots here are all **one centimetre** apart.
This square has a side of one centimetre.
Its area is therefore 1 cm × 1 cm = 1 cm².

This square has a side of 2 cm.
Its area is therefore 2 cm × 2 cm = 4 cm².

This square has a side of 3 cm.
Its area is therefore 3 cm × 3 cm = 9 cm².

This square has a side of 4 cm.
Its area is therefore 4 cm × 4 cm = 16 cm².

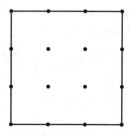

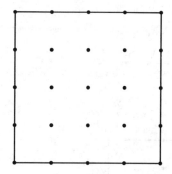

Now look at these squares which do not have a horizontal base. Find the area of the squares below. You can count whole and half squares, to find the total area.

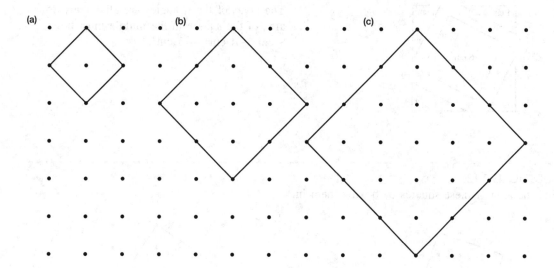

You should have found the areas to be: (a) 2 cm².   (b) 8 cm².   (c) 18 cm².

What is the area of this square?

The easiest way to find the area of this square is to box in the original square like this:

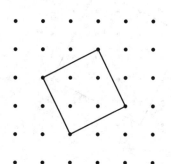

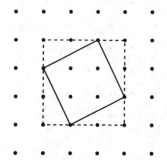

SHAPE AND SPACE

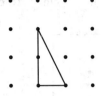

Remember that the area of a triangle is half the base times the vertical height.

So, the area of this shape is given by:

$A = \frac{1}{2} \times 1 \times 2 = 1 \text{ cm}^2$.

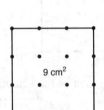

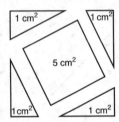

So, I can find the area of the original square, by considering the area of the outside square, which is 9 cm².

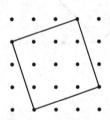

The areas of the triangles are all 1 cm². So, the area of the square in the middle must be 9 cm² – 4 cm² = 5 cm².

QUESTIONS 3.13

Find the area of these squares by boxing them in.

1.

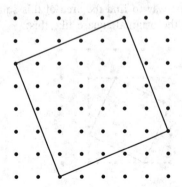

2.

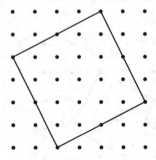

3.

4.

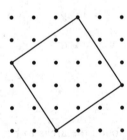

SHAPE AND SPACE

5.

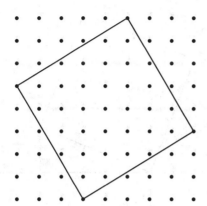

6.

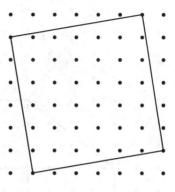

RIGHT-ANGLED TRIANGLES AND SQUARES

You can now discover a very famous Mathematical Theorem yourself! I have arranged some squares surrounding right-angled triangles in the diagrams below.

QUESTIONS 3.14
Work out the area of each of these squares. What do you notice?

1.

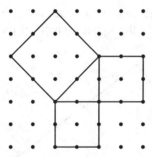

2.

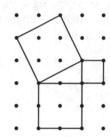

3.

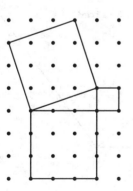

4.

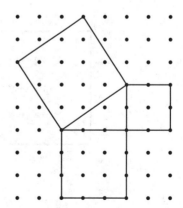

5.   6.

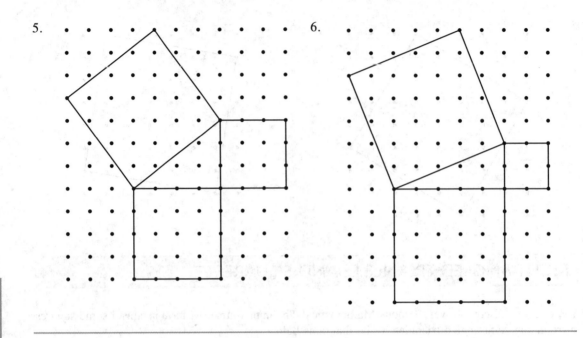

▲ PYTHAGORAS' THEOREM ▼

Read the previous section on Squares and Triangles on Dotted Paper before you read on!

Pythagoras was an ancient Greek, who lived about 582 BC to 510 BC.

His famous theorem concerns right-angled triangles. Draw a triangle which has sides of 3 cm, 4 cm and 5 cm. Check that one angle is a right angle. Now draw in the squares which sit on each side of the triangle, like this:

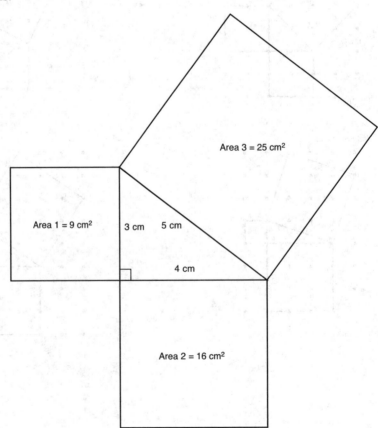

Area 3 = 25 cm²

Area 1 = 9 cm²   3 cm   5 cm

4 cm

Area 2 = 16 cm²

Pythagoras' Theorem is about the *areas* of the squares we have just drawn.

> **Pythagoras' Theorem**:
>
> Area 1 + Area 2 = Area 3

Or, in words:

> **Pythagoras' Theorem, in words**:
>
> The area of the two smaller squares add together to make the area of the largest square.

The triangle we have used in the diagram has sides of 3 cm, 4 cm and 5 cm. These numbers are the smallest whole numbers which make a right-angled triangle. The numbers 3, 4, 5 are referred to as a **Pythagorean triple**, because: $3^2 + 4^2 = 5^2$

FINDING LENGTHS USING PYTHAGORAS' THEOREM

EXAMPLE I

What is the length of the hypotenuse of this right-angled triangle?

Remember that the word hypotenuse means the longest side of a right-angled triangle.

We need to consider the squares which sit on the sides of the triangle:

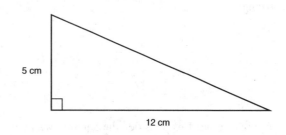

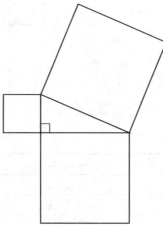

Pythagoras' Theorem states that the areas of the smaller two squares add together to make the area of the larger square.

Side of Triangle	Area of Square
5 cm	25 cm²
12 cm	144 cm²
	169 cm²

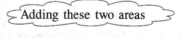
Adding these two areas

So, the area of the larger square is 169 cm². What length side will a square have if its area is 169 cm²? You probably recognise that $13 \times 13 = 169$.

So, the length of the side will be 13 cm. If you didn't know $13 \times 13 = 169$, you can use your calculator. Type in 169 and then press the square root button. This is what the square root button is for. It tells you the length of the side of the square, when you know the area of the square.

Side of Triangle	Area of Square
5 cm	25 cm²
12 cm	144 cm²
13 cm	169 cm²

Adding these two areas

So, to get from here to here, use the square root button.

So, 5, 12, 13 is another Pythagorean Triple. Again, draw a 5 cm, 12 cm, 13 cm triangle and show that it is a right-angled triangle.

EXAMPLE 2

Pythagoras' Theorem will work whether the numbers used are whole numbers or not. This is why it is such a powerful theorem.

Find the length of the hypotenuse for this triangle:

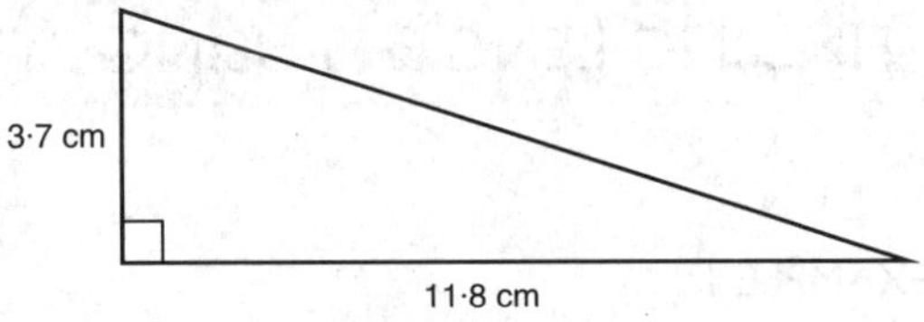

3·7 cm

11·8 cm

Again, we need to consider the squares which sit on the sides of the triangle:

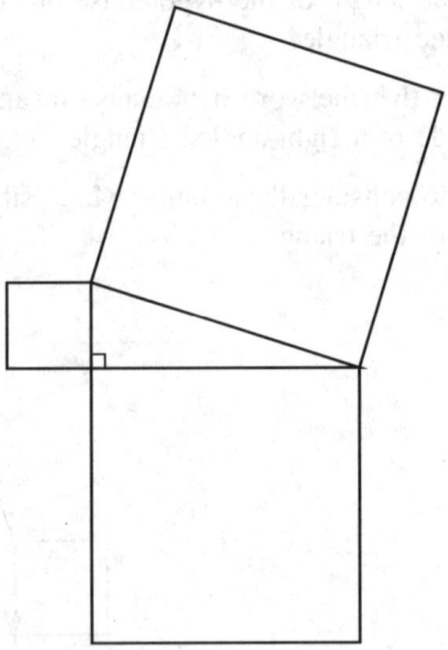

Side of Triangle	Area of Square
3·7 cm	13·69 cm²
11·8 cm	139·24 cm²
12·366 cm	152·93 cm²

Adding these two areas together

Using the square root button on my calculator.

So, I would give the answer as 12·4 cm (to one decimal place), for the length of the hypotenuse.

EXAMPLE 3

Find the length of the side of this triangle marked with an x.

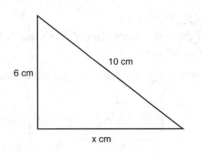

This time we are not asked to find the longest side, the hypotenuse. The areas of the two smallest squares must still add together to make the area of the largest square.

Area 1 + Area 2 = Area 3

$36 \text{ cm}^2 + \text{Area 2} = 100 \text{ cm}^2$

$36 + \boxed{} = 100$

Clearly, the missing area must be 64 cm².

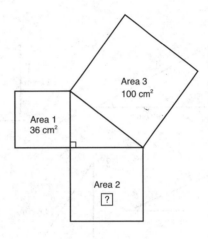

Or, using the same grid as before:

	Side of Triangle	Area of Square
length of hypotenuse.......	10 cm	100 cm²
length of other side we know.....	6 cm	36 cm²
	x = 8 cm	64 cm²

This time we must subtract

CAUTION!

Many pupils add 100 to 36 instead of subtracting. This gives them a total of 136, which when square rooted would give an answer of 11·7 cm. This is clearly incorrect, as the longest side is only 10 cm. Check to see if your answers make sense or not!

QUESTIONS 3.15

In these diagrams, find the missing lengths which are marked by a letter. Give your answers to one decimal place.

1.
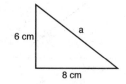

2.
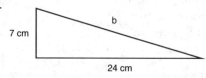

3.
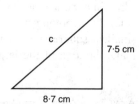

4.
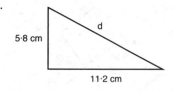

5.
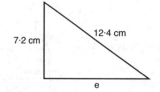

6.
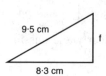

7.
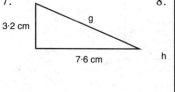

8.
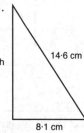

9.
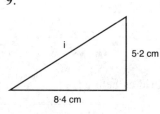

10.
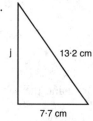

PYTHAGORAS' THEOREM USING ALGEBRA

If we label the sides of a right-angled triangle
a and b for the two shorter lengths and c for the
length of the hypotenuse, the triangle will look like this:

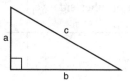

Now we need to consider the squares which sit
on each side as before:

Pythagoras' Theorem states that the areas of the
smaller two squares add together to make the
area of the largest square.

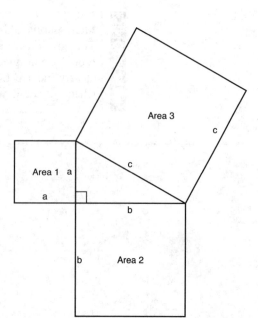

Side of Triangle	Area of Square
a cm	$a \times a = a^2$
b cm	$b \times b = b^2$
c cm	$c \times c = c^2$

Adding these two smaller squares as before

So, Pythagoras' theorem is often stated as:

Pythagoras' Theorem:

$$a^2 + b^2 = c^2$$

This is exactly the same as Area 1 + Area 2 = Area 3, as we had before.

If you are happy with the algebra version, you could dispense with doing a table each time.

EXAMPLE 1

Find the length of the hypotenuse for this triangle.

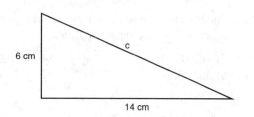

Remember that a and b are the lengths of the two smaller sides, and it doesn't matter which way round you use them, but c is always the hypotenuse. So, let's call a = 6 cm and b = 14 cm.

Pythagoras' Theorem states that: $\qquad a^2 + b^2 \qquad = c^2$

Substituting into Pythagoras' Theorem: $\quad 6^2 + 14^2 \quad = c^2$

$$36 + 196 \quad = c^2$$
$$232 \qquad = c^2$$

So, square rooting both sides: $\qquad 15\cdot23 \qquad = c$

So, the length of the hypotenuse is $15\cdot2$ cm (to one decimal place)

EXAMPLE 2

Find the length of the side marked a cm in this triangle.

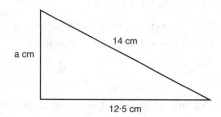

Pythagoras' Theorem states that: $\qquad a^2 + b^2 \qquad = c^2$

Substituting into Pythagoras' Theorem: $\quad a^2 + 12\cdot5^2 \quad = 14^2$

$$a^2 + 156\cdot25 \quad = 196$$

Subtracting $156\cdot25$ from both sides $\qquad a^2 \quad = 196 - 156\cdot25$

$$a^2 \quad = 39\cdot75$$

Square rooting both sides: $\qquad a \quad = 6\cdot304...$

So, the length of the side a is $6\cdot3$ cm (to one decimal place)

SHAPE AND SPACE

QUESTIONS 3.16

1. An equilateral triangle has sides of length 12 cm. Use Pythagoras' Theorem to find the height of the triangle.

2. A right-angled isosceles triangle has a hypotenuse of length 22 cm. Use Pythagoras' Theorem to find the length of the other two sides.

3. An isosceles triangle has base 7 cm and height 10 cm. Find the lengths of the other two sides.

4. An isosceles triangle has two equal sides of 18 cm and a base of 13·5 cm. Find the height.

5. A horse owner keeps two horses in a rectangular field measuring 100 m by 80 m. She is thinking of putting up a fence to go diagonally across the field to split it into two fields. How many metres of fencing will she need? Give your answer to one decimal place.

6. A 6 m ladder rests against a vertical wall. The foot of the ladder is 2 m away from the base of the wall. How high is the top of the ladder up the wall?

7. Draw a triangle with sides of 6·6 cm, 11 cm and 13·5 cm. Is this triangle a right-angled triangle? Use Pythagoras' Theorem to confirm your answer.

8. Some points are plotted on a 1 cm square grid. Find the distance between these pairs of points. Give your answer to one decimal place.

(a) (3, 7) and (8, 9)   (c) (−4, 7) and (6, 3)
(b) (4, 8) and (9, 7)   (d) (−2, −8) and (−5, 8)

▲ TRIGONOMETRY ▼

At this level, trigonometry is about right-angled triangles.

I asked my class to draw some right-angled triangles. The sides could be any length, but one angle had to be 30°. Some pupils drew very big triangles, some very small ones and there were many in between.

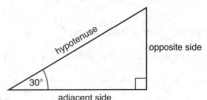

I asked everyone to label the sides of their triangle in the same way.

The longest side of a right-angled triangle is called the **hypotenuse**. Put this in:

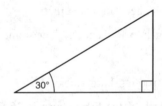

The 30° angle was the chosen angle. This is the side **opposite** our angle:

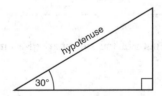

The last side to be labelled is called the **adjacent** side. 'Adjacent' means 'next to'. The adjacent side is the side next to our 30° angle.

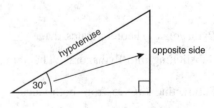

SHAPE AND SPACE

Next, I asked everyone to measure the sides of their triangle, correct to the nearest mm. Here are some of their results:

	opposite side	adjacent side	hypotenuse
Abigail	6·5	11·1	12·8
Barry	8·1	13·5	15·7
Charlotte	4·2	7·6	8·7
Helen	5·5	9·4	10·9
Bradley	9·5	15·9	18·5
Dan	8·6	14·9	17·2

I then asked everyone to use their calculators to do some divisions. I asked pupils to find the answer to these calculations:

The length of the opposite side ÷ The length of the hypotenuse

The length of the adjacent side ÷ The length of the hypotenuse

The length of the opposite side ÷ The length of the adjacent side

They have recorded their results like this:

	opposite side	adjacent side	hypotenuse	opp ÷ hyp	adj ÷ hyp	opp ÷ adj
Abigail	6·5	11·1	12·8	0·5078	0·8672	0·5856
Barry	8·1	13·5	15·7	0·5159	0·8599	0·6
Charlotte	4·2	7·6	8·7	0·4828	0·8736	0·5526
Helen	5·5	9·4	10·9	0·5046	0·8624	0·5851
Bradley	9·5	15·9	18·5	0·5135	0·8594	0·5975
Dan	8·6	14·9	17·2	0·5	0·8663	0·5772

You can see that the answers to the opposite side ÷ the hypotenuse are all very nearly the same!

	opposite side	adjacent side	hypotenuse	opp ÷ hyp	adj ÷ hyp	opp ÷ adj
Abigail	6·5	11·1	12·8	0·5078	0·8672	0·5856
Barry	8·0	13·5	15·7	0·5096	0·8599	0·5926
Charlotte	4·3	7·6	8·7	0·4943	0·8736	0·5658
Helen	5·5	9·4	10·9	0·5046	0·8624	0·5851
Bradley	9·5	15·9	18·5	0·5135	0·8594	0·5975
Dan	8·6	14·9	17·2	0·5	0·8663	0·5772

The answers in the other two columns are also very nearly the same.

This is remarkable! Whatever size triangle pupils have drawn, the answers to the divisions have turned out to be very nearly the same. Clearly, there will be some inaccuracies in the scale drawings done by the pupils, but the more accurate the diagrams, the more nearly the answers will agree!

These are the ideas that lie at the heart of trigonometry. If you have a right-angled triangle, where one angle is 30°, then the length of the side opposite the 30° angle, divided by the length of the hypotenuse, will give you an answer of about 0·5. Draw your own right-angled triangle, where one angle is 30° and check out these findings!

Fortunately, we do not have to keep making accurate drawings and taking measurements to use trigonometry. Mathematicians have already worked out the answers to these divisions. They have also given the last three columns special names, so we can refer to them easily.

> The opposite side ÷ the hypotenuse is called the **Sine** of our angle.
>
> The adjacent side ÷ the hypotenuse is called the **Cosine** of our angle.
>
> The opposite side ÷ the adjacent side is called the **Tangent** of our angle.

Sine is often shortened to Sin (still pronounced Sine).

Cosine is often shortened to Cos.

Tangent is often shortened to Tan.

So, the three formulae are most neatly written as:

$$\text{Sin } \theta = \frac{\text{opp}}{\text{hyp}}$$

$$\text{Cos } \theta = \frac{\text{adj}}{\text{hyp}}$$

$$\text{Tan } \theta = \frac{\text{opp}}{\text{adj}}$$

Notice that I have used θ (theta, a Greek letter) as my chosen angle.
For my class the chosen angle is 30°, so θ = 30°.

Look at your calculator and find the Sin, Cos and Tan buttons. On my calculator, I press "30°", *then* "Sin", to find that Sin 30° = 0·5. On other calculators, you will need to press "Sin", *then* "30°", to find that Sin 30° = 0·5. Make sure you know how your own calculator works. Use your calculator to check that:

Sin 30° = 0·5

Cos 30° = 0·86602....

Tan 30° = 0·57735.....

You can see that these are about the same answers as my pupils obtained.

These are some of the triangles which my pupils drew:

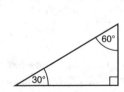 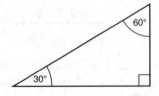 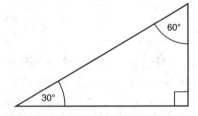

You can see that they all have the same angles. They all have a right angle, which is 90°. They all have an angle of 30°, so of course the third angle in each triangle must be 60°, so that the angles of a triangle add to 180°. So, all of the triangles are **similar**. This is why we get the same answer for the opposite divided by the hypotenuse. Look at the section on Similar Shapes if you need more clarification here.

USING TRIGONOMETRY TO FIND LENGTHS

EXAMPLE I
Find the length of the side marked x, in this triangle:

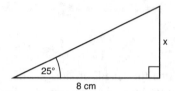

We need to find the length of side x. This is the side opposite the angle of 25°, so label this side opposite, like this:

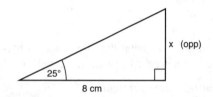

The side of 8 cm is the side adjacent to the angle of 25°, so label this side adjacent, like this:

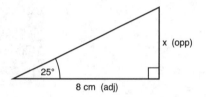

I am not going to label the other side as hypotenuse, as we don't know the length of the hypotenuse and we are not asked to find the length of it either.

Look at our three formulae:

$$\text{Sin } \theta = \frac{\text{opp}}{\text{hyp}}$$

$$\text{Cos } \theta = \frac{\text{adj}}{\text{hyp}}$$

$$\text{Tan } \theta = \frac{\text{opp}}{\text{adj}}$$

We need to use Tan, as this is the only formula which includes just opposite (the side we need to find) and adjacent (the side we know).

So, write down the formula we need to use:

$\text{Tan } \theta = \dfrac{\text{opp}}{\text{adj}}$ Substitute in what we know. The angle, θ, is 25°. The opposite side is x. The adjacent side is 8 cm.

$\text{Tan } 25° = \dfrac{x}{8}$ Use your calculator to find that Tan 25° = 0·466 (three decimal places will be enough), and substitute this into the formula, like this:

$0·466 = \dfrac{x}{8}$ Multiply both sides by 8 to find that:

So, x = 0·466 × 8

So, x = 3·728 cm

So, x = 3·7 cm (to 1 decimal place)

EXAMPLE 2

Find the length of the side marked y, in this triangle:

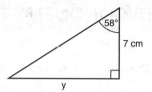

We need to find the length of side y. This is the side opposite to the angle we know, so label this side opposite. The side of 7 cm is the side adjacent to the angle of 58°, so label this side adjacent, like this:

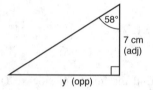

I am not going to label the other side as hypotenuse, as we don't know the length of the hypotenuse and we are not asked to find the length of it either.

Look at our three formulae:

$$\text{Sin } \theta = \frac{\text{opp}}{\text{hyp}}$$

$$\text{Cos } \theta = \frac{\text{adj}}{\text{hyp}}$$

$$\text{Tan } \theta = \frac{\text{opp}}{\text{adj}}$$

We still need to use Tan, as this is the only formula which includes just opposite (the side we want to find) and adjacent (the side we know).

So, write down the formula we need to use:

$\text{Tan } \theta = \frac{\text{opp}}{\text{adj}}$ Substitute in what we know. The angle, θ, is 58°. The opposite side is y. The adjacent side is 7 cm.

$\text{Tan } 58° = \frac{y}{7}$ Use your calculator to find that Tan 58° = 1·600 (three decimal places will be enough), and substitute this into the formula, like this:

$1·600 = \frac{y}{7}$ Multiply both sides by 7 to find that:

$1·600 \times 7 = y$

So, y = 11·2 cm

EXAMPLE 3

Find the length of the side marked z, in this triangle:

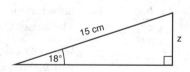

We need to find the length of side z. This is the side opposite the angle of 18°, so label this side opposite. The side of 15 cm is the hypotenuse, so label this side hyp, like this:

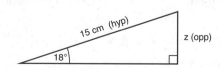

I am not going to label the other side as adjacent, as we don't know the length of the adjacent and we are not asked to find the length of it either.

Look at our three formulae:

$$\text{Sin } \theta = \frac{\text{opp}}{\text{hyp}}$$

$$\text{Cos } \theta = \frac{\text{adj}}{\text{hyp}}$$

$$\text{Tan } \theta = \frac{\text{opp}}{\text{adj}}$$

We need to use Sin, as this is the only formula which includes just opposite (the side we need to find) and hypotenuse (the side we know).

So, write down the formula we need to use:

$\text{Sin } \theta = \dfrac{\text{opp}}{\text{hyp}}$	Substitute in what we know. The angle, θ, is 18°. The opposite side is z. The hypotenuse is 15 cm.
$\text{Sin } 18° = \dfrac{z}{15}$	Use your calculator to find that Sin 18° = 0·309 (three decimal places will be enough), and substitute this into the formula, like this:
$0·309 = \dfrac{z}{15}$	Multiply both sides by 15 to find that:

$0·309 \times 15 = z$

So, z = 4·635 cm

So, z = 4·6 cm (to 1 decimal place)

EXAMPLE 4 (SLIGHTLY HARDER!)

Find the length of the side marked x, in this triangle:

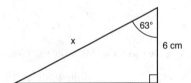

We need to find the length of side x. This time this is the hypotenuse, so label this side hyp. The side of 6 cm is the side adjacent to the angle of 63°, so label this side adjacent, like this:

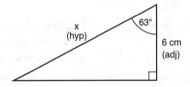

I am not going to label the other side as opposite, as we don't know the length of the opposite and we are not asked to find the length of it either.

Look at our three formulae:

$$\text{Sin } \theta = \frac{\text{opp}}{\text{hyp}}$$

$$\text{Cos } \theta = \frac{\text{adj}}{\text{hyp}}$$

$$\text{Tan } \theta = \frac{\text{opp}}{\text{adj}}$$

We need to use Cos, as this is the only formula which includes just adjacent (the side we know) and hypotenuse (the side we need to find).

So, write down the formula we need to use:

$Cos\ \theta = \dfrac{adj}{hyp}$ Substitute in what we know. The angle, θ, is 63°. The adjacent is 6 cm. The hypotenuse is x.

$Cos\ 63° = \dfrac{6}{x}$ Use your calculator to find that Cos 63° = 0·454 (three decimal places will be enough), and substitute this into the formula, like this:

$0·454 = \dfrac{6}{x}$ This is now ever so slightly harder, because we need to find the value of x, which is on the bottom line of the equation. So, we must multiply both sides by x first of all, like this:

$0·454 \times x = 6$ Now, divide both sides by 0·454, like this:

$\dfrac{0·454 \times x}{0·454} = \dfrac{6}{0·454}$

So, x = 13·2 cm (to 1 decimal place)

USING TRIGONOMETRY TO FIND ANGLES

EXAMPLE I
Find the angle marked θ in this triangle:

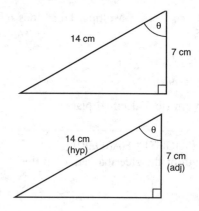

Label the sides we know. The side of 7 cm is the adjacent side and the side of 14 cm is the hypotenuse, like this:

So, we need to use the formula for Cosine.

$Cos\ \theta = \dfrac{adj}{hyp}$ Substitute in the values for the adjacent side and the hypotenuse, like this:

$Cos\ \theta = \dfrac{7}{14}$

$Cos\ \theta = 0·5$ I now need to know what angle has this cosine. So far I have known the angle and have used my calculator to find the cosine of the angle. Now I already know the cosine and I need to get back to the angle.

This is how my calculator works:

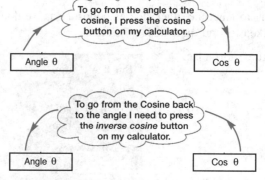

Make sure you know how your calculator works.

Cos θ = 0·5   So 0·5 is showing on my calculator display. Now I press the inverse cosine button, to find that the angle is 60°.

So θ = 60°.

EXAMPLE 2
Find the angle θ in this triangle:

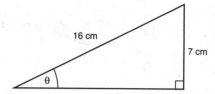

Label the sides we know:

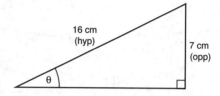

So, we need to use the formula for Sine.

Sin θ = opp / hyp

Substitute in the values for the opposite and the hypotenuse, like this:

Sin θ = 7 / 16

Sin θ = 0·4375   This time I will need to press the inverse Sin button, to find θ, like this:

θ = 25·9° (to 1 decimal place)

QUESTIONS 3.17
1. Use your calculator to find the Sine, Cosine and Tangent for these angles. Give your answers to 3 decimal places.

Angle	Sin	Cos	Tan
30°			
60°			
45°			
15°			
55°			

2. Use your calculator to find the angle θ in degrees, correct to 1 decimal place, when:

(a) Sin θ = 0·673   (c) Tan θ = 1·386   (e) Cos θ = 0·845
(b) Cos θ = 0·295   (d) Sin θ = 0·318   (f) Tan θ = 0·858

SHAPE AND SPACE

3. Find the length of the marked sides in these right-angled triangles. Give your answers to 1 decimal place.

(a)

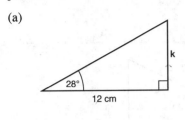

(b)

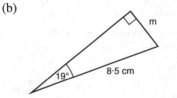

(c)

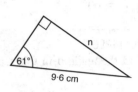

(d)

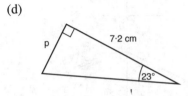

(e)

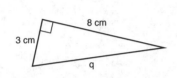

(f)

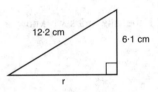

(g)

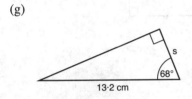

(h)

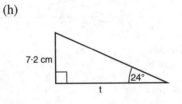

(i)

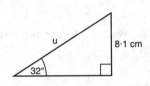

4. Find the marked angles in these right-angled triangles. Give your answers to the nearest degree.

(a)

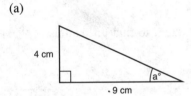

(b)

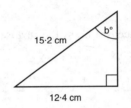

(c)

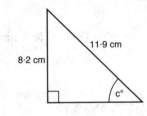

(d)

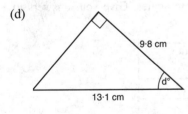

(e)

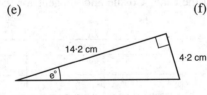

(f)

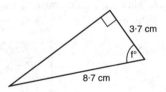

(g)

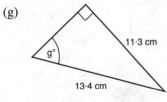

(h)

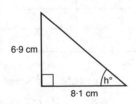

5. A surveyor uses an inclinometer to measure the angle of elevation when he is looking at the top of a tower. He is standing 50 m away from the tower and the angle of elevation is 52°.

Find the height of the tower.

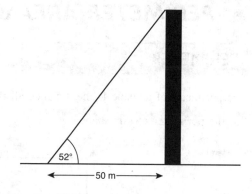

6. A strut on a building needs to join a horizontal surface to a vertical surface. The architect wants the angle to be 40° and the strut to join the vertical surface 5m up, like this:

Find the length of the strut.

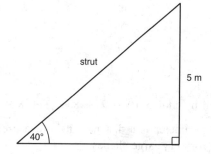

7. (a) Find the height of an equilateral triangle of side 8 cm. (b) Use your answer to find the area of the triangle.

8. Find the acute angle between the diagonals of a rectangle measuring 5 cm by 8 cm.

9. An isosceles triangle has sides of 14 cm, 14 cm and 8 cm. Find (a) the angle between the two equal sides (b) the height (c) the area of the triangle.

10. Find the length of side x:

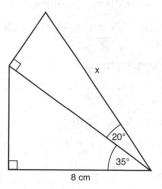

▲ *PERIMETER, AREA & VOLUME* ▼

PERIMETER

The perimeter of a shape is the distance all the way around the outside of a shape.

So, the perimeter of this shape:

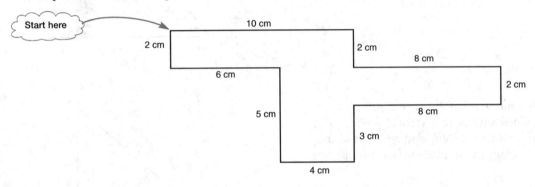

is found by adding $10 + 2 + 8 + 2 + 8 + 3 + 4 + 5 + 6 + 2 = 50$ cm

As the perimeter is a distance, it is measured in centimetres, or metres for larger shapes, or kilometres for very large shapes.

AREA

The area of a shape is the amount of surface that the shape covers.

This square has sides which are 1 cm long:

The area of this square is 1 cm $\times$ 1 cm which is 1 square centimetre.

We write 1 square centimetre as 1 cm^2.

EXAMPLE 2
The area of this rectangle is 12 cm^2.

You can see that 6 cm $\times$ 2 cm $= 12$cm^2

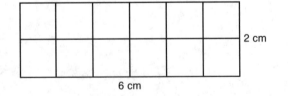

EXAMPLE 3
The area of this rectangle is 15 cm^2.

You can see that 6 cm $\times$ 2·5 cm $= 15$ cm^2.

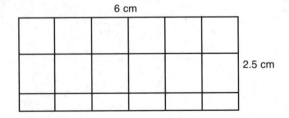

The area of any rectangle is given by length × width.

Area of this rectangle = a × b

This formula will give you the area of any rectangle, no matter how 'difficult' the numbers involved.

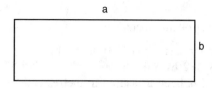

EXAMPLE 4

The area of this rectangle is:

6·2 cm × 2·7 cm = 16·74 cm².

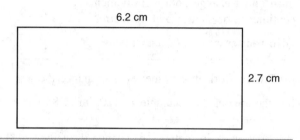

EXAMPLE 5: COMPOUND SHAPES

Find the area of this shape:

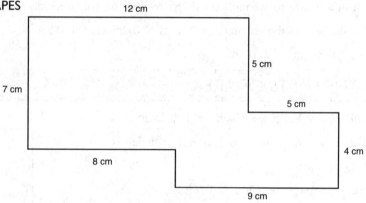

We can split the shape into rectangles, like this:

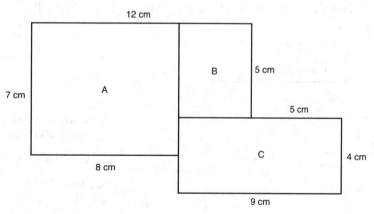

Area A is a rectangle of area 8 cm × 7 cm = 56 cm²
Area B is a rectangle of area 4 cm × 5 cm = 20 cm²
Area C is a rectangle of area 9 cm × 4 cm = 36 cm²

So, the area of the whole shape is 56 + 20 + 36 = 112 cm²

SHAPE AND SPACE

EXAMPLE 6

Find the area of this rectangle:

Notice that the answer is NOT found by
multiplying $1 \cdot 2$ by 85!
The length has been measured in metres and
the width has been measured in centimetres, so
we cannot just multiply them together! We
must either change both measurements to
centimetres or change both to metres.

Give your answer in (a) cm^2 (b) m^2

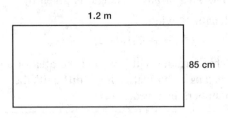

1.2 m

85 cm

(a) Firstly, work in centimetres, so, change the length of $1 \cdot 2$ m to 120 cm.

So, the area of the rectangle = 120 cm $\times$ 85 cm = 10200 cm^2

(b) Now, work in metres, so, change the length of 85 cm to metres. Remember that there are 100
cm in a metre, so we must divide 85 by 100 to give $0 \cdot 85$ m.

So, the area of the rectangle = $1 \cdot 2$ m $\times$ $0 \cdot 85$ m = $1 \cdot 02$ m^2

So, 10200 cm^2 = $1 \cdot 02$ m^2

THE UNITS OF AREA

This square has sides which are 1 m long:

The area of this square is 1 m $\times$ 1 m which is

1 square metre.

We write 1 square metre as 1 m^2.

To find the area of the square in square
centimetres, remember that there are 100 cm
in 1 m.

1 m

1 m

1 m = 100 cm

1 m = 100 cm

Each row contains 100 cm^2.
There are 100 rows.

So, the area of this square is 1 m $\times$ 1 m = 1 m^2.

But, also the area of this square is
100 cm $\times$ 100 cm = 10 000 cm^2.

So

$$1 \text{ m}^2 = 10\ 000 \text{ cm}^2$$

CAUTION!

Many pupils seem surprised by how many
1 square centimetres are needed to make one
square metre! Notice that the number needed is
NOT 100!

SHAPE AND SPACE

You can change between other units of area in the same way.

$1 \text{ km}^2 = 1 \text{ km} \times 1 \text{ km}$ ...there 1000 m in 1 km

$1 \text{ km}^2 = 1000 \text{ m} \times 1000\text{m}$

$1 \text{ km}^2 = 1\,000\,000 \text{ m}^2$

So

$$1 \text{ km}^2 = 1\,000\,000 \text{ m}^2$$

THE AREA OF A TRIANGLE

Take a piece of card and cut out a rectangle which is 8 cm by 12 cm. Draw in one of the diagonals.

Cut along the diagonal that you have drawn.

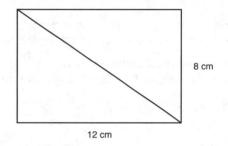

8 cm

12 cm

You now have two right-angled triangles which are **congruent**. This means that both triangles are exactly the same shape and size. One triangle will fit exactly on top of the other.

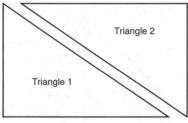

Triangle 2

Triangle 1

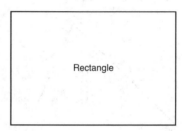

Rectangle

Area of Triangle 1 + Area of Triangle 2 = Area of Rectangle

We know the area of our rectangle is given by: Area = length × width

so: Area = 8 cm × 12 cm = 96 cm²

Area of Triangle 1 = Area of Triangle 2

So, the area of each triangle must be 48 cm².

We have found the area of this right-angled triangle by taking half of 8×12.

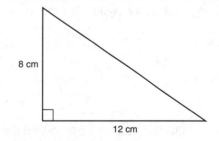

8 cm

12 cm

$$\begin{aligned} \text{Area of triangle} \quad &= \text{half of } 8 \times 12 \\ &= \tfrac{1}{2} \text{ of } 8 \times 12 \\ &= \tfrac{1}{2} \times 8 \times 12 \\ &= 48 \text{ cm}^2 \end{aligned}$$

In words:

The area of the triangle is half the base times the height.

SHAPE AND SPACE

Using algebra, we could call the sides of the
triangle a and b, like this:

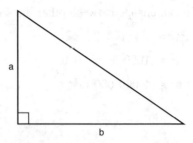

In algebra:

$$\text{Area} = \tfrac{1}{2} \times a \times b$$

What if your triangle is not a right-angled one?

Cut out another rectangle which is
8 cm × 12 cm and draw in a triangle like this:

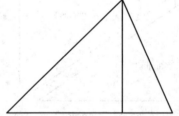

Cut out the triangle and rearrange the pieces like this:

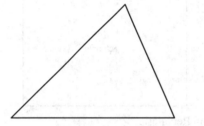

Again, we have formed two congruent triangles. They must both have the same area and, just as before, the two areas must add up to the area of the rectangle.

So, the area of this triangle is 48 cm², just the
same as the area of the right-angled triangle.

Using algebra, we could label the triangle like this:

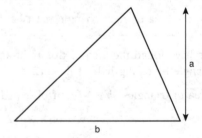

Notice that this time we have labelled the base 'b' and the **vertical height** 'a'. This distance is sometimes called the **perpendicular** height. Perpendicular means 'at right angles to'. The height is at right angles to the base of the triangle.

So, the area of this triangle is $\tfrac{1}{2} \times a \times b$ just as before.

In words:

> The area of the triangle is half the base times the height.

In algebra:

> Area $= \frac{1}{2} \times a \times b$

So far we have found the area of a right-angled triangle. We have also found the area of a triangle which is not a right-angled triangle, but was still inside the original rectangle. The area for both of these triangles is given by:

> The area of the triangle is half the base times the height.

What if I draw a triangle which has the same base as before and the same **vertical** height as before, but goes **outside** the original rectangle which we drew? A triangle like this one:

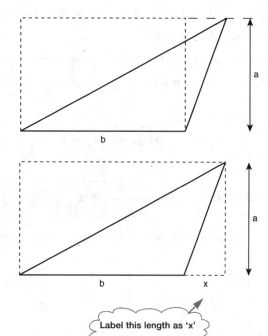

Draw in a rectangle which surrounds the whole triangle, like this:

The length of this rectangle is (b + x) and the width is a.

So, the area of the rectangle is given by the formula:

Label this length as 'x'

Area of rectangle = length $\times$ width
Area of rectangle = (b + x) $\times$ a
Area of rectangle = ab + ax

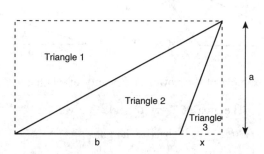

So, the areas of these three triangles must equal the area of the rectangle:

So, Triangle 1 + Triangle 2 + Triangle 3 = Area of Rectangle

We know the areas of Triangles 1 and 3, using what we have found out already. Fill these areas in on the diagram, like this:

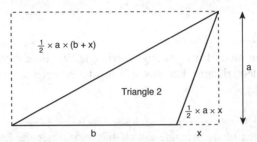

So, to find the area of Triangle 2, substitute into the formula:

Triangle 1 + Triangle 2 + Triangle 3 = Area of Rectangle

$\frac{1}{2}ab + \frac{1}{2}ax + $ Triangle 2 $ + \frac{1}{2}ax = ab + ax$

So, Triangle 2 $ = \frac{1}{2}ab$

So, Triangle 2 also has an area given by "half the base times the height"!

The formula for the area of a triangle is given by:

In words:

> The area of the triangle is half the base times the height.

In algebra:

> Area $= \frac{1}{2} \times a \times b$

So, amazingly, the area of all these triangles below will be given by the same formula:

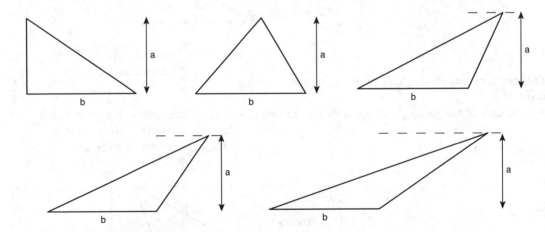

This is another example of the power and beauty of Maths!

> The area of every triangle is given by:
>
> Area $= \frac{1}{2} \times$ base $\times$ height
>
> Area $= \frac{1}{2} \times a \times b$

EXAMPLE I
Find the area of this triangle:

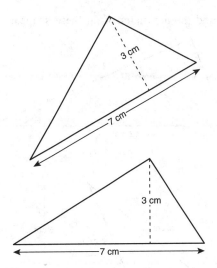

If you prefer, turn the triangle round so that the 7 cm side is horizontal. This helps some pupils to obtain the right answer.

The formula tells us:

Area = $\frac{1}{2}$ × base × height

Area = $\frac{1}{2}$ × 7 cm × 3 cm

Area = 10·5 cm²

QUESTIONS 3.18

1. If these dots are spaced 1 cm apart, find the area of each shape.

(a)

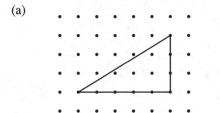

(b)

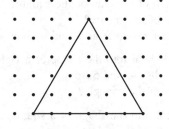

(c)

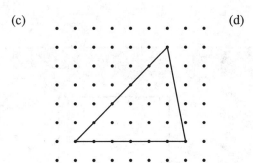

(d)

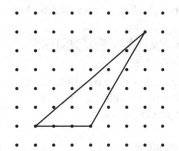

(e)

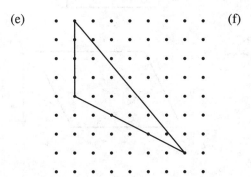

(f)

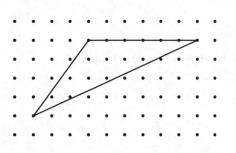

2. Find the perimeter of all these shapes:

(a)

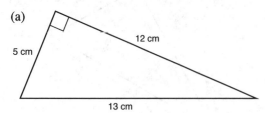

(b)

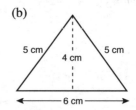

(c)

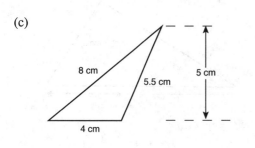

(d)

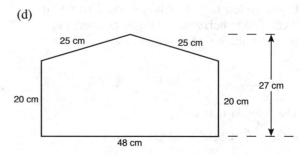

3. Find the area of all the shapes in question 2.

4. A piece of wire is bent into the shape of a right-angled triangle.
Its sides are 12 cm, 16 cm and 20 cm.
(a) What is the area of the triangle?

The wire is then bent into the shape of a square.
(b) What is the length of the side of the square?
(c) What is the area of the square?
(d) Which shape has the bigger area and by how much?

5. A piece of wire is bent into the shape of a right-angled triangle.
Its sides are 20 cm, 48 cm and 52 cm.
(a) What is the area of the triangle?

The wire is then bent into the shape of a square.
(b) What is the length of the side of the square?
(c) What is the area of the square?
(d) Which shape has the bigger area and by how much?

AREA OF A PARALLELOGRAM

A rectangle is a special sort of parallelogram.
It has two pairs of parallel sides. It happens to
have angles which are right angles.

The area of this rectangle is a × b

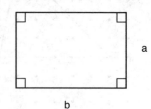

What is the area of this parallelogram?

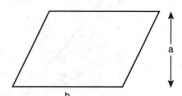

SHAPE AND SPACE

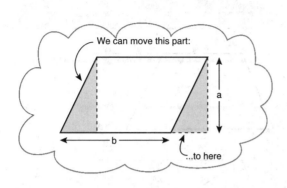

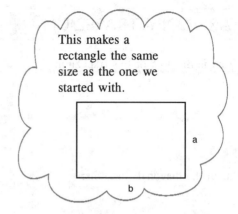

So the area of the parallelogram is also a × b.

The area of all these parallelograms is also a × b.

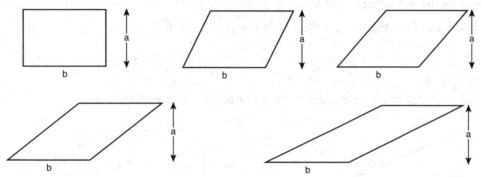

Another way of showing this, is to think of each parallelogram as being made up of two triangles, like this:

Each triangle has area = $\frac{1}{2}$ × a × b

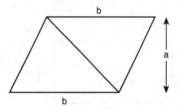

Each parallelogram has the area of two triangles = $2 \times \frac{1}{2} \times a \times b = a \times b$

AREA OF A TRAPEZIUM

What is the area of this trapezium?

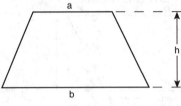

Put in the diagonal, like this:

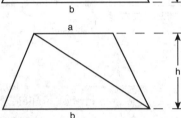

The area of the top triangle is $\frac{1}{2}$ah.

The area of the bottom triangle is $\frac{1}{2}$bh.

So, the total area of the trapezium is $\frac{1}{2}$ah + $\frac{1}{2}$bh = $\dfrac{(a + b)}{2} \times h$

QUESTIONS 3.19

1. Find the perimeter of all these shapes. (They are not drawn to scale!)

(a)

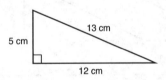

(b)

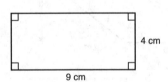

(c)

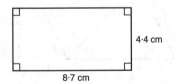

(d)

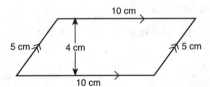

(e)

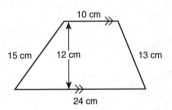

(f)

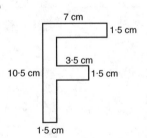

2. Find the area of the shapes in question 1.

3. Find the shaded area in this shape:

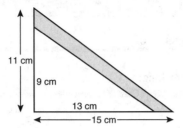

4. Find the area of these shapes. One square represents 1 cm².

(a)

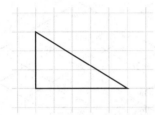

(b)

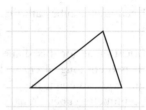

(c)

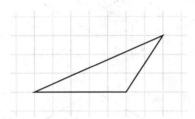

(d)

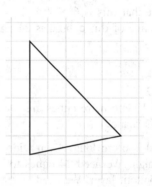

(e)

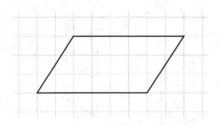

(f)

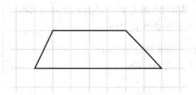

5. Find the area of these rectangles in (i) cm² (ii) m²

(a)

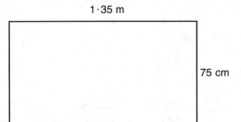

(b)

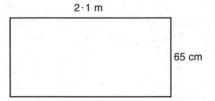

VOLUME

The volume of a solid shape is the amount of space that it occupies.

This cube has sides which are all 1 cm long:

The volume of this cube is:

1 cm $\times$ 1 cm $\times$ 1 cm = 1 cm^3

This is called '1 cubic centimetre'.

EXAMPLE 1

How many 1 centimetre cubes are there in this shape?

The mathematical name for this shape is a cuboid. It is 6 cm long, 4 cm wide and 1 cm high. You can count the number of 1 centimetre cubes. You need 24 of them to make this shape.

You can see that this is $6 \times 4 \times 1 = 24$
So, the volume of this cuboid is 24 cm^3.

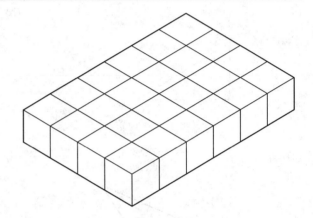

EXAMPLE 2

How many 1 centimetre cubes are there in this shape?

This cuboid is 6 cm long, 4 cm wide and 2 cm high. We need 24 cubes to make the bottom layer. We need another 24 cubes to make the top layer. Altogether, the shape needs 48 one centimetre cubes.

You can see that this is
$6 \times 4 \times 2 = 48$

So, the volume of this cuboid is 48 cm^3.

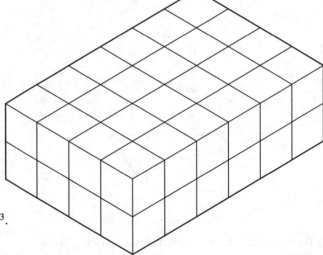

SHAPE AND SPACE

EXAMPLE 3

Find the volume of this cuboid:

This cuboid is 6 cm long, 4 cm wide and 1·5 cm high. We need 24 cubes to make the bottom layer. We need another 12 cubes cut in half to make 24 pieces for the top layer. Altogether, the shape needs 36 one centimetre cubes.

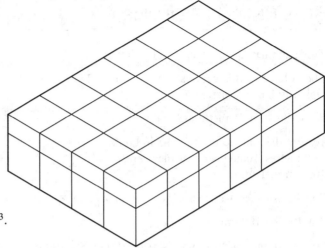

You can see that this is
6 × 4 × 1·5 = 36

So, the volume of this cuboid is 36 cm³.

So, in general, the volume of any cuboid is given by this formula:

> Volume of a cuboid = length × width × height

EXAMPLE 4

Find the volume of a cuboid 6·3 cm long, 4·2 cm wide and 2·5 cm high.

Volume of a cuboid = length × width × height

Volume = 6·3 × 4·2 × 2·5 = 66·15

So, the volume of this cuboid is 66·15 cm³.

EXAMPLE 5

Find the volume of a cuboid 1·2 m long, 85 cm wide and 40 cm high.

CAUTION! Notice that the answer is NOT found by multiplying 1·2 by 85 by 40! The length has been measured in metres and the width and the height have been measured in centimetres, so we cannot just multiply these numbers together! We must either change all measurements to centimetres or to metres.

Give your answer in (a) cm³ (b) m³

(a) Firstly, work in centimetres, so change the length of 1·2 m to 120 cm.

So, the volume of the cuboid = 120 cm × 85 cm × 40 cm = 408 000 cm³

(b) Now, work in metres, so, change the width of 85 cm to metres. Remember that there are 100 cm in a metre, so we must divide 85 by 100 to give 0·85 m.

Change the height of 40 cm to metres, by dividing by 100 to give 0·4 m.

So, the volume of the cuboid = 1·2 m × 0·85 m × 0·4 m = 0·408 m³

So, 408 000 cm³ = 0·408 m³

SHAPE AND SPACE

THE UNITS OF VOLUME

This cube has sides which are 1 m long:

The volume of this cube is 1 m $\times$ 1 m $\times$ 1 m which is 1 cubic metre.

We write 1 cubic metre as 1 m^3.

To find the volume of the cube in cubic centimetres, remember that there are 100 cm in 1 m.

So, the volume of this cube is: 1 m $\times$ 1 m $\times$ 1 m = 1 m^3.

But 1 m = 100 cm.

So, the volume of this cube is also: 100 cm $\times$ 100 cm $\times$ 100 cm = 1 000 000 cm^3.

$$1 \text{ m}^3 = 1\ 000\ 000 \text{ cm}^3$$

CAUTION!

Many pupils seem surprised by how many one cubic centimetres are needed to make one cubic metre! The number needed is NOT 100!

CAPACITY

The capacity of a container is the amount of liquid that it can hold. Capacity is measured in litres and millilitres.

This is a **solid** cube. Its sides are all 10 cm long. 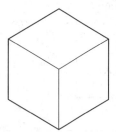	This is an open **container**. The inside edges of this container are all 10 cm in length. 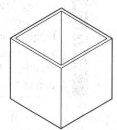
This solid occupies 10 cm $\times$ 10 cm $\times$ 10 cm = 1000 cm^3 space. The volume of the solid = 1000 cm^3 of space.	**This container is said to hold 1 litre of a liquid.** The capacity of the container = 1 litre

So,

$$1000 \text{ cm}^3 = 1 \text{ litre}$$

1 litre can be sub-divided into 1000 millilitres.

So, 1000 cm³   = 1 litre = 1000 ml

So, 1000 cm³   = 1000 ml

So, 1 cm³   = 1 ml

So,

> 1 cm³ = 1 millilitre
> 1 cm³ = 1 ml

VOLUME OF PRISMS

What is the volume of this shape?

The shape is made from 1 centimetre cubes and from half cubes.

There are 6 whole cubes and 4 halves, so the volume is 8 cubes.

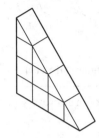

If I make an identical shape and stack it next to my first shape, the new solid will look like this:

The new volume will be 8 cubes × 2 = 16 cubes.

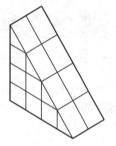

Add another layer and the new shape will look like this:

The new volume will be 8 cubes × 3 = 24 cubes.

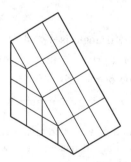

If you had 10 identical layers stacked together, the new shape would look like this:

The new volume will be 8 cubes × 10 = 80 cubes.

The area of the triangular face of our shape is 8 cm².

The volume of all of these shapes has been found by taking the area of the cross-section (shown shaded) and multiplying by the length.

All of these shapes are prisms. They are called triangular prisms, because they have a triangular face.

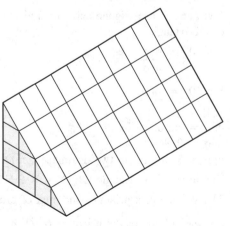

The shapes below are also prisms. Can you describe the property that all prisms have?

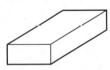

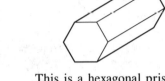

This is a rectangular prism. We usually call it a cuboid!

This is a hexagonal prism.

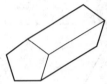

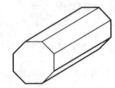

This is a pentagonal prism.

This is an octagonal prism.

All prisms have a uniform cross-section.

So,

> The volume of a prism = the area of cross-section × length

EXAMPLE I

Find the volume of the triangular prism, whose face is this triangle and is 10 cm long.

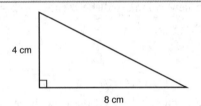

The area of the triangle is $\frac{1}{2} \times 4 \times 8 = 16$ cm².

The volume of a prism = the area of cross-section × length

So, the volume of the prism = $16 \times 10 = 160$ cm³.

EXAMPLE 2

Find the volume of the triangular prism, whose face is this equilateral triangle and whose length is 15 cm long.

The area of the triangle is $\frac{1}{2} \times$ base × height

You need to use trigonometry to find the height of the triangle.

$\text{Sin } 60° = \dfrac{\text{opp}}{\text{hyp}}$

$\text{Sin } 60° = \dfrac{\text{opp}}{4}$

opp = sin 60° × 4

opp = 0·866 × 4

opp = 3·46 cm (to two decimal place)

The area of the triangle is $\frac{1}{2} \times 4 \times 3·46 = 6·92$ cm².

The volume of a prism = the area of cross-section × length

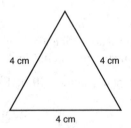

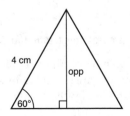

So, the volume of the prism = $6·92 \times 15 = 103·8$ cm³.

VOLUME OF CYLINDERS

A cylinder is a prism with a circular cross-section. So, we can use the same formula:

The volume of a prism = the area of cross-section × length

This time, the cross-section is a circle. So, the area of cross-section is given by πr^2, where r is the radius of the circle.

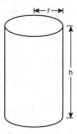

So,

> Volume of a cylinder = $\pi r^2 \times h$
> Volume of a cylinder = $\pi r^2 h$

EXAMPLE I

Find the volume of a tin of baked beans of diameter 7·5 cm and height 11 cm.

We have been told the diameter, so we need to divide by 2 to find the radius.

So, radius = 7·5 cm ÷ 2 = 3·75 cm.

Volume of a cylinder = $\pi r^2 h$

Volume of a cylinder = $\pi \times 3·75^2 \times 11$ [Remember that the 3·75 *only* is squared!]

Volume of a cylinder = 485·7 cm³ (to one decimal point)

QUESTIONS 3.20

1. Find the volume of these cuboids, if all dots are 1 cm apart.

(a)

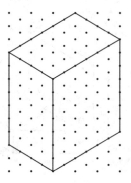

(b)

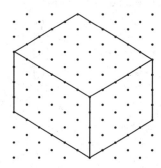

(c)

(d)

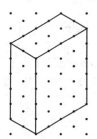

2. Which tank holds most water?

Cuboid 1which has dimensions: 4 m by 7 m by 2·5 m

Cuboid 2 which has dimensions: 4·8 m by 4·2 m by 3·4 m

3. A cuboid has dimensions: 1·5 m by 80 cm by 2 m

Find the volume of this cuboid in (a) cm³ (b) m³.

4. A cuboid has dimensions: 2·4 m by 95 cm by 1·8 m

Find the volume of this cuboid in (a) cm³ (b) m³.

5. How many cuboids can you find that have a volume of 60 m³?

6. I have measured the outside dimensions of a carton of UHT milk. The dimensions are 9·5 cm, 6·2 cm and 8·8 cm.

(a) What is the maximum amount of milk that the carton can hold? Give your answer in millilitres.

(b) What do you think the label gives as the amount of milk in the carton?

(c) Why would there be a slight difference in your answers to (a) and (b)?

7. A long-jump pit is constructed to be 15 m long, 2 m wide and 60 cm deep. How many cubic metres of sand do I need to order to fill the pit?

8. Find the volume of these prisms. The end faces are drawn below and they are all 15 cm long.

(a)

5 cm

9 cm

(b)

5 cm

6 cm

(c)

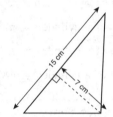

15 cm

7 cm

9. Find the volume of these prisms.

(a)

10 cm

3 cm

6 cm

8 cm

(b)

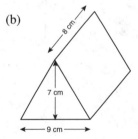

8 cm

7 cm

9 cm

(c)

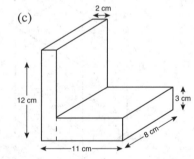

2 cm

12 cm

3 cm

11 cm

8 cm

10. Find the volume of a tin of soup, where the diameter is 6·8 cm and the height is 10 cm.

11. Find the volume of a tin of baked beans, where the diameter is 4·3 cm and the height is 11·2 cm.

12. Find the volume of a tin of molasses, where the diameter is 9 cm and the height is 10·8 cm.

▲ *BEARINGS* ▼

Bearings are used to give precise information about the position of objects, particularly when navigating.

EXAMPLE 1

What is the bearing of the Island from the Port?

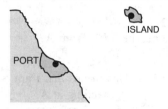

When using bearings, you must remember to:

- Start by facing North.
- Always turn in a clockwise direction.

It will help to draw in a North line, and to join the Port to the Island with a straight line, like this:

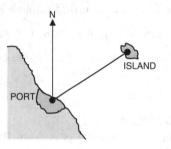

Now we need to measure the correct angle. Remember to imagine that you are standing at the Port, looking along the North line. Now turn clockwise, until you are looking at the Island. So, the correct angle is this one:

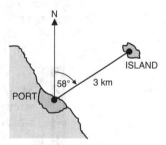

So, using a protractor, you can measure the angle, to give the bearing of the island from the port as 58°.

THREE-FIGURE BEARINGS

You might be asked to give the answer as a 3-figure bearing. So, a bearing of 58° would be given as 058°.

EXAMPLE 2
What is the bearing of B **from A**?

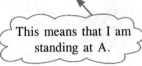

So, I am standing at the point A.

I face North.

Then I turn clockwise until I am looking at B.

The angle I have turned through is 75°.

So, the bearing of B from A is 75°.

If you were asked for a 3-figure bearing, give your answer as: "The bearing of B from A is 075°."

EXAMPLE 3
What is the bearing of A **from B**?

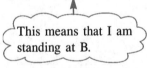

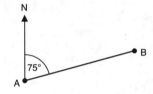

CAUTION!

> Many pupils give the answer to this question, wrongly, as 75°, just because this is the angle which is given in the diagram.

In this example I am standing **at B.** I face north and turn clockwise, until I am looking at A.

SHAPE AND SPACE

Put in another North line at B, to help us, like this:

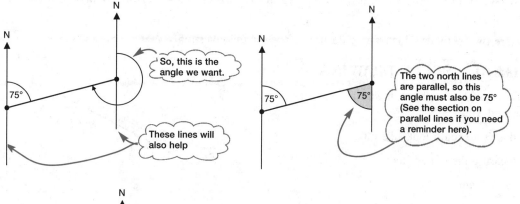

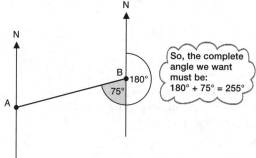

So, the bearing of A **from B** is 225°

Notice that, this time, the bearing already is a 3-figure bearing.

QUESTIONS 3.21

In questions 1 to 4, for each diagram, complete these two statements:

(a) The bearing of X from Y is _____ .

(b) The bearing of Y from X is _____ .

1.

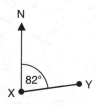

2.

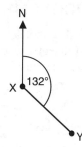

3.

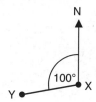

4.

SHAPE AND SPACE

EXAMPLE 4

A ship sails from a port on a bearing of 63°, for a distance of 2·5 km. How far (a) north and (b) east has it gone?

There are two methods which we could use to answer this question.

METHOD 1: SCALE DRAWING

Choose a suitable scale, such as 2 cm to represent 1 km.

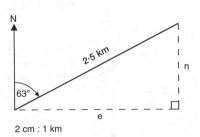

Your diagram should look like this:

Now measure the dotted lines.

(a) n = 2·2 cm

(b) e = 4·4 cm

2 cm : 1 km

(a) DISTANCE TRAVELLED NORTH

Using the scale we have chosen:

> Look up the section on Maps and Scale Drawings, under Ratio, if you need a reminder here.

    2 cm   :   1 km
    1 cm   :   0·5 km
    2·2 cm :   0·5 × 2·2 km = 1·1 km

So, the ship has sailed 1·1 km north.

(b) DISTANCE TRAVELLED EAST

    2 cm : 1 km

    1 cm : 0·5 km

4·4 cm : 0·5 × 4·4 km = 2·2 km

So, the ship has sailed 2·2 km east.

METHOD 2: TRIGONOMETRY

Notice that I have added in the 27° angle.
(63° and 27° must add together to make 90°, as the North line and the East line must be at right angles to each other.)

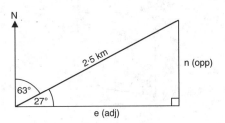

(a) DISTANCE TRAVELLED NORTH

As 'n' is opposite the angle of 27°, I can use the formula for sine, like this:

$$\text{Sin } 27° = \frac{\text{opp}}{\text{hyp}}$$

$$\text{Sin } 27° = \frac{n}{2·5}$$

$$0·454 = \frac{n}{2·5}$$ Multiply both sides by 2·5, to give:

$$n = 1·135$$

So, the distance travelled north is 1·1km, to one decimal place.

(b) DISTANCE TRAVELLED EAST

As 'e' is adjacent to the angle of 27°, I can use the formula for cosine, like this:

$$Cos\ 27° = \frac{adj}{hyp}$$

$$Cos\ 27° = \frac{e}{2 \cdot 5}$$

$$0 \cdot 891 = \frac{e}{2 \cdot 5} \qquad \text{Multiply both sides by } 2 \cdot 5, \text{ to give:}$$

$$e = 2 \cdot 2275$$

So, the distance travelled east is $2 \cdot 2$ km, to one decimal place.

QUESTIONS 3.22

Use either a scale drawing method or trigonometry to answer questions 1 to 3:

1. A ship sails from a harbour on a bearing of 127°, for a distance of $3 \cdot 2$ km.

How far (a) south and (b) east has it gone?

2. A ship sails from a harbour on a bearing of 221°, for a distance of $4 \cdot 1$ km.

How far (a) south and (b) west has it gone?

3. A ship sails from a harbour on a bearing of 309°, for a distance of $3 \cdot 8$ km.

How far (a) north and (b) west has it gone?

4. A small boat goes on a fishing trip. It leaves the harbour and sails for $2 \cdot 7$ km on a bearing of 058°. The crew aren't catching any fish, so they change course and sail for $1 \cdot 2$ km on a bearing of 174°. Use an accurate scale drawing to find (a) the distance that they must travel and (b) the bearing that they must sail, to return to the harbour directly. Could you have used trigonometry to answer this question?

▲ *POSITION AND MOVEMENT* ▼

CO-ORDINATES

Co-ordinates are numbers which are used to describe the position of points on a grid, like this:

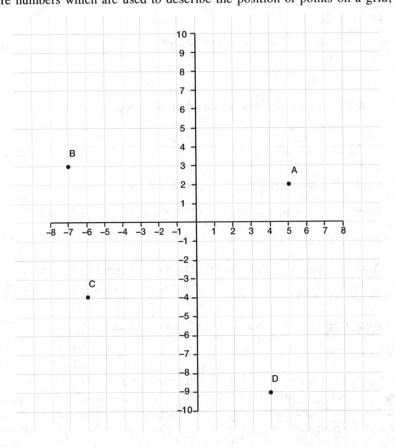

The grid is formed by the x-axis going horizontally and the y-axis going vertically. These axes cross at right-angles to each other at the **origin**. The co-ordinates of the origin are (0, 0).

To get to point A, start at the origin, and go 5 along to the right and 2 up.

To get to point B, start at the origin, and go 7 along to the left and 3 up.

To get to point C, start at the origin, and go 6 along to the left and 4 down.

To get to point D, start at the origin, and go 4 along to the right and 9 down.

When using co-ordinates, the first number in the bracket always tells you the horizontal position and the second number always tells you the vertical position.

So, the co-ordinates of A are (5, 2)

The co-ordinates of B are (−7, 3)

The co-ordinates of C are (−6, −4)

The co-ordinates of B are (4, −9)

Use positive and negative signs to indicate the directions, like this:

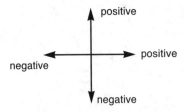

SHAPE AND SPACE

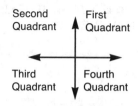

Second Quadrant | First Quadrant

Third Quadrant | Fourth Quadrant

The co-ordinate grid is split into for quadrants by the axes:

A is said to be in the first quadrant.
B is said to be in the second quadrant.
C is said to be in the third quadrant.
D is said to be in the fourth quadrant.

QUESTIONS 3.23

1. Write down the co-ordinates of these points:

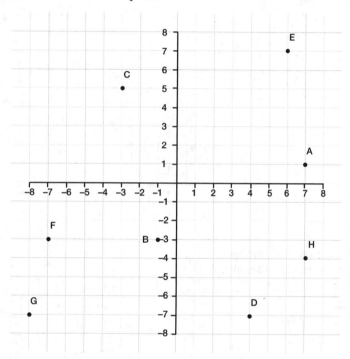

P is the mid-point of AB
Q is the mid-point of CD

R is the mid-point of EF
S is the mid-point of GH

Write down the co-ordinates of P, Q, R and S.

2. The points L(2, 6), M(7, 3) and N(10, 8) are three vertices (corners) of a square. What are the co-ordinates of the other vertex?

3. Plot the points W(5, 4), X(4, −1), Y(−2, −2) and Z(−1, 3).

Join W to X, X to Y, Y to Z and Z to W.

What is the name of the shape you have drawn?

4. ABCD is a square. A is the point (1, 5) and C is the point (−1, −3). What are the co-ordinates of the points B and D?

5. PQRS is a parallelogram. P is (4, 7), Q is (5, −2) and R is (−1, −4). What are the co-ordinates of S?

6. The centre of a square is (−1, −2). One vertex is (4, −5). What are the co-ordinates of the other vertices?

7. Plot these points: A(−1, 3), B(6, 1), C(3, 3) and D(−4, −1).

(a) What is the name of this shape?

(b) Find the area of the shape ABCD.

[Hint: Draw a rectangle with vertices given by: W(6, 3), X(6, −3), Y(−4, −3) and Z(−4, 3). Find the area of the triangles ABW etc and subtract from the area of the rectangle WXYZ.]

8. Plot these points: A(3, 4), B(10, −2), C(3, −8) and D(−4, −2).
(a) What is the name of this shape?
(b) Find the area of the shape ABCD.

TRANSLATIONS

Plot the points A(3, 6), B(6, 5), C(3, 4) and D(3, 1) to form the flag F shown in the diagram:

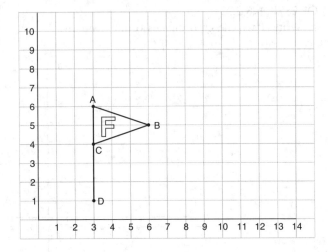

Now trace the flag and move the tracing paper, so the diagram now looks like this, labelling the new flag F' (called F dashed):

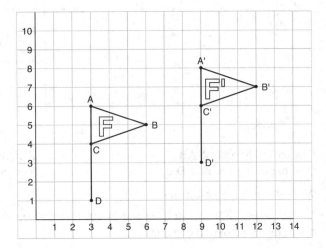

The flag F is called the **object** and the flag F' is called the **image**.

Notice that the point A on the object has been labelled A' on the image, the point B on the object has been labelled B' on the image and so on.

To go from A to A', you need to move 6 units along and 2 units up.
To go from B to B', you need to move 6 units along and 2 units up.
To go from C to C', you need to move 6 units along and 2 units up.
To go from D to D', you need to move 6 units along and 2 units up.

So, every point on F (including all the points that we haven't even labelled with a specific letter) has moved 6 units along and 2 up. This type of movement is called a **translation**.

A translation can be written neatly as a **column vector**, like this: $\begin{pmatrix} 6 \\ 2 \end{pmatrix}$

Column Vector	Description of the Movement
$\begin{pmatrix} 6 \\ -2 \end{pmatrix}$	This moves the object 6 unit to the **right** and 2 units **down.**
$\begin{pmatrix} -6 \\ 2 \end{pmatrix}$	This moves the object 6 unit to the **left** and 2 units **up.**
$\begin{pmatrix} -6 \\ -2 \end{pmatrix}$	This moves the object 6 unit to the **left** and 2 units **down**.

Use positive and negative signs to indicate the direction, just as we did when using co-ordinates, like this:

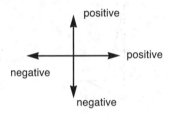

A translation is a type of **transformation**, as it transforms (or changes) F into F'. Other types of transformations are reflection, rotations and enlargements, which we will also cover in this section.

You can represent a translation by an arrow, like this:

$\begin{pmatrix} 5 \\ -2 \end{pmatrix}$

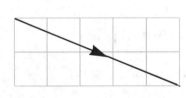

$\begin{pmatrix} -7 \\ 3 \end{pmatrix}$

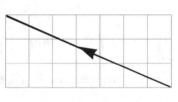

$\begin{pmatrix} -8 \\ -5 \end{pmatrix}$

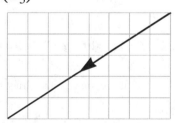

QUESTIONS 3.24

1. Write down the column vectors which describe the following translations:

(a)

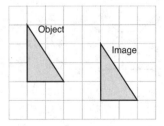

(b)

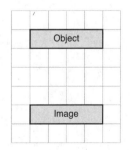

(c)

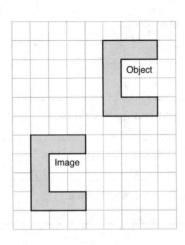

(d)

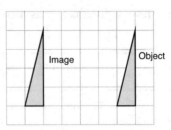

(e)

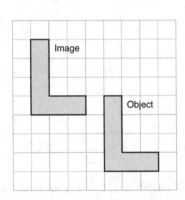

(f)

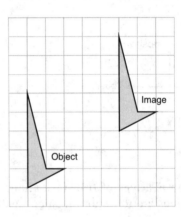

2. Draw arrows which represent these translations:

(a) $\begin{pmatrix} 3 \\ 5 \end{pmatrix}$ (b) $\begin{pmatrix} 0 \\ 4 \end{pmatrix}$ (c) $\begin{pmatrix} 6 \\ 0 \end{pmatrix}$ (d) $\begin{pmatrix} -5 \\ 0 \end{pmatrix}$ (e) $\begin{pmatrix} -2 \\ 7 \end{pmatrix}$ (f) $\begin{pmatrix} -6 \\ 4 \end{pmatrix}$

(g) $\begin{pmatrix} -4 \\ -5 \end{pmatrix}$ (h) $\begin{pmatrix} -3 \\ 0 \end{pmatrix}$ (i) $\begin{pmatrix} 0 \\ -7 \end{pmatrix}$ (j) $\begin{pmatrix} 3 \\ 7 \end{pmatrix}$ (k) $\begin{pmatrix} -8 \\ 2 \end{pmatrix}$ (l) $\begin{pmatrix} 4 \\ -4 \end{pmatrix}$

3. Copy these shapes and draw the image when translated by the given vector:

(a)

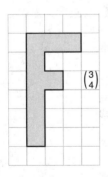

$\begin{pmatrix} 3 \\ 4 \end{pmatrix}$

(b)

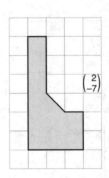

$\begin{pmatrix} 2 \\ -7 \end{pmatrix}$

(c)

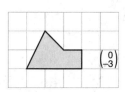

$\begin{pmatrix} -5 \\ 3 \end{pmatrix}$

(d)

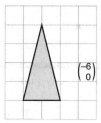

$\begin{pmatrix} -6 \\ 0 \end{pmatrix}$

(e)

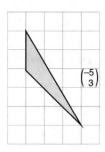

$\begin{pmatrix} 0 \\ -3 \end{pmatrix}$

(f)

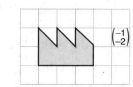

$\begin{pmatrix} -1 \\ -2 \end{pmatrix}$

4. A translation has column vector $\begin{pmatrix} 3 \\ -4 \end{pmatrix}$

A is the point (2, 5). Write down the co-ordinates of A′, the point A after it has been translated by this column vector. Do the same for the points B(1, −7), C(−6, 8) and D(−3, −7).

5. The point (5, 2) is translated onto the point (7, 5), then onto the point (2, −6).
(a) What are the column vectors for these two translations?
(b) What is the column vector which will translate (5, 2) onto (2, −6) in one move?
(c) How are your answers to (a) and (b) related?

6. Plot the points A(3, 4), B(−2, 7), C(2, 8), D(5, 3), E(−3, −6) and F(4, 5).

(a) Write down the column vectors which will take you to from (i) A to B (ii) B to C (iii) C to D (iv) D to E (v) E to F.
(b) Now write down the column vector which will take you from A to F in one move.
(c) What is the connection between your answers to (a) and (b)?

REFLECTIONS

The point A′ is the reflection of the point A in the mirror line M (or the line of reflection M).

If you join A to A′, then the line AA′ must be at right angles to the line M, like this:

Also, the distance A to X, must equal the distance A′ to X. Notice that this is shown on the diagram by the two lines drawn through AX and also through AX′.

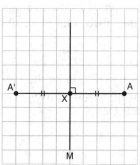

EXAMPLE 2

Plot the reflection of the point B in the mirror line M.

CAUTION!

Once the mirror line is no longer placed vertically on the page, many pupils do not plot B′ correctly!

METHOD

Draw a line at right angles to the mirror line.

Now measure the distance BX, and draw in XB′, so that these two lengths are the same, like this:

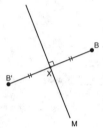

Remember that:

• BB′ must be at right angles to the mirror line.

• The length BX = The length XB′

EXAMPLE 3

Plot the reflection of this flag in the mirror line M.

CAUTION!

Once again, this is a question which many pupils will complete incorrectly, because the mirror line goes through the flag itself.

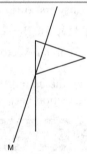

METHOD

Use the same method as before. Label the key points of the flag A, B, C and D, like this:

Draw a line from A at right angles to the mirror line.

Now measure the distance A to the mirror line and draw in A′ so that the two lengths 'A to the mirror line' and 'A′ to the mirror line' are the same. Do exactly the same for the other points and your image of the flag, after reflection in the mirror line M should look like this:

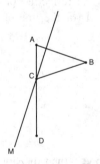

Notice that the point C is on the mirror line M, so the reflection of C will be the same point. Any point actually on the mirror line doesn't move when reflected.

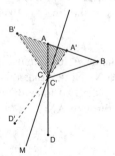

SHAPE AND SPACE

QUESTIONS 3·25

1. Reflect these flags in the given mirror lines:

(a)

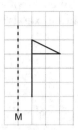

(b)

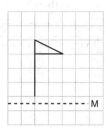

(c)

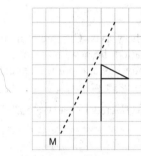

(d)

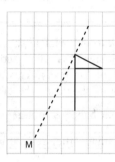

(e)

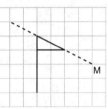

(f)

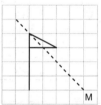

2. Reflect these letters in the given mirror lines:

(a)

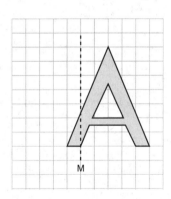

(b)

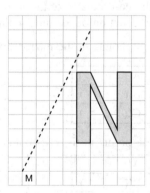

3(a) Plot these points A(4, 7), B(6, 6), C(4, 5) and D(4, 1) to form the flag F. Reflect the flag F in the y-axis, then write down the co-ordinates of the images of A, B, C and D.
(b) Repeat by reflecting flag F in the x-axis.
(c) Repeat by reflecting flag F in the line x = 3
(d) Repeat by reflecting flag F in the y = −2

4(a) Draw a co-ordinate grid for values of x between −8 and +8, and values of y between −8 and +8. Plot the points given in the table below. Join A to B, B to C etc, to make a closed shape. Reflect the shape in the x-axis, then complete the co-ordinates of the images of each point in the table. Can you say what happens to a general point (x, y) when it is reflected in the x-axis?

Object	Image after reflection in the x-axis
A(1, 1)	A'(,)
B(2, 4)	B'(,)
C(4, 2)	C'(,)
D(5, 6)	D'(,)
E(7, 2)	E'(,)
(x, y)	

(b) Now go back to the original shape ABCDE and reflect it in the y-axis. Complete the table below, giving the new image of A, B, C and so on. Notice that I have called the new image of A, A″ (which is read as 'A double dashed'). This is because my diagram already has one point labelled A', so the second image of A should not be labelled the same as the first image of A.

Can you say what happens to a general point (x, y) when it is reflected in the y-axis?

Object	Image after reflection in the y-axis
A(1, 1)	A″(,)
B(2, 4)	B″(,)
C(4, 2)	C″(,)
D(5, 6)	D″(,)
E(7, 2)	E″(,)
(x, y)	

5. A is the point (−2, 5), B(4, 8) and C(5, 3). Plot the triangle ABC. The image of two points after a reflection are (8, 4) and (5, −2).
(a) What are the co-ordinates of the third point?
(b) What is the equation of the mirror line?

6(a) Reflect these points in the mirror line y = 2

A(2, 7)	A'(,)
B(−2, −2)	B'(,)
C(0, 0)	C'(,)

(b) Reflect these points in the mirror line x = −3

A(1, 3)	A'(,)
B(−2, −2)	B'(,)
C(0, 0)	C'(,)

(c) Reflect these points in the mirror line y = −x

A(4, 1)	A'(,)
B(2, 6)	B'(,)
C (−2, 4)	C'(,)

(d) Reflect these points in the mirror line y = 2x −1

A(6, −1)	A'(,)
B(1, −5)	B'(,)
C(4, −5)	C'(,)

ROTATIONS

Use a piece of tracing paper to make a copy of the flag. Draw in the axes as well on the tracing paper.

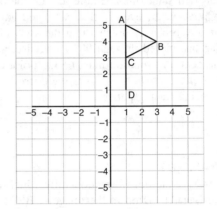

Put the tracing paper copy exactly over the original flag. Put the point of your compasses on the origin, the point (0, 0), and turn the tracing paper through 90°, turning clockwise. The axes will line up again when you have made your quarter turn. Draw in the new image. Your diagram should look like this:

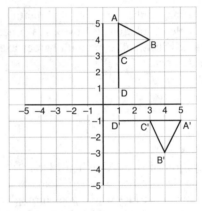

When describing a rotation, there are three pieces of information which must be given:

A ROTATION is described by:

- The Centre of Rotation
- The Angle Turned Through
- A Clockwise or Anticlockwise Turn

EXAMPLE I

Describe the transformation fully which moves the flag ABCD on to the image A′B′C′D′.

Use tracing paper, if this helps.

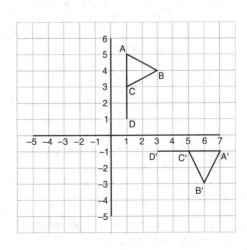

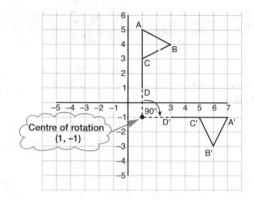

You will sometimes be able to spot the centre of rotation 'by eye'. In this case, you have already probably noticed that the stick of the flag has moved through 90° clockwise, and so the centre of rotation must be the point $(1, -1)$. You can confirm that this is the correct answer by using tracing paper.

EXAMPLE 2

Describe the transformation fully which moves the flag ABCD on to the image A'B'C'D'.

This time, neither the centre of rotation, nor the angle of rotation, is obvious. We need a method which will cope with harder examples, like this one.

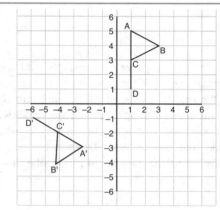

I have joined A to A'. Then I have halved the distance between A and A', and drawn the line which goes through this half-way point, which is at right angles to the line AA'. This is called the **perpendicular bisector** of the line AA'.

['Perpendicular' is another word for being at right angles. 'Bisector' refers to a line which cuts another exactly into two.]

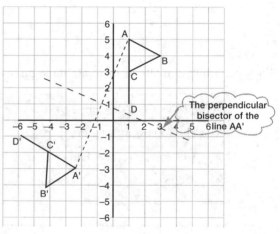

The centre of rotation must lie on the perpendicular bisector of the line AA', because every point on this line is exactly the same distance form A as it is from A'. Check some points yourself with a ruler on the diagram to confirm that this is the case:

Now I know that the centre of rotation lies somewhere on the perpendicular bisector of the line AA', but I still don't know exactly where. So now I am going to do the same thing to the two points D and D', like this:

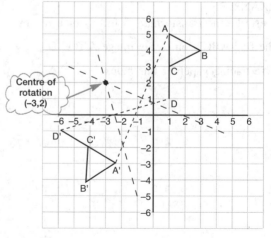

I can now see that the two perpendicular bisectors cross at the point $(-3, 2)$, so this must be the centre of rotation.

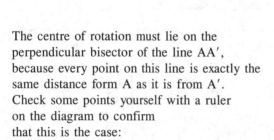

I can work out the angle of rotation now by taking one point and its image and joining these two points to the centre of rotation. I have chosen to use the point D and its image D'. I can now measure the angle through which D has moved. Use your own protractor to confirm that the angle of rotation is 120° clockwise.

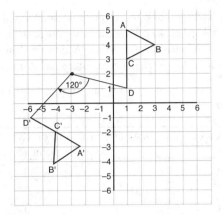

It would not have made any difference to the final answer if I had chosen a different point and its image. Try looking at the point A and its image A', to confirm that you still make the angle of rotation 120° clockwise.

QUESTIONS 3.26

1. Rotate these flags about the given centre of rotation (marked by the letter O), by the given angle:

(a)

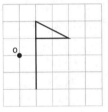

90°, clockwise

(b)

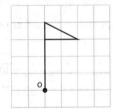

120°, clockwise

(c)

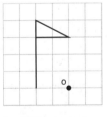

150°, clockwise

(d)

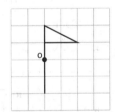

20°, anti-clockwise

2(a) Draw a co-ordinate grid for values of x between −6 and +6, and values of y between −6 and +6. Plot the points given in the table below. Join A to B, B to C etc, to make a closed shape. Rotate the shape 90° clockwise about the point (0, 0), then complete the co-ordinates of the images of each point in the table.

Can you say what happens to a general point (x, y) when it is rotated 90° clockwise about the point (0, 0)?

Object	Image after rotation of 90° clockwise about the point (0, 0)
A(2, 1)	A'(,)
B(3, 3)	B'(,)
C(4, 2)	C'(,)
D(5, 4)	D'(,)
E(5, 1)	E'(,)
(x, y)	

(b) Now go back to the original shape ABCDE and rotate it 180° about the point (0, 0). Complete the table below, giving the new image of A, B, C and so on. Notice that I have called the new image of A, A″ (which is read as 'A double dashed'). This is because my diagram already has one point labelled A′, so the second image of A must be labelled differently from the first image of A.

Can you say what happens to a general point (x, y) when it is rotated 180° clockwise about the point (0, 0)?

Object	Image after rotation of 180° clockwise about the point (0, 0)
A(2, 1)	A″(,)
B(3, 3)	B″(,)
C(4, 2)	C″(,)
D(5, 4)	D″(,)
E(5, 1)	E″(,)
(x, y)	

(c) Once again, go back to the original shape ABCDE and rotate it 270° clockwise about the point (0, 0). Complete the table below, giving the new image of A, B, C and so on. Notice that I have called the new image of A, A‴ (which is read as 'A triple dashed').

Can you say what happens to a general point (x, y) when it is rotated 270° clockwise about the point (0, 0)?

Object	Image after rotation of 270° clockwise about the point (0, 0)
A(2, 1)	A‴(,)
B(3, 3)	B‴(,)
C(4, 2)	C‴(,)
D(5, 4)	D‴(,)
E(5, 1)	E‴(,)
(x, y)	

3. A is the point (−3, 1), B(3, 4) and C(1, 8). Plot the triangle ABC. The images of two of these points after a rotation are (−4, −2) and (−1, −8).

(a) What are the co-ordinates of the third point?

(b) What is the centre of rotation?

(c) Through what angle has the triangle been rotated?

4. Describe fully the transformation which moves X onto Y for these diagrams:

(a)

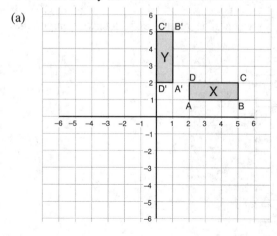

(b)

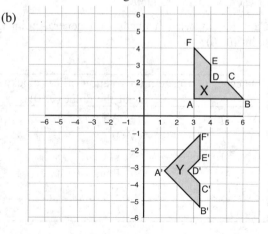

(c)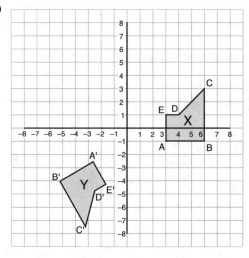

(d)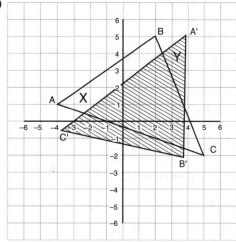

ENLARGEMENTS

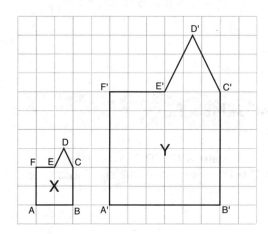

Shape Y is an enlargement of shape X, with scale factor 3.

The length of AB is 1 cm.

The length of A′B′ is 3 cm.

A′B′ = 3 × AB

In fact, each corresponding side is three times longer on the image than on the object. So I can write:

B′C′ = 3 × BC   E′F′ = 3 × EF
C′D′ = 3 × CD   F′A′ = 3 × FA
D′E′ = 3 × DE

> Length on the Image = 3 × Length on the Object

> Length on the Image = Scale Factor × Length on the Object

QUESTIONS 3.27

1. Copy these shapes onto squared paper and draw an enlargement of each shape, with the given scale factor:

(a)

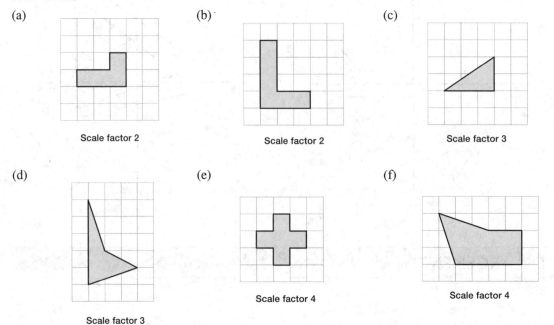

Scale factor 2

(b)

Scale factor 2

(c)

Scale factor 3

(d)

Scale factor 3

(e)

Scale factor 4

(f)

Scale factor 4

CENTRE OF ENLARGEMENT

In all of these three diagrams, the shape A′B′C′D′E′ is an enlargement of the shape ABCDE, scale factor 2, but the image A′B′C′D′E′ appears in a different place in each diagram!

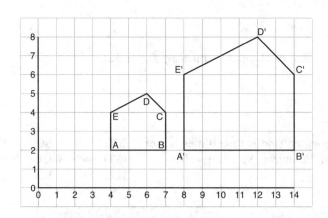

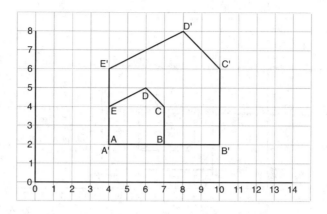

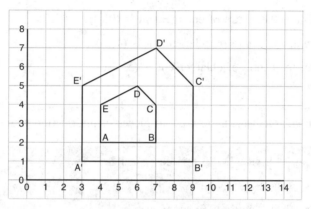

If I draw in on each diagram a line which joins A to A′, B to B′ and so on, all these lines cross at a particular point. This point is called the **centre of enlargement**.

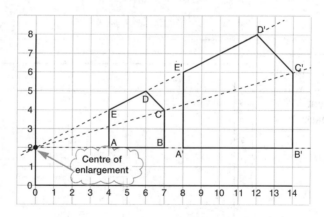

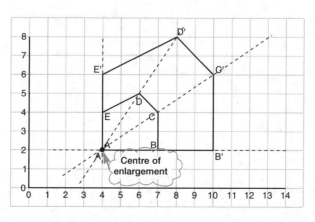

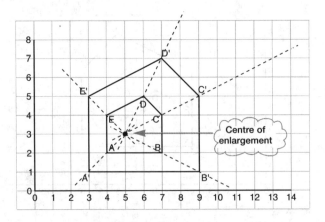

So, in the first diagram, the centre of enlargement is (0, 2).

In the second diagram, the centre of enlargement is (4, 2).

In the third diagram, the centre of enlargement is (5, 3).

When describing an enlargement, there are two pieces of information which must be given:

An ENLARGEMENT is described by:

- The Scale Factor
- The Centre of Enlargement

EXAMPLE 1

Draw an enlargement of this shape, scale factor 2, with centre of enlargement the point (2, 1), marked with the letter O.

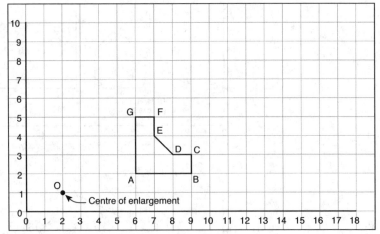

SHAPE AND SPACE

I have drawn a line from O to A and measured the length of this line. The length of OA is 2·1 cm. I have been asked to draw an enlargement scale factor 2, so I double this length, to give me the length of OA′.

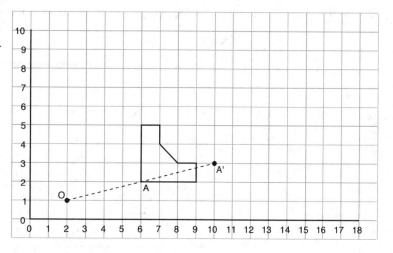

OA′ = OA × 2

OA′ = 2·1 cm × 2

OA′ = 4·2 cm

I can now continue the straight line OA, so that it now measures 4·2 cm, and mark that point as A′.

For this example, as I am working on squared paper, it is probably easier to make use of those squares! Starting at the centre of enlargement, O to A is 4 squares along and 1 square up. As I have been asked to draw an enlargement, scale factor two, I must double both of these, to give the distance O to A′ as 8 squares along and 2 squares up. If you are asked to draw an enlargement on plain paper, then you must rely on measuring with your ruler.

Now do the same for all the other points, and join them up to form the image, like this:

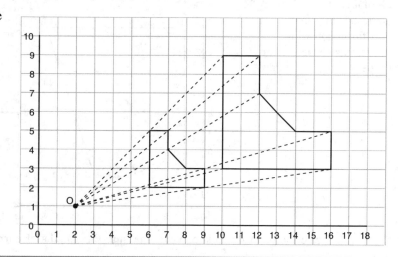

EXAMPLE 2

Draw an enlargement of this shape, scale factor 3, with centre of enlargement the point marked with the letter O. Notice that this time we are working on plain paper, and also that the centre of enlargement is inside the shape. This makes no difference – simply do as we did in Example 1.

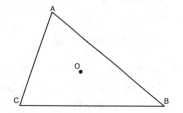

I have drawn in the line O to A and measured this distance. It is 1·8 cm.

I have been asked to draw an enlargement scale factor 3, so I multiply this length by 3, to give me the length of OA′.

OA′ = OA × 3

OA′ = 1·8 cm × 3

OA′ = 5·4 cm

I can now continue the straight line OA, so that it now measures 5·4 cm, and mark that point as A′.

Now do the same for the other points, and join them up to form the image, like this:

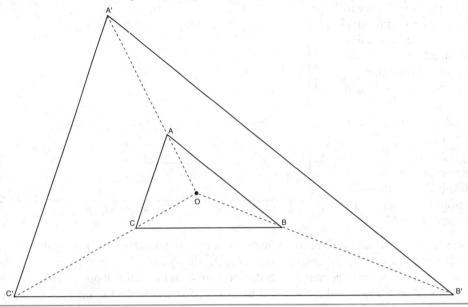

EXAMPLE 3

Describe fully the transformation which transforms shape X onto shape Y:

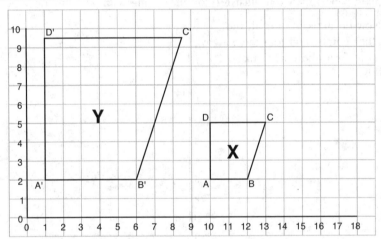

To find the scale factor of the enlargement, measure the lengths of corresponding sides, like this:

AB = 1 cm and A′B′ = 2·5 cm

So, A′B′ = 2·5 × AB

The Scale Factor must be 2·5

Check another pair of corresponding sides:

AD = 1·5 cm and A′D′ = 3·75 cm

So, A′D′ = 2·5 × AD

Again, the Scale Factor must be 2·5

Check the other two pairs of corresponding sides yourself, to check that they agree with the formulae:

> Length on the Image = 2·5 × Length on the Object

> Length on the Image = Scale Factor × Length on the Object

So, the Scale Factor = 2·5

Notice that the Scale Factor does not have to be a whole number!

To find the centre of the enlargement, join A to A', join B to B' and so on, like this:

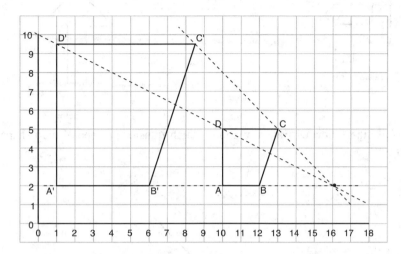

The Centre of Enlargement is where these lines cross, so the Centre of Enlargement is the point (16, 2).

So, a full description of this transformation is:

An enlargement, scale factor 2·5, centre of enlargement (16, 2).

QUESTIONS 3.28

1. Draw an enlargement of each of these shapes by the given scale factor, using the centre of enlargement marked by the letter O. Use the squared paper to help you.

(a)

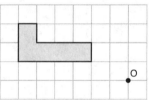

Scale factor 2

(b)

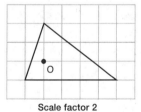

Scale factor 2

(c)

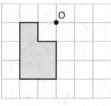

Scale factor 3

(d)

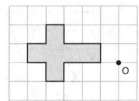

Scale factor 2·5

2. Draw an enlargement of each of these shapes by the given scale factor, using the centre of enlargement marked by the letter O. The paper is not squared this time! Use your ruler to make the measurements and work very accurately.

(a)

Scale factor 2

(b)

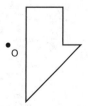

Scale factor 3

(c)

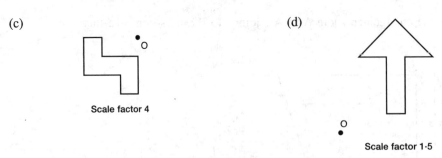

Scale factor 4

(d)

Scale factor 1·5

3. Describe fully the following transformations which transform shape X onto shape Y for each of these diagrams:

(a)

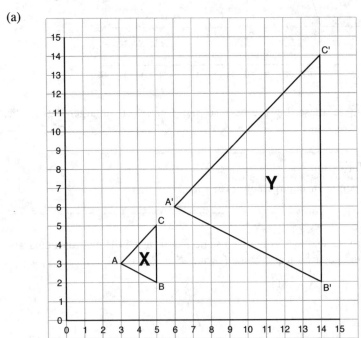

(b)

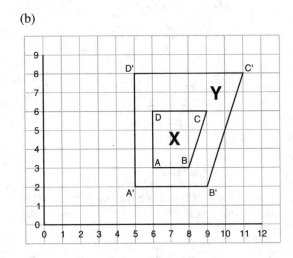

(c)

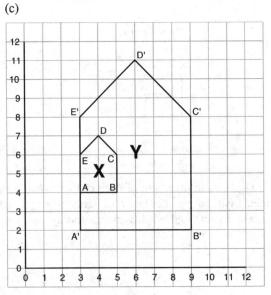

(d)

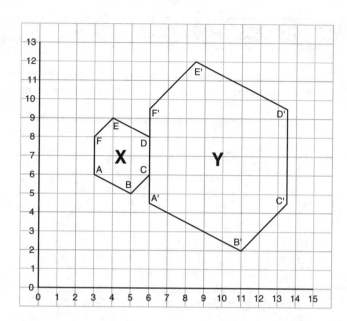

4(i) Enlarge all of the following shapes, scale factor 2, with the given centre of enlargement:

(a)

(b)

(c)

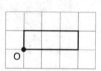

(d)

(e)

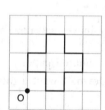

(f)

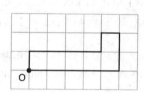

Find the area of each object and the area of each image after an enlargement scale factor 2, and put your answers into this table of results:

Shape	Area of Object	Area of Image after an enlargement, scale factor 2
(a)		
(b)		
(c)		
(d)		
(e)		
(f)		

Can you write down an equation which connects the area of the object, the area of the image and the scale factor?

(ii) Repeat the process for an enlargement of scale factor 3.

(iii) Repeat for an enlargement of scale factor 4.

SCALE FACTORS LESS THAN ONE

EXAMPLE 1

Draw an enlargement of this shape, scale factor $\frac{1}{3}$, centre of enlargement (1, 5).

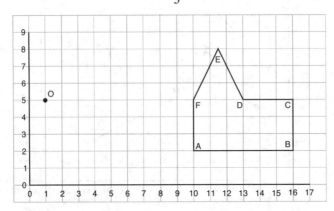

Use exactly the same method as before! Join the centre of enlargement, O, to the point A. Now use the same formula as before to find the length of OA'.

> Length on the Image = Scale Factor × Length on the Object

> Length on the Image = $\frac{1}{3}$ × Length on the Object

The length of OA is 4·3 cm.

OA' = $\frac{1}{3}$ × 4·3 cm = 1·43 cm, so the point A' can now be plotted.

Once again, it is easier to make use of the squared paper.

O to A is 9 squares along and 3 squares down. I want a third of this, so O to A' will be 3 along and 1 down.

Do the same for all the other points. For example, O to E is 10·5 squares along and 3 squares up. Take one third of this, to give O to E' as 3·5 squares along and 1 square up.

So, the image looks like this:

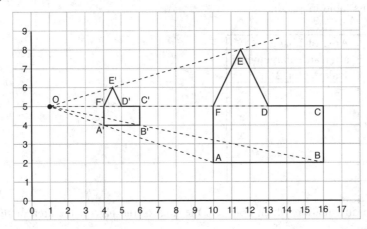

Notice that, although the image is actually *smaller* than the object, Mathematicians, (strange to say!), still refer to this as an *enlargement* scale factor $\frac{1}{3}$.

All corresponding sides on the image are one third of the length of the sides on the object.

QUESTIONS 3.29

1. Draw an enlargement of each of these shapes by the given scale factor, using the centre of enlargement marked by the letter O. Use the squared paper to help you.

(a)

O

Scale factor $\frac{1}{2}$

(b)

O

Scale factor $\frac{1}{3}$

(c)

O

Scale factor $\frac{1}{4}$

(d)

O

Scale factor $\frac{1}{5}$

2. Draw an enlargement of each of these shapes by the given scale factor, using the centre of enlargement marked by the letter O. The paper is not squared this time! Use your ruler to make the measurements and work very accurately.

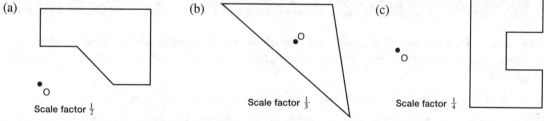

(a)

O

Scale factor $\frac{1}{2}$

(b)

O

Scale factor $\frac{1}{3}$

(c)

O

Scale factor $\frac{1}{4}$

3. Describe fully the following transformations which transform shape X onto shape Y for each of these diagrams:

(a)

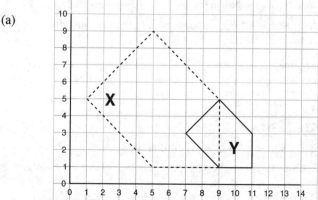

(b)

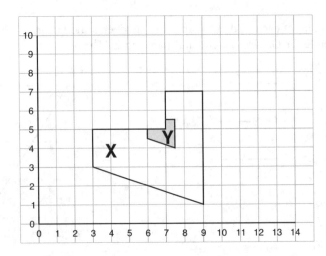

(c)

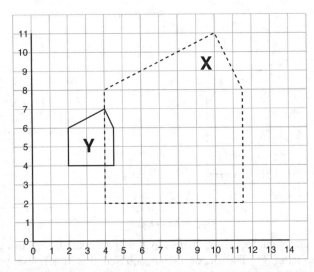

CONGRUENT SHAPES, SIMILAR SHAPES

When I used **Translations**, **Reflections** and **Rotations,** the image was always the *same shape* and the *same size* as the object. For these transformations, the image and the object are said to be **congruent**.

If you drew the image and the object onto card and cut them out, they would fit exactly over each other.

> **CONGRUENT SHAPES**
> * Same Shape (All corresponding angles are the same.)
> * Same Size (All corresponding lengths are the same.)

Now that I am using Enlargements, the image is the *same shape* as the object, but the *size is different*. [Except, of course, if I choose the scale factor to be one!] Now, the image and the object are said to be **similar**.

> **SIMILAR SHAPES**
> * Same Shape (All corresponding angles are the same.)
> * Different Size (All corresponding sides have been enlarged by the same scale factor.)

Shape X and Shape Y are similar shapes:

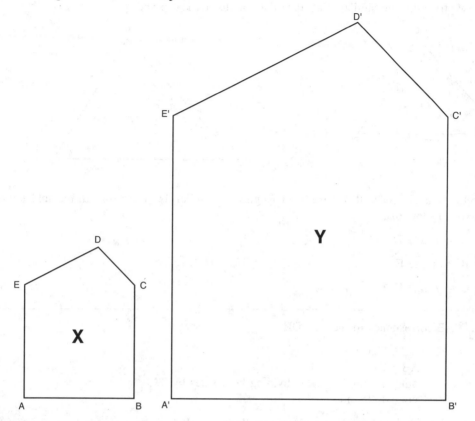

LOOKING AT THE ANGLES

Use your protractor to check that:

Angle A = Angle A′
Angle B = Angle B′
Angle C = Angle C′
Angle D = Angle D′
Angle E = Angle E′

LOOKING AT THE LENGTHS

Shape X : Shape Y

   AB : A′B′
3 cm : 7·5 cm   ......dividing both sides by 3 .....
1 cm : 2·5 cm

So, every 1 cm on the object X is 2·5 cm on the image Y.

> Length on the Image = Scale Factor × Length on the Object

> Length on the Image = 2·5 × Length on the Object

Check that:

$B′C′ = 2·5 × BC$ $D′E′ = 2·5 × DE$

$C′D′ = 2·5 × CD$ $E′A′ = 2·5 × EA$

So, Shape Y is an enlargement of Shape X, with scale factor 2·5.

So, Shape X and Shape Y are indeed similar.

EXAMPLE I

These two triangles are similar. Calculate the lengths marked p and q.

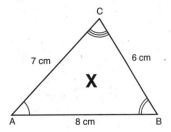
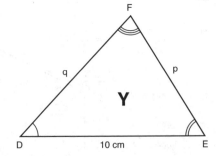

Notice that you can check that these two triangles *are* similar, by measuring all the angles. Use your protractor to show that:

Angle A = Angle D

Angle B = Angle E

Angle C = Angle F

The side AB corresponds to the side DE

$$\text{Shape X : Shape Y}$$
$$\text{AB : DE}$$
$$\text{8 cm : 10 cm} \quad \text{......dividing both sides by 8 ....}$$
$$\text{1 cm : 1·25 cm}$$

So every 1 cm on the Shape X is 1·25 cm on the Shape Y

Shape Y is an enlargement of Shape X, with scale factor 1·25.

To calculate the length of side p:

The side marked p corresponds to the side length 6 cm.

> Length on the Image = Scale Factor × Length on the Object

> Length on the Image = 1·25 × Length on the Object

Substitute into this formula, like this:

EF = 1·25 × BC
p = 1·25 × 6 cm
p = 7·5 cm

So, the length of side p is 7·5 cm.

To calculate the length of side q:

The side marked q corresponds to the side length 7 cm.

> Length on the Image = Scale Factor × Length on the Object

> Length on the Image = 1·25 × Length on the Object

Substitute into this formula, like this:

DF = 1·25 × AC
q = 1·25 × 7 cm
q = 8·75 cm

So, the length of side q is 8·75 cm.

EXAMPLE 2

These two triangles are similar. Calculate the lengths marked r and s.

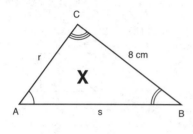
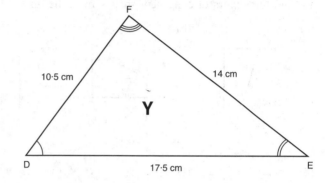

The side BC corresponds to the side EF

Shape X : Shape Y

   BC : EF
  8 cm : 14 cm   ......dividing both sides by 8 .....
  1 cm : 1·75 cm

So, every 1 cm on the Shape X is 1·75 cm on the Shape Y

Shape Y is an enlargement of shape X, with scale factor 1·75.

To calculate the length of side r:

The side marked r corresponds to the side length 10·5 cm.

> Length on the Image = Scale Factor × Length on the Object

> Length on the Image = 1·75 × Length on the Object

Substitute into this formula, like this:

DF = 1·75 × AC
10·5 cm = 1·75 × r   [Make sure you substitute in the correct way round!]
r = 10·5 cm ÷ 1·75
r = 6 cm

So, the length of side r is 6 cm.

To calculate the length of side s:

The side marked s corresponds to the side length 17·5 cm.

> Length on the Image = Scale Factor × Length on the Object

> Length on the Image = 1·75 × Length on the Object

Substitute into this formula, like this:

DE = 1·75 × AB
17·5 cm = 1·75 × s   [Make sure you substitute in the correct way round!]
s = 17·5 cm ÷ 1·75
s = 10 cm

So, the length of side s is 10 cm.

QUESTIONS 3.30

1. Find three pairs of congruent shapes from the ones drawn below:

(a) 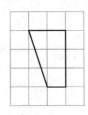   (b) 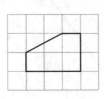   (c) 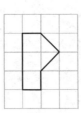   (d)

(e) 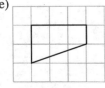   (f) 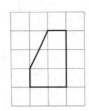   (g) 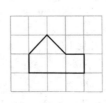   (h)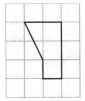

2. Find three pairs of similar shapes from the ones drawn below:

(a)   (b) 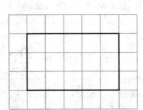   (c)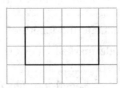

(d) 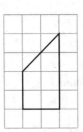   (e) 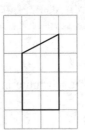   (f)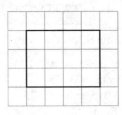

(g) 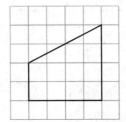   (h) 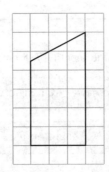   (i)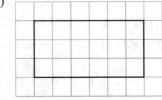

3. These pairs of triangles are similar. Find the length of the marked sides.

(a)

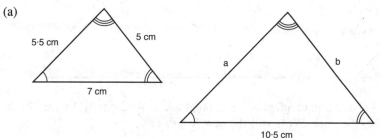

(b)

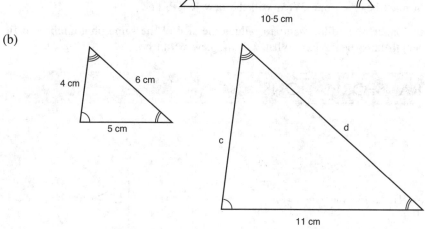

(c)

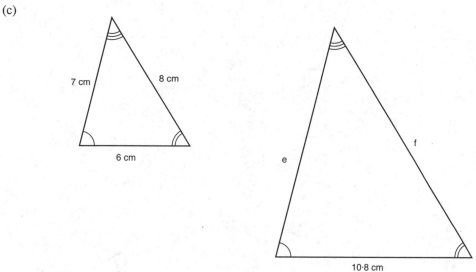

4. These pairs of triangles are similar. Find the length of the marked sides.

(a)

(b)

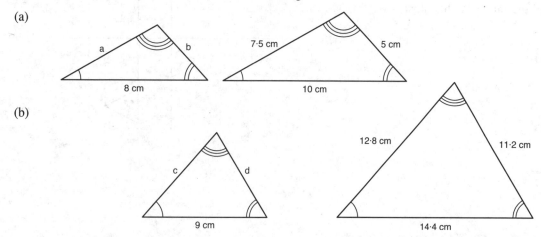

(c)

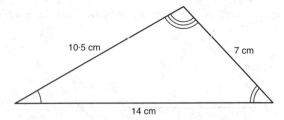

5. A newspaper editor wants to enlarge a photograph. The photograph is 10·2 cm by 15 cm. To fit the space, the new width must be 15·3 cm. What will the new length be?

6. In a later edition of the paper, the editor wants to reduce the size of the same photograph. To fit the space this time the length must be 12 cm. What will the new width be?

COMBINING TRANSFORMATIONS

Plot the points (2, 5), (4, 4), (2, 3) and (2, 1) to make the flag L:

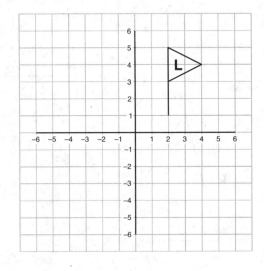

Reflect the flag L in the x-axis, and label the image M, like this:

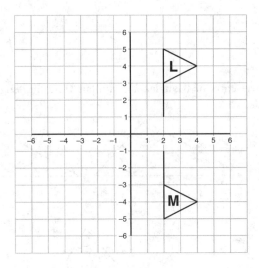

Now, reflect the *flag M* in the y-axis, and label the image N, like this:

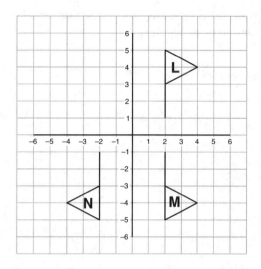

What *single* transformation will move the flag L onto the flag N?

Use tracing paper to confirm that flag L moves onto the flag N with a 180° rotation about the point (0, 0).

So, a reflection in the x-axis, followed by a reflection in the y-axis has the same effect as a 180° rotation about the point (0, 0).

EXAMPLE 2

Plot the points (4, 5), (6, 4), (4, 3) and (4, 1) to make the flag P:

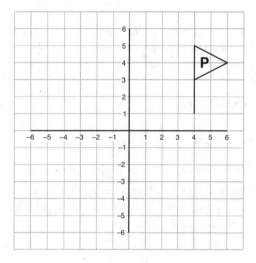

Reflect the flag P in the line x = 3, and label the image Q, like this:

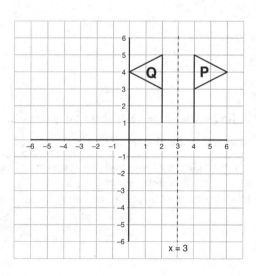

Now, reflect the *flag Q* in the y-axis, and label the image R, like this:

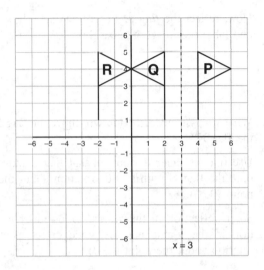

What *single* transformation will move the flag P onto the flag R?

You can see that you can move flag P onto flag R with a translation of $\begin{pmatrix} -6 \\ 0 \end{pmatrix}$

So, a reflection in the line x = 3, followed by a reflection in the y-axis has the same effect as a translation of $\begin{pmatrix} -6 \\ 0 \end{pmatrix}$

QUESTIONS 3.31

1. Reflect the shape in the x-axis.

Now reflect the image in the line y = x.

What single transformation has the same effect as a reflection in the x-axis, followed by a reflection in the line y = x?

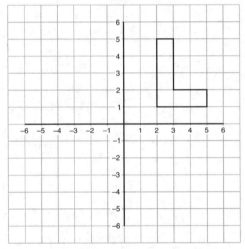

2. Rotate the shape 180° about the point (0, 0).

Now reflect the image in the y-axis.

What single transformation has the same effect as a rotation of 180° about the point (0, 0), followed by a reflection in the y-axis?

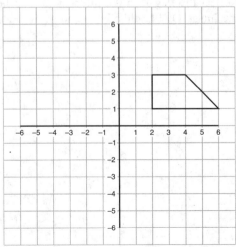

3. Rotate the shape 180° about the point (0, 0).

Now rotate the image 180° about the point (1, −2).

What single transformation has the same effect as a rotation of 180° about the point (0, 0), followed by a rotation of 180° about the point (1, −2)?

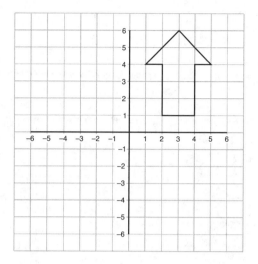

4. Reflect the shape in the line y = 1.

Now reflect the image in the x-axis.

What single transformation has the same effect as a reflection in the line y = 1, followed by a reflection in the x-axis.

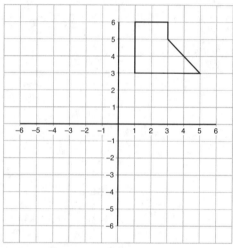

5.
X = a reflection in the x-axis
Y = a reflection in the x-axis
Q = a quarter turn anti-clockwise about (0, 0)
H = a half turn about (0, 0)
T = a three-quarter turn anti-clockwise about (0, 0)
M = a reflection in the line y = x
N = a reflection in the line y = −x

Choose a shape of your own to find the single transformation which has the same effect as:

(a) X followed by N
(b) N followed by X
(c) H followed by X
(d) X followed by H
(e) Q followed by X
(f) X followed by Q
(g) T followed by M
(h) M followed by T

STATISTICS

MEAN, MEDIAN & MODE

The Mean, Median and Mode are all types of **average.**

The Headteacher, who does not realise that there are three types of average, has asked me to find out the average amount of spending money that Year 7 pupils have each week. I have assumed that he wants the Mean!

These are the replies from the first twelve pupils that I've asked:

Brian	£10·00
Angela	£3·00
Jill	£2·50
Jean	£3·00
Raj	£8·00
Susan	£3·00
William	£0·00
David	£5·00
Anastasia	£4·50
Galya	£5·00
Fred	£6·00
Claire	£3·25
	£53·25

Now divide £53·25 by 12

Brian	£10·00
Angela	£3·00
Jill	£2·50
Jean	£3·00
Raj	£8·00
Susan	£3·00
William	nothing at all
David	£5·00
Anastasia	£4·50
Galya	£5·00
Fred	£6·00
Claire	£3·25

To find the Mean amount of spending money, add up all the amounts of money and then divide by the number of pupils that I've asked.

Notice that we must divide by 12, even though we only have 11 amounts of money. We have actually asked 12 people.

The answer on my calculator is 4·4375. This isn't a good way to leave an answer for an amount of money, so I am going to round it up to the nearest whole penny, making it £4·44

This is the **Mean**. So, the mean amount of spending money is £4·44

> To find the MEAN, add up all your data and divide by the number of pieces of data that you have collected.

This answer is based on the data gathered from a very small **sample** of pupils. If I asked more pupils I would almost certainly get a different answer. You could experiment for yourself to see what happens if you ask another 12 pupils and then calculate the mean for all 24 pupils together. What do you think the new answer would be? What do you think would happen if you increased the size of your sample to 50? Or to 100? How do people doing market research decide on how many people they will include in their sample?

HEIGHTS

What if the Headteacher had asked me to find out the average height of pupils in Year 7?

I have asked 11 of my class to stand at the front of the classroom in a line. Here they are:

First of all I am going to ask them to stand in order of size:

Then a I asked the tallest and the shortest, Melissa and Charlotte, to sit on the floor. The line now looks like this:

Then I asked Stanley and Simon to sit on the floor. The line of people now looks like this:

I continue this process until everyone except one person is sitting down.

So I now measure Zoe's height. She is 155 cm tall.

So the **MEDIAN** height is 155 cm.

Note the spelling!

> To find the MEDIAN for an odd number of pieces of data:
>
> 1. Put the data in order of size.
>
> 2. Take the middle piece of data.

Supposing that I had originally asked 12 people to come to the front of the class. I've asked Graham to join the others at the front of the classroom and the new line up now looks like this:

Charlotte Stanley Roy Graham Gary Ferdinand Zoe Tessa Devon Rita Simon Melissa

Then I repeat the same process as before, asking the tallest and the shortest, still Melissa and Charlotte, to sit on the floor.

I carry this process on until there are now **TWO** people standing, like this:

Charlotte Stanley Roy Graham Gary Ferdinand Zoe Tessa Devon Rita Simon Melissa

I now measure Ferdinand's height and Zoe's height.

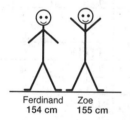

Ferdinand Zoe
154 cm   155 cm

To find the Median, now that I have an even number of people, I must go half way between Ferdinand's height and Zoe's height.

Ferdinand's height is 154 cm
Zoe's height is 155 cm

Add them together: $154 + 155 = 309$
Now divide 309 cm by 2: $309 \div 2 = 154 \cdot 5$ cm

So, the new MEDIAN, for an even number of pupils is 154·5 cm.

> To find the MEDIAN for an even number of pieces of data:
>
> 1. Put the data in order of size.
>
> 2. Take the middle two pieces of data.
>
> 3. Go half-way between the middle two pieces of data by adding together and dividing by two.

SHOE SIZES

What if the Headteacher asked me to find out the average shoe size for Year 7 pupils?

I have asked all 28 pupils in my group what their shoe size is and these are their replies:

So, what shall I tell the Headteacher? What is the average shoe size?

SIZE	TALLY	TOTAL
3	I	1
$3\frac{1}{2}$	I	1
4	II	2
$4\frac{1}{2}$	IIII	4
5	JHTT	5
$5\frac{1}{2}$	I	1
6	JHTT	5
$6\frac{1}{2}$	JHTT II	7
7	I	1
$7\frac{1}{2}$		0
8	I	1

More pupils take size $6\frac{1}{2}$ than any other size

The natural answer seems to be to say that the average shoe size is $6\frac{1}{2}$ as there are more pupils with this shoe size than any other. This is called the **MODE**. So the Mode is size $6\frac{1}{2}$.

> To find the MODE, look for the most frequently occurring piece of data.

However, if you ran a shoe shop, you would actually need to consider girls and boys shoe sizes separately, as not all styles are worn by both sexes!

These are the class shoe sizes looked at separately:

The Mode for boys is still size $6\frac{1}{2}$.

BOYS			GIRLS		
SIZE	TALLY	TOTAL	SIZE	TALLY	TOTAL
3		0	3	I	1
$3\frac{1}{2}$		0	$3\frac{1}{2}$	I	1
4	II	2	4		0
$4\frac{1}{2}$		0	$4\frac{1}{2}$	IIII	4
5	I	1	5	IIII	4
$5\frac{1}{2}$		0	$5\frac{1}{2}$	I	1
6	III	3	6	II	2
$6\frac{1}{2}$	JHTT I	6	$6\frac{1}{2}$	I	1
7	I	1	7		0
$7\frac{1}{2}$		0	$7\frac{1}{2}$		0
8	I	1	8		0

But when we look at the girls, we see that two sizes (size $4\frac{1}{2}$ and size 5) are both equally popular.

In this situation we would give both answers. So, the Mode for the girls is size $4\frac{1}{2}$ **AND** size 5. This set of results is referred to as being **bi-modal**, as there are two modes.

If you really did run a shoe shop, you would be interested in a much larger sample than one class of 28 pupils, before you decided which sizes in which styles to stock in your shop! However, the principle is the same!

DIFFERENT TYPES OF AVERAGE

We have now looked at three different situations and used three different types of average!

Why did I choose the mean for spending money? Could I also have chosen the mode and the median?

Why did I choose the median for height? Why not the mean or the mode?

Why did I choose the mode for shoe sizes? Why not the mean or the median?

If we consider all three situations and all three types of average, there are nine possibilities altogether.

	Spending Money	Height	Shoe Size
Mean	£4·44		
Median		154·5 cm	
Mode			$6\frac{1}{2}$

Try to find the other entries in the table. See if you can work out the entries before you read the next few pages.

SPENDING MONEY: THE MEDIAN

1. Put them all in order.

0·00
2·50
3·00
3·00
3·00
3·25
4·50
5·00
5·00
6·00
8·00
10·00

2. We asked an even number of people, so look at the middle two, which in this case is £3·25 and £4·50

3. Go half-way between. We can do this by adding them together and dividing by two:

£3·25 + £4·50 = £7·75

£7·75 ÷ 2 = £3·875

So, we would probably round the answer up to £3·88

So, the MEDIAN SPENDING MONEY is £3·88

SPENDING MONEY: THE MODE

More pupils have £3·00 a week spending money than any other amount, so the MODE is £3·00

HEIGHT: THE MEAN

This entails more work than finding the median, where I had to measure the height of either one or two pupils. Now I will have to measure the height of all those pupils who stood in the line. I'll include Graham in my sample.

These are their heights:

1872·5 ÷ 12 = 156·04166…. on my calculator

The MEAN HEIGHT is 156 cm, to the nearest centimetre.

Charlotte	147 cm
Stanley	148·5 cm
Roy	150 cm
Graham	152 cm
Gary	154 cm
Ferdinand	154 cm
Zoe	155 cm
Tessa	157·5 cm
Devon	158·5 cm
Rita	160 cm
Simon	167·5 cm
Melissa	168·5 cm
Total	1872·5 cm

STATISTICS

HEIGHT: THE MODE

Only two people in my sample were measured as being the same height. So, looking at my list of measurements, the mode is 154 cm.

Do you think that Gary and Ferdinand would be **exactly** the same height in reality? I have, in fact, chosen to measure their heights to the nearest half a centimetre. Height is said to be a **continuous variable** because it can take any value, depending on how accurately you measure! But, realistically, when measuring someone's height, I think that the most accurate that I can aim to be, is to measure to the nearest half a centimetre. Do you think if I measured someone's height today and again tomorrow, that I would get the same answer? It might depend on how straight they were standing or whether they were 'stretching'!

In contrast, the number of cats that you have, the number of books, the number of bicycles your family members own, are all said to be **discrete variables** because you don't (usually!) have $3 \cdot 75$ cats, for example. Discrete variables can take certain values only, such as whole numbers.

When the Headteacher asked me to find the average height for Year 7 pupils, I deliberately chose to use the Median. I knew that, unlike using the Mean or the Mode, I would have to measure **either** one **or** two pupils only. Also, Gary and Ferdinand probably **aren't** exactly the same height. This suggests that the mode may not be a very useful average for height.

SHOE SIZE: THE MEAN

Remember that I asked 28 pupils their shoe size. If I write the data out long hand the list will look like this:

$3, 3\frac{1}{2}, 4, 4, 4\frac{1}{2}, 4\frac{1}{2}, 4\frac{1}{2}, 4\frac{1}{2}, 5, 5, 5, 5, 5, 5\frac{1}{2}, 6, 6, 6, 6, 6, 6\frac{1}{2}, 6\frac{1}{2}, 6\frac{1}{2}, 6\frac{1}{2}, 6\frac{1}{2}, 6\frac{1}{2}, 6\frac{1}{2}, 7, 8$

Adding all these numbers gives a total of $153 \cdot 5$

Take this total and divide by 28, which is the number of people that I asked. Use your calculator:

$153 \cdot 5 \div 28 = 5 \cdot 48$

So, the MEAN SHOE SIZE is $5 \cdot 48$

SHOE SIZE: THE MEDIAN

1. Put the list of shoe sizes in order:

$3, 3\frac{1}{2}, 4, 4, 4\frac{1}{2}, 4\frac{1}{2}, 4\frac{1}{2}, 4\frac{1}{2}, 5, 5, 5, 5, 5, \underline{5\frac{1}{2}, 6}, 6, 6, 6, 6, 6\frac{1}{2}, 6\frac{1}{2}, 6\frac{1}{2}, 6\frac{1}{2}, 6\frac{1}{2}, 6\frac{1}{2}, 6\frac{1}{2}, 7, 8$

2. Look at the middle two shoe sizes in the list as I asked an even number of people.

The middle two sizes are $5\frac{1}{2}$ and 6

3. Go half way between $5\frac{1}{2}$ and 6, which is $5 \cdot 75$

So, the MEDIAN SHOE size is $5 \cdot 75$

Both the mean shoe size and the median shoe size give us answers which are not actual shoe sizes. Would it help a shoe shop owner to know that the "average" shoe size is $5 \cdot 48$ or $5 \cdot 75$? In this case, it wouldn't help at all, as you cannot buy shoes size $5 \cdot 75$, so the mode does seem to be the most useful average for shoes sizes. However, the mean and the mode are still mathematically correct answers. All three answers are correct answers, even though they are all different!

We have now managed to calculate all nine possibilities, as follows:

For each of our three situations, we have got three different answers! In each situation, all these answers are mathematically correct, although there are definite advantages and disadvantages in choosing one average rather than another.

	Spending Money	Height	Shoe Size
Mean	£4·44	156 cm	5·48
Median	£3·88	154·5 cm	5·75
Mode	£3·00	154 cm	$6\frac{1}{2}$

Next time someone tells you "the average" for something, it would be a good idea to ask them which average they have used and why they chose to use that one rather than another.

A year 7 pupil who wanted more spending money could use the argument that: "I have only £3·00 spending money per week. As the (mean) average is £4·44 I should therefore have an increase". A knowledgeable parent might reply that the (modal) average **is** £3·00, so that no increase is justified!!

This situation may seem trivial, but apply the same reasoning to firms, employees and employers and you begin to see how important it is to treat Statistics with respect and some scepticism!

EXAMPLE 2

The Head of Biology has given her class of 30 pupils a test, which she has marked out of 20. These are their results:

Mark	12	13	14	15	16	17	18	19	20
Number of Pupils	1	2	5	2	6	8	3	2	1

Find (a) the Mean (b) the Median (c) the Mode.

CAUTION! When the data is presented in this way, many, many pupils do not end up with correct answers! There seems to be a temptation, when finding the mean for example, to divide by '9', possibly because there are 9 columns with numbers in them.

Remember that, to find the mean, we need to add up the scores of the 30 pupils, then divide by 30. It may be useful to write the table out like this, so that you remember that the table is giving you **30** pieces of information:

Mark	List of the Marks Obtained
12	12
13	13, 13
14	14, 14, 14, 14, 14
15	15, 15
16	16, 16, 16, 16, 16, 16
17	17, 17, 17, 17, 17, 17, 17, 7
18	18, 18, 18
19	19, 19
20	20

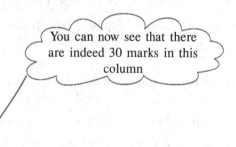

You can now see that there are indeed 30 marks in this column

It is now easy to find the correct answer for the mean. Adding in some extra columns in the table, like this, will help:

Mark	List of the Marks Obtained		Row Total
12	12	1 × 12 =	12
13	13, 13	2 × 13 =	26
14	14, 14, 14, 14, 14	5 × 14 =	70
15	15, 15	2 × 15 =	30
16	16, 16, 16, 16, 16, 16	6 × 16 =	96
17	17, 17, 17, 17, 17, 17, 17, 17	8 × 17 =	136
18	18, 18, 18	3 × 18 =	54
19	19, 19	2 × 19 =	38
20	20	1 × 20 =	20
		Total	482

(a) The Mean = 482 ÷ 30 = 16·0666.. = 16·1 marks (to decimal place)

(b) The Median:

Mark	List of the Marks Obtained
12	12
13	13, 13
14	14, 14, 14, 14, 14
15	15, 15
16	16, 16, 16, 16, 16, 16
17	17, 17, 17, 17, 17, 17, 17, 17
18	18, 18, 18
19	19, 19
20	20

The marks that the 30 pupils obtained are already in order, so we need to find the middle two marks (as there are an even number of pupils in the class).

So, the Median is 16 marks

(c) More pupils scored 17 marks than any other score, so the mode is 17 marks.

Once again, the mean, median and mode have given us three different answers!

QUESTIONS 4.1

1. Find the Mean, Median and Mode for these sets of data:

(a) 20, 38, 28, 27, 20, 37, 38, 21, 25, 38, 35, 22, 28, 26, 38
(b) 56, 58, 59, 56, 51, 58, 54, 53, 56, 58, 57, 56, 58, 59
(c) 4·6, 5·2, 3·6, 5·5, 4·7, 3·7, 3·9, 4·0, 4·1, 3·3
(d) 23, 0, 25, 17, 0, 34, 45, 19, 32, 23, 34, 29, 0, 14, 21, 0, 18, 21, 35, 26

2. The weights of 20 adults (measured in kg) are: 57, 67, 98, 67, 76, 58, 87, 85, 59, 90, 72, 81, 55, 71, 63, 52, 68, 65, 68, 93. Find the mean and median weights.

3. The heights of 12 pupils (measured in cm) are: 149, 166, 157, 152, 162, 172, 159, 165, 173, 182, 149, 164. Find the mean and median heights.

4. These are the scores of pupils in class 10B in their Maths test: 49, 91, 76, 34, 56, 22, 47, 82, 63, 67, 23, 43, 90, 92, 45, 67, 46, 63, 64, 74, 29, 45, 43, 59, 66, 82, 47, 56. Find the mean and median scores.

5. In sixteen hockey games the School First Eleven have scored this number of goals: 4, 5, 0, 1, 3, 4, 5, 3, 3, 0, 1, 3, 3, 4, 2, 3. Find the mean, median and modal number of goals scored.

6. If the mean of four numbers is 9, what is the total of the four numbers?

7. The mean age of a class of 28 pupils is 13 years 4 months. What is the total of their ages?

8. A football team scores 1, 2, 0 and 1 goals in 4 matches.
(a) What is the mean number of goals per game?
(b) How many goals must the team score in the 5th match, if the team is to double the mean?

9. A class of 30 pupils have sat a History test. These are their results:

Mark	12	13	14	15	16	17	18	19	20
Number of Pupils	2	0	7	1	5	10	3	1	1

Find (a) the Mean (b) the Median (c) the Mode.

10. The same class have also sat a Geography test. These are their results:

Mark	12	13	14	15	16	17	18	19	20
Number of Pupils	1	0	1	2	1	7	13	3	2

Find (a) the Mean (b) the Median (c) the Mode.

11. The whole of Year 10 have just had their Science Module test results (marked out of 25 marks). These are their results:

Mark	12	13	14	15	16	17	18	19	20	21	22	23	24	25
Number of Pupils	4	7	13	18	17	19	23	27	25	23	15	9	6	3

Find (a) the Mean (b) the Median (c) the Mode.

12. The results from the neighbouring school for module 1 on the same science syllabus are:

Mark	12	13	14	15	16	17	18	19	20	21	22	23	24	25
Number of Pupils	5	9	14	17	18	21	25	24	26	23	16	11	6	3

Find (a) the Mean (b) the Median (c) the Mode.
(d) Compare the results at the two schools.

SO, WHAT IS STATISTICS ALL ABOUT?

Why is there a branch of Maths called Statistics? Our work on Mean, Median and Mode all started because the Headteacher wanted to know some information. We are not sure **why** he wanted to know about spending money, shoe sizes and height, but he must have had his reasons!

Once someone has started to ask questions such as:

> How much money do people spend on buying their car?
> Did Class A do better in their Maths exam than class B?
> Do pupils do better academically at single sex schools?

then some statistics will be required.

COLLECTING DATA

An important part of Statistics is collecting the **data**, or information. This can be done with a **tally chart**, as we did before, or you may need to organise a **survey** or a **questionnaire** to gather facts or opinions from people.

HANDLING THE DATA

Once you have collected your information, or **raw data** as it is called before you have done anything with it, you will want to process it in some way. Statisticians have devised ways to display data visually. You are probably already familiar with many of the different ways that you can use to represent data, such as **pictograms**, **bar charts**, **pie charts** and **scatter graphs** for example.

The job of the statistician is to find ways of looking at the data which tell you something useful about whatever it is you are researching, or to enable you to draw conclusions from the data.

To help analyse the data, statisticians might calculate the **mean**, **median** or **mode**, as a simple way of representing the entire set of data. If someone simply says that "the average is........." people usually understand that they have used the mean as the average. Instead of listing all the data that you have collected, the "average", be it mean, median or mode, is one number (or possibly two in the case of the mode) which represents the entire collection of data that you have made.

Statisticians might find the **range** for a set of data ...... or draw a **scatter graph** to look for **correlations** between two sets of data.... More of these later!

Now look at some more examples to put some of these ideas into practice:

DISPLAYING DISCRETE DATA

TEST RESULTS IN BIOLOGY

In the section on Mean, Median and Mode, we looked at these results for 30 pupils in a Biology test:

Mark	12	13	14	15	16	17	18	19	20
Number of Pupils	1	2	5	2	6	8	3	2	1

This is called **discrete data**, as the marks awarded were only **whole numbers** in this particular test. No pupil could score 13·5 marks or 18·3 marks, for example.

The Head of Biology could choose to draw a **bar chart** of her results, like this:

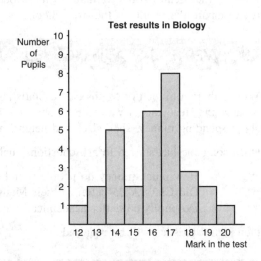

GROUPING DISCRETE DATA

EXAMINATION MARKS IN FRENCH

Again, marks for the French exam are all whole numbers (you cannot score 52·86 marks, for example), so we are dealing with **discrete** data.

These are the results obtained by 100 students on their French exam:

15	64	19	62	23	84	49	80	21	81
29	34	58	29	18	50	24	98	30	16
3	44	50	30	71	31	23	25	45	33
89	68	32	52	34	42	87	60	83	78
77	87	98	43	75	23	73	49	90	45
34	63	82	62	66	10	37	56	94	56
33	52	82	93	45	65	76	76	48	55
40	20	36	86	58	94	86	40	44	73
55	73	74	77	65	60	70	50	50	76
52	48	49	60	62	58	63	64	62	63

Marks	Tally	Total
0–9	I	1
10–19	ⵋ	5
20–29	ⵋ IIII	9
30–39	ⵋ ⵋ I	11
40–49	ⵋ ⵋ IIII	14
50–59	ⵋ ⵋ IIII	14
60–69	ⵋ ⵋ ⵋ I	16
70–79	ⵋ ⵋ III	13
80–89	ⵋ ⵋ I	11
90–99	ⵋ I	6
	Total	100

With such a large array of numbers, it is sometimes convenient to put the data into a **grouped frequency table**.

Cross off each piece of data as you put a tally in the tally chart. Use the 'five bar gate' counting system. Then put the total in the final column.

Your grouped frequency table should now look like this.

Check that the grand total is 100 (it is, so we haven't lost any data in the process!)

0–9, 10–19, 20–29 and so on are called the **class intervals**.

DISPLAYING GROUPED DISCRETE DATA

EXAMINATION MARKS IN FRENCH

We could choose to draw a **bar chart** of this information. It will look like this:

Notice how we have drawn the scale along the horizontal axis.

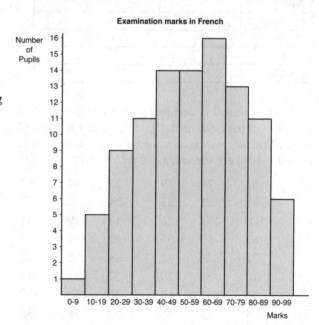

How else can we analyse the data? We could find the average mark. Unless there is a good reason to do otherwise, usually you would chose to calculate the mean.

So, add up the 100 exam marks and then divide by 100.

All the marks together add up to 5517. Now divide by 100.

$5517 \div 100 = 55 \cdot 17$

So, the mean is 55 marks (to the nearest whole mark)

STATISTICS

QUESTIONS 4.2

1. These are the marks of 80 pupils in their German exam:

34	55	52	48	67	37	34	29	45	90
65	48	37	55	48	32	46	23	64	35
19	73	43	81	83	46	75	35	63	17
77	86	73	80	73	65	46	47	28	45
48	56	71	72	56	37	45	83	39	53
34	23	89	67	18	63	27	73	43	82
50	38	91	61	20	84	71	65	71	88
48	62	44	33	31	92	28	23	70	49

Marks	Tally	Totals
0–9		
10–19		
20–29		
30–39		
40–49		
50–59		
60–69		
70–79		
80–89		
90–99		

(a) Group the data, by completing the tally chart.

(b) Draw a bar chart to display the data.

(c) Find the mean mark for these 80 pupils in their German exam.

2. A local council is deciding whether or not to close a long-stay car park in a small town. When full, the car park can hold 120 cars. Each car pays a flat rate of £5 for a day's parking. The council decide that they will keep a record of the number of cars which use the car park over a three month period. These are the results of their survey:

25	82	28	19	23	44	55	98	34	45
34	48	101	36	28	38	52	36	45	64
84	120	71	28	11	29	51	39	41	62
62	62	32	55	102	51	72	47	40	61
67	32	28	32	63	38	43	35	60	28
12	51	51	29	27	47	28	55	59	39
8	26	81	89	48	49	60	20	103	35
37	34	38	45	39	38	38	38	87	34
39	72	45	23	29	29	18	90	97	52

No. of Cars	Tally	Totals
0–9		
10–19		
20–29		
30–39		
40–49		
50–59		
60–69		
70–79		
80–89		
90–99		
100–109		
110–120		

(a) Group the data, by completing the tally chart.

(b) Draw a bar chart to display the data.

(c) Find the mean number of cars using the car park per day.

(d) What is the expected income from the car park for a complete year?

FINDING THE MEAN FROM GROUPED DATA

EXAMINATION MARKS IN PHYSICS

The same 100 students who took a French exam, have also taken a Physics exam. The Head of Physics has already put all the marks into a grouped frequency table, as follows:

Marks	Total
0–9	0
10–19	0
20–29	1
30–39	3
40–49	17
50–59	32
60–69	40
70–79	7
80–89	0
90–99	0

Unfortunately, the Head of Physics has lost the piece of paper with the raw data of pupils' scores. How can we find the mean for the Physics exam from the grouped frequency table?

The only sensible thing to do in the circumstances is to assume that the one person who scored somewhere between 20 and 29, scored **half-way** between 20 and 29.

To find half-way between 20 and 29, add the two numbers together and divide by two:

20 + 29 = 49
49 ÷ 2 = 24·5

So, we will assume that this pupil has scored 24·5 marks.

Then we will assume that the three pupils who have scored between 30 and 39 again have all scored exactly half-way, which is 34·5 marks.

Marks	Mid-mark	Total
0–9	4·5	0
10–19	14·5	0
20–29	24·5	1
30–39	34·5	3
40–49	44·5	17
50–59	54·5	32
60–69	64·5	40
70–79	74·5	7
80–89	84·5	0
90–99	94·5	0

I can now start to write out a list of an approximation to the marks for these 100 pupils

I have assumed that 1 pupil scored 24·5
I have assumed that 3 pupils scored 34·5
I have assumed that 17 pupils scored 44·5   and so on........

If I write out the 100 pupils' scores long hand, it will look like this:

24·5
34·5, 34·5, 34·5
44·5, 44·5, 44·5, 44·5, 44·5, 44·5, 44·5, 44·5, 44·5, 44·5, 44·5, 44·5, 44·5, 44·5, 44·5, 44·5, 44·5,
and so on.....

Rather than carry on writing all 100 scores out separately, you can see that I have:
1 score of 24·5   or 1 times 24·5
3 scores of 34·5   or 3 times 34·5
17 scores of 44·5   or 17 times 44·5 and so on.....

When I want to add up the grand total for all 100 pupils scores, the easiest way is to add extra columns to the frequency table, like this:

Marks	Mid-mark	Total number of pupils	Mid-mark × Number of Pupils	Row Total
0–9	4·5	0	0 × 4·5	0
10–19	14·5	0	0 × 14·5	0
20–29	24·5	1	1 × 24·5	24·5
30–39	34·5	3	3 × 34·5	103·5
40–49	44·5	17	17 × 44·5	756·5
50–59	54·5	32	32 × 54·5	1744
60–69	64·5	40	40 × 64·5	2580
70–79	74·5	7	7 × 74·5	521·5
80–89	84·5	0	0 × 84·5	0
90–99	94·5	0	0 × 94·5	0
			Total	5730

$5730 \div 100 = 57 \cdot 3$

So, an approximation for the mean for the Physics exam is 57 (to the nearest mark).

Just when I have finished finding an approximation for the mean for the Physics exam – guess what! The eccentric old Head of Physics has found his piece of paper with the raw scores of the 100 pupils on it! Here it is:

Marks	Actual Marks
0–9	
10–19	
20–29	27
30–39	37, 37, 39
40–49	40, 40, 41, 41, 41, 42, 42, 44, 46, 47, 47, 47, 47, 48, 48, 49, 49
50–59	50, 50, 50, 52, 52, 52, 52, 52, 53, 53, 53, 54, 54, 54, 54, 55, 55, 55, 55, 55, 55, 56, 57, 57, 57, 57, 57, 57, 57, 58, 58, 59
60–69	60, 60, 60, 61, 61, 61, 62, 62, 62, 63, 63, 63, 63, 63, 63, 63, 63, 64, 64, 64, 64, 65, 65, 65, 65, 65, 65, 65, 65, 65, 65, 66, 66, 67, 67, 68, 69, 69, 69, 69
70–79	71, 74, 74, 76, 76, 77, 79
80–89	
90–99	

Adding in another column will help to find the total of all the marks:

Marks	Actual Marks	Row Total
0–9		
10–19		
20–29	27	27
30–39	37, 37, 39	113
40–49	40, 40, 41, 41, 41, 42, 42, 44, 46, 47, 47, 47, 47, 48, 48, 49, 49	759
50–59	50, 50, 50, 52, 52, 52, 52, 52, 53, 53, 53, 54, 54, 54, 54, 55, 55, 55, 55, 55, 55, 56, 57, 57, 57, 57, 57, 57, 57, 58, 58, 59	1745
60–69	60, 60, 60, 61, 61, 61, 62, 62, 62, 63, 63, 63, 63, 63, 63, 63,	
	63, 64, 64, 64, 64, 65, 65, 65, 65, 65, 65, 65, 65, 65, 65, 66, 66, 67, 67, 68, 69, 69, 69, 69	2571
70–79	71, 74, 74, 76, 76, 77, 79	527
80–89		
90–99		
	Total	5742

$5742 \div 100 = 57 \cdot 42$

So, the actual Mean, when we are able to go back to the raw data, is 57·42 compared to 57·3 when we had to make some intelligent assumptions. So, we can see that our assumptions have not let us down too badly, because we are so close with our two answers. In fact, to the nearest whole mark, they both give the same answer, namely a mean of 57 marks.

QUESTIONS 4.3

1. These are the GCSE mock results for Year 11 in Geography. Fill in the table below to help you to find an estimate for the mean mark in Geography:

Marks	Mid-mark	Total number of pupils	Mid-mark × Number of Pupils	Row Total
0–9		0		
10–19		1		
20–29		5		
30–39		7		
40–49		14		
50–59		58		
60–69		52		
70–79		67		
80–89		15		
90–99		2		
			Total	

2. These are the GCSE mock results for Year 11 in History:

Marks	Total
0–9	0
10–19	0
20–29	4
30–39	3
40–49	17
50–59	47
60–69	62
70–79	55
80–89	32
90–99	1

Find an estimate for the mean mark in History.

THE RANGE

COMPARING THE FRENCH AND PHYSICS MARKS

An important task for the statistician is to compare different sets of data. What can we say about the marks of pupils in their French exam compared to their mark in their Physics exam?

We have already calculated the mean for both exams as follows:

French Exam: mean is 55 marks
Physics Exam: mean is 57 marks

Can we conclude, as these means are very close, that the pupils found the French exam about as hard as the Physics exam and vice versa?

In French: the highest score was 98
the lowest score was 3

The difference between the highest and the lowest score is 98 − 3 = 95 marks.

This is called the **range**.

> The Range — The Highest Score — The Lowest Score

In Physics: the highest score   = 79
                the lowest score   = 27 .....subtracting
                The Range   = 52

So, the range for Physics is 52 marks.

The range for French is 95 marks
The range for Physics is 52 marks

You can see that the **spread** of marks that the pupils achieved in French was much greater than in Physics. So, although the mean for both exams was very nearly the same, the spread of marks is very different, as shown by the range for each subject. In French, there were many pupils who gained extremely high marks and also pupils who didn't score many marks at all. In Physics, no-one scored an extremely high mark, but no-one scored a very low one either.

QUESTIONS 4.4

1.These are the marks for class 10A in their Latin exam:

78	53	67	88	54	72	98	70	100	83
54	59	62	83	75	54	51	78	83	77
77	89	90	58	85	61	55	62	97	73

(a) Find the mean.
(b) Find the range.

2. These are the marks for class 10B in their Latin exam:

70	19	73	76	71	63	98	78	99	77
99	90	91	56	97	81	97	70	87	80
29	92	55	96	45	45	10	62	93	74

(a) Find the mean.
(b) Find the range.
(c) Compare the Latin results for class 10A with those of class 10B.

SCATTER GRAPHS

COMPARING THE FRENCH AND PHYSICS MARKS

Pupil	French Mark	Physics Mark
1	15	55
2	29	65
3	3	79
4	89	77
5	77	58
6	34	53
7	33	27
8	40	52
9	55	57
10	52	65
11	64	74
12	34	65
13	44	49
14	68	37
15	87	40
16	63	39
17	52	64
18	20	76
19	73	69
20	48	59

I have selected 20 pupils at random from the 100 pupils who did both exams. Here are these 20 pupils and their marks for French and Physics.

I am going to represent each pupil by one dot on a **scatter graph**, which looks like this:

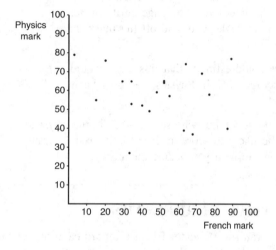

You can see that some pupils have done well in both exams, some have done badly in both and some have done well in one, but badly in the other. There is no clear connection between these two sets of data, because how good you are at French does not seem to have any bearing on how good you are at Physics. The dots on the scatter graph are distributed randomly. So, for this group of pupils, there appears to be no connection between ability in French and ability in Physics. There is said to be no **correlation** between the French and Physics exam marks.

POSITIVE CORRELATION

When I plot a scatter graph for these same 20 pupils for their Physics exam marks and their Maths exam marks, this is what it looks like:

This time you can see that for most pupils, the better they are at Maths the better they are at Physics. Those pupils who are not that good at Maths tend to be not that good at Physics either.

This is described as **positive correlation**.

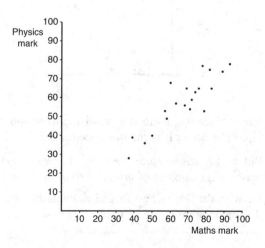

We can draw in the **line of best fit**, which is
the straight line that appears to best represent
the data. I think the line should be about here:

Notice that there are approximately equal
numbers of pupils either side of my straight line.

A pupil who scored 70% in their Maths exam
was absent for the Physics exam. What would
you expect that pupil to have scored in their
Physics exam?

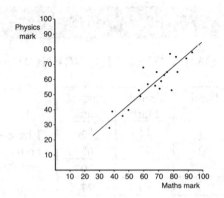

We can use the line of best fit to make an
estimate for the mark this pupil might have
scored in Physics. Find 70% on the Maths
scale. Draw a vertical line up the page until
you reach the line of best fit. Then draw a
horizontal line across the page until you reach
the Physics scale, and read off the mark there,
which is 60%.

So, we could estimate that this pupil would
have scored 60% in Physics, had they been
present.

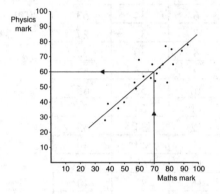

What would a pupil who scored 45% in the Physics
exam be likely to score in their Maths exam? Draw
a line in, to help you decide the answer.

NEGATIVE CORRELATION

When I ran a small cafe, I kept a record each day of three pieces of data:
1. The temperature at lunchtime outside in the street.   2. The number of ice-creams that I sold.
3. The number of bowls of soup that I sold.

I then plotted scatter graphs of my results over several days, like this:

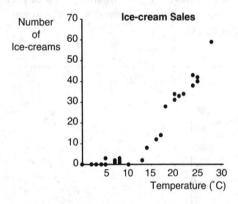

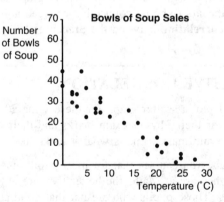

You can see that there is a positive correlation between the number of ice-creams and the temperature. The hotter it is the more ice-creams I sell.

But as the temperature goes up, the **less** bowls of soup I sell. There is **a negative correlation**
between the number of bowls of soup that I sell and the temperature.

Draw in the line of best fit and estimate the number of bowls of soup that I will sell on a day when
the temperature is (a) 20°C (b) 30°C

QUESTIONS 4.5

1. These are the marks that a group of Year 11 pupils obtained on their GCSE mock exam in Maths and the mark they obtained in the final exam:

Pupil	A	B	C	D	E	F	G	H	I	J	K	L
Mock Mark	80	62	72	35	57	28	49	45	60	92	87	72
Final Mark	88	71	55	40	57	45	65	63	60	94	88	86

Pupil	M	N	O	P	Q	R	S	T	U	V	W	X
Mock Mark	75	42	55	40	66	56	50	60	59	81	61	71
Final Mark	74	48	66	85	75	76	53	65	67	68	91	82

(a) Draw a scatter graph of this information.

(b) Draw in a line of best fit.

(c) A pupil who was present for the mock exam and scored 65%, was absent for the final exam. Estimate her final mark using your line of best fit.

(d) Estimate the mock mark for a pupil who scored 60% in the final exam.

2. These are the heights and weights of some young men:

Heights (cm)	175	176	183	179	183	180	182	171	181
Weights (kg)	72	72	79	73	78	76	76	69	75

Heights (cm)	178	172	173	169	170	170	168	169	169
Weights (kg)	74	71	70	69	70	68	68	67	68

(a) Draw a scatter graph of this information. Notice that your scales do not have to start at zero! On the horizontal axis, go from 165 cm to 184 cm, taking 1cm for each unit. On the vertical scale, go from 67 kg to 80 kg, taking 1cm for each unit.

(b) Draw in a line of best fit.

(c) Estimate the weight of someone whose height is 177 cm.

(d) Estimate the height of someone weighing 70 kg.

GROUPING CONTINUOUS DATA

WEIGHTS OF WORMS IN THE LABORATORY:

A scientist, working on a project in a biology laboratory, has kept worms in two separate containers at different temperatures.

These are the weights of the worms from container A (in grams):

12·6	9·8	10·5	11·6	12·2
8·4	16·0	13·6	12·8	9·8
7·3	14·3	15·6	9·6	8·8
10·8	10·9	11·9	10·8	16·0
15·7	9·6	8·9	12·6	13·6
20·1	14·0	12·9	13·3	10·1
8·0	8·6	6·7	15·6	12·2
13·7	11·7	17·9	6·8	5·7
12·0	18·0	18·6	13·6	12·7
11·4	13·7	14·8	12·1	10·0

Weight is a continuous variable, as it can take any value. The scientist has measured the weight to one decimal place, but he could have decided to measure the weights to 2 decimal places, or 3 decimal places, if he had wanted to be even more accurate. He knows that he will have a lot of data to analyse, so he puts the information into groups. Imagine that you are the scientist and put the data into groups, using a tally chart, like this:

Weight	Tally	Total
4–6		
6–8		
8–10		
10–12		
12–14		
14–16		
16–18		
18–20		
20–22		

Some pieces of data are difficult to place in the tally chart! Does 14·0 go into the 12–14 category or the 14–16 category?

We need to be careful to decide what happens at the boundaries of each group. We could decide that the class interval 4 – 6 will include weights of exactly 4 grams or more, up to very nearly as heavy as 6 grams.

We can write this much more neatly as $4 \leqslant$ weight < 6

or $4 \leqslant w < 6$

$4 \leqslant w$ ....this means the weight can equal and be greater than 4 grams.

$w < 6$ ....this means the weight is strictly less than 6 grams.

Weight	Tally	Total
$4 \leqslant w < 6$	I	1
$6 \leqslant w < 8$	III	3
$8 \leqslant w < 10$	LHT IIII	9
$10 \leqslant w < 12$	LHT LHT	10
$12 \leqslant w < 14$	LHT LHT LHT	15
$14 \leqslant w < 16$	LHT I	6
$16 \leqslant w < 18$	III	3
$18 \leqslant w < 20$	II	2
$20 \leqslant w < 22$	I	1

We now need to do our tally chart again, paying particular attention to the weights like 14·0 grams.

This is the completed tally chart.

EXAMPLE 2

A different scientist has measured the weights of worms in container B. These are the results:

4	10	9	9	8
8	7	10	6	10
9	9	9	11	9
11	11	10	12	11
11	8	12	6	7
6	12	5	9	15
14	7	13	12	8
9	13	8	5	11
10	10	12	10	8
7	8	9	9	7

This scientist has taken his measurements to the **nearest** gram.

So, a weight given as 7 grams, will be greater than 6·5 grams but smaller than 7·5 grams. (See the section on Accuracy for a reminder here.)

We can most neatly express this using symbols as: $6 \cdot 5 \leqslant w < 7 \cdot 5$

Weight	Tally	Total
$3 \cdot 5 \leqslant w < 5 \cdot 5$	|||	3
$5 \cdot 5 \leqslant w < 7 \cdot 5$	ⅢⅢ |||	8
$7 \cdot 5 \leqslant w < 9 \cdot 5$	ⅢⅢ ⅢⅢ ⅢⅢ ||	17
$9 \cdot 5 \leqslant w < 11 \cdot 5$	ⅢⅢ ⅢⅢ |||	13
$11 \cdot 5 \leqslant w < 13 \cdot 5$	ⅢⅢ ||	7
$13 \cdot 5 \leqslant w < 15 \cdot 5$	||	2
$15 \cdot 5 \leqslant w < 17 \cdot 5$		0
$17 \cdot 5 \leqslant w < 19 \cdot 5$		0
$19 \cdot 5 \leqslant w < 21 \cdot 5$		0

The class intervals $3 \cdot 5 \leqslant w < 5 \cdot 5$ and $5 \cdot 5 \leqslant w < 7 \cdot 5$ and so on, take account of the fact that weight is a continuous variable.

This is the completed tally chart.

DISPLAYING CONTINUOUS DATA: BAR CHARTS

WEIGHTS OF WORMS IN THE LABORATORY:

Weight	Total
$4 \leqslant w < 6$	1
$6 \leqslant w < 8$	3
$8 \leqslant w < 10$	9
$10 \leqslant w < 12$	10
$12 \leqslant w < 14$	15
$14 \leqslant w < 16$	6
$16 \leqslant w < 18$	3
$18 \leqslant w < 20$	2
$20 \leqslant w < 22$	1

This is the frequency table for the worms in Container A.

We can now display the weights of the worms using a bar chart.

The bar chart for these results will look like this:

Notice how the horizontal axis has been drawn.
We are dealing with a continuous variable (weight), so the horizontal axis has been drawn as a continuous number line.

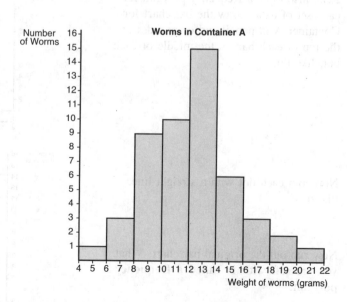

EXAMPLE 2

Weight	Total
$3·5 \leqslant w < 5·5$	3
$5·5 \leqslant w < 7·5$	8
$7·5 \leqslant w < 9·5$	7
$9·5 \leqslant w < 11·5$	13
$11·5 \leqslant w < 13·5$	7
$13·5 \leqslant w < 15·5$	2
$15·5 \leqslant w < 17·5$	0
$17·5 \leqslant w < 19·5$	0
$19·5 \leqslant w < 21·5$	0

This is the frequency table for the worms in Container B.

We can draw the bar chart for container B.

Notice that the horizontal axis is once again a continuous number line. The bars are still plotted opposite the class boundaries, just as in Example 1. So, the first bar sits between $3·5$ and $5·5$, the second bar sits between $5·5$ and $7·5$ and so on.

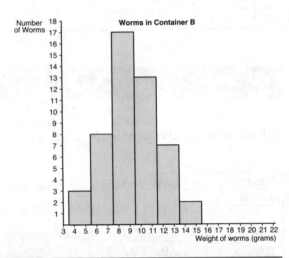

FREQUENCY POLYGONS

GROUPED CONTINUOUS DATA

I can also draw a frequency polygon for each set of data. Draw the bar chart for Container A in pencil and draw a dot at the top of each bar, in the middle of each bar, like this:

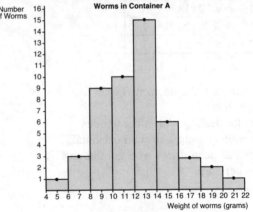

Now join each dot with a straight line, like this:

Now rub out the original bar chart. What you are left with is called a **frequency polygon**.

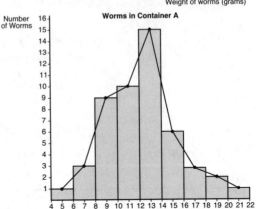

This is the frequency polygon for Container A:

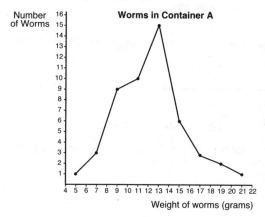

This is the frequency polygon for Container B:

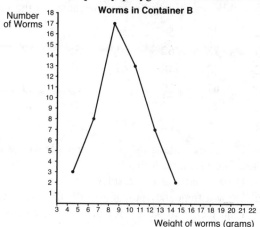

We can also put these two frequency polygons on the same axes, so we can compare them, like this:

Notice that the dots for the two sets of data come in the middle of the bars. So, for container A on the horizontal axis, the dots are opposite 5, 7, 9, 11 and so on.

For container B on the horizontal axis, the dots are opposite 4·5, 6·5, 8·5, 10·5 and so on.

Putting the two frequency polygons on the same axis gives a very useful visual representation of what is happening. Clearly the weights of the worms in container B are generally smaller than those in container A.

QUESTIONS 4.6

1. A scientist is trying to develop a new variety of tomato. She keeps a record of the weight of each tomato, in grams, recording her results to one decimal place. These are the weights of 60 tomatoes:

60·2	44·8	57·3	72·9	50·3	40·4	63·8	52·1	63·5	54·8
56·4	48·9	62·9	70·1	48·7	74·3	71·0	49·9	62·9	59·3
44·8	51·0	72·1	69·5	67·3	60·7	65·0	55·6	52·0	55·6
63·8	62·3	50·6	43·1	52·9	49·4	46·7	59·4	44·9	67·3
71·0	70·9	49·4	42·9	53·8	52·8	41·9	66·3	68·9	56·8
65·8	47·6	48·3	66·0	60·1	67·4	52·7	68·5	64·8	62·9

Weight	Tally	Total
$40 \leqslant w < 45$		
$45 \leqslant w < 50$		
$50 \leqslant w < 55$		
$55 \leqslant w < 60$		
$60 \leqslant w < 65$		
$65 \leqslant w < 70$		
$70 \leqslant w < 75$		

(a) Group the data by completing the tally chart.

(b) Draw a bar chart to display the data.

(c) Draw a frequency polygon to display the data.

(d) Find the mean weight for these 60 tomatoes.

2. On another day, a member of her research team measures the weight of a new batch of 60 tomatoes, this time giving his measurements to the nearest gram, like this:

42	45	56	55	57	55	52	60	62	71
67	72	62	61	56	60	55	59	67	60
72	48	48	67	52	63	53	46	62	68
41	67	50	41	62	64	69	58	50	70
56	71	49	73	71	48	71	49	41	56
68	60	62	63	50	51	52	55	52	64

(a) Group the data using a similar table to the one in question 1, but remembering to change the class intervals appropriately.
(b) Draw a bar chart to display the data.
(c) Draw a frequency polygon to display the data.
(d) Find the mean weight for these 60 tomatoes.

FINDING THE MEAN FROM CONTINUOUS GROUPED DATA

WEIGHTS OF WORMS IN THE LABORATORY

We can find the mean from continuous grouped data using the same ideas as we did when dealing with discrete grouped data.

Weight	Total
$4 \leq w < 6$	1
$6 \leq w < 8$	3
$8 \leq w < 10$	9
$10 \leq w < 12$	10
$12 \leq w < 14$	15
$14 \leq w < 16$	6
$16 \leq w < 18$	3
$18 \leq w < 20$	2
$20 \leq w < 22$	1

This is the frequency table for worms in Container A.

We assume as before that the one worm in the class interval $4 \leq w < 6$ weighs the middle weight of 5 grams. We assume that the worms in the class interval $6 \leq w < 8$ weigh the middle weight of 7 grams, and so on.

We can use the same table as we did before, like this:

Weight	Mid-weight	Total number of worms	Mid-weight × Number of Worms	Row Total
$4 \leq w < 6$	5	1	5×1	5
$6 \leq w < 8$	7	3	7×3	21
$8 \leq w < 10$	9	9	9×9	81
$10 \leq w < 12$	11	10	11×10	110
$12 \leq w < 14$	13	15	13×15	195
$14 \leq w < 16$	15	6	15×6	90
$16 \leq w < 18$	17	3	17×3	51
$18 \leq w < 20$	19	2	19×2	38
$20 \leq w < 22$	21	1	21×1	21
			Total	612

The total number of worms is 50, so the mean weight is given by:

$612 \div 50 = 12 \cdot 24$ grams $= 12 \cdot 2$ grams (to one decimal place)

EXAMPLE 2

We can use exactly the same table for the worms in container B, except that the middle weights will be slightly different. The middle of the class interval $3 \cdot 5 \leqslant w < 5 \cdot 5$ will be $4 \cdot 5$ and so on for the other classes. The table will look like this:

Weight	Mid-weight	Total number of worms	Mid-weight × Number of Worms	Row Total
$3 \cdot 5 \leqslant w < 5 \cdot 5$	$4 \cdot 5$	3	$4 \cdot 5 \times 3$	$13 \cdot 5$
$5 \cdot 5 \leqslant w < 7 \cdot 5$	$6 \cdot 5$	8	$6 \cdot 5 \times 8$	52
$7 \cdot 5 \leqslant w < 9 \cdot 5$	$8 \cdot 5$	17	$8 \cdot 5 \times 17$	$144 \cdot 5$
$9 \cdot 5 \leqslant w < 11 \cdot 5$	$10 \cdot 5$	13	$10 \cdot 5 \times 13$	$136 \cdot 5$
$11 \cdot 5 \leqslant w < 13 \cdot 5$	$12 \cdot 5$	7	$12 \cdot 5 \times 7$	$87 \cdot 5$
$13 \cdot 5 \leqslant w < 15 \cdot 5$	$14 \cdot 5$	2	$14 \cdot 5 \times 2$	29
$15 \cdot 5 \leqslant w < 17 \cdot 5$	$16 \cdot 5$	0	$16 \cdot 5 \times 0$	0
$17 \cdot 5 \leqslant w < 19 \cdot 5$	$18 \cdot 5$	0	$18 \cdot 5 \times 0$	0
$19 \cdot 5 \leqslant w < 21 \cdot 5$	$20 \cdot 5$	0	$20 \cdot 5 \times 0$	0
			Total	463

The total number of worms is 50, so the mean weight is given by:

$463 \div 50 = 9 \cdot 26$ grams $= 9 \cdot 3$ grams (to one decimal place)

So, the mean weight for Container A $= 12 \cdot 2$ grams

And, the mean weight for Container B $= 9 \cdot 3$ grams

This confirms what we thought from plotting the two frequency polygons on the same axes.

QUESTIONS 4.7

1. An apple grower is keeping a record of the weights of a new variety of apple. She weighs each apple in grams to one decimal place, and puts each piece of data into a tally chart. These are her results for all the apples picked on a particular day:

Weight (in grams)	Total
$110 \leqslant w < 120$	18
$120 \leqslant w < 130$	23
$130 \leqslant w < 140$	41
$140 \leqslant w < 150$	69
$150 \leqslant w < 160$	83
$160 \leqslant w < 170$	54
$170 \leqslant w < 180$	21

(a) How many apples are in her sample?

(b) Draw a bar chart to display the data.

(c) Draw a frequency polygon to display the data.

(d) Find an estimate for the mean weight for these apples.

2. A tomato grower keeps a note of the weight of each tomato picked on certain days. He takes his measurements to the nearest gram, so his table of results looks like this:

Weight (in grams)	Total
$49 \cdot 5 \leqslant w < 54 \cdot 5$	8
$54 \cdot 5 \leqslant w < 59 \cdot 5$	16
$59 \cdot 5 \leqslant w < 64 \cdot 5$	34
$64 \cdot 5 \leqslant w < 69 \cdot 5$	53
$69 \cdot 5 \leqslant w < 74 \cdot 5$	67
$74 \cdot 5 \leqslant w < 79 \cdot 5$	49
$79 \cdot 5 \leqslant w < 89 \cdot 5$	23
$84 \cdot 5 \leqslant w < 89 \cdot 5$	13

(a) How many tomatoes are in his sample?

(b) Draw a bar chart to display the data.

(c) Draw a frequency polygon to display the data.

(d) Find an estimate for the mean weight for these tomatoes.

PIE CHARTS

So far, we haven't done any work on pie charts! They deserve a chapter all to themselves as, unlike pictograms, bar charts and frequency polygons, they require you to know about angles.

EXAMPLE 1

At Advantage College, there are 360 students, who are on the following courses:

200 Maths & Science
45 Business Studies
65 Humanities
20 Law
30 Modern Languages

We could choose to draw a bar chart of this information. However, a pie chart is often used for this type of situation, because we can use it to represent the **entire** college, with just one circle or pie. This (as I'm sure you spotted!) is a particularly easy situation.

There are 360 degrees in a circle and there just happen to be 360 students at Advantage College! So, each student is represented on the pie chart by one degree.

Course	No. of Students	Angle on the Pie Chart
Maths & Science	200	200°
Business Studies	45	45°
Humanities	65	65°
Law	20	20°
Modern Languages	30	30°

The pie chart will look like this:

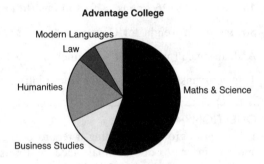

EXAMPLE 2

At Brainwave College, there are 180 students, who are on the following courses:

25 Engineering
15 Law
30 Psychology
28 Music
12 Theatre Studies
33 Journalism
37 Accountancy

This time 180 students will be represented by 360° in the complete circle.

So, every student will be represented by 2° on the pie chart.

Course	No. of Students	Angle on the Pie Chart
Engineering	25	50°
Law	15	30°
Psychology	30	60°
Music	28	56°
Theatre Studies	12	24°
Journalism	33	66°
Accountancy	37	74°

The pie chart will look like this:

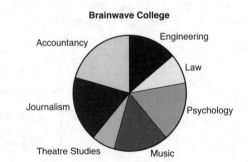

Check that the numbers in this column add up to 360°. They do!

EXAMPLE 3

At Curiosity College, the principal, who is a mathematician, has worked out that the numbers of students on various courses at her college as percentages:

35% of students study Mathematics
25% of students study Physics
14% of students study Chemistry
19% of students study Biology
7% of students study Environmental Sciences

Until we know the total number of students at the college – from which we could work out the number of students on each course – we cannot draw a bar chart. However, we can easily turn this information into a pie chart.

Pie charts are good at showing various proportions of the whole and we know the proportion of the students who are following each course. So we can work out the angles for the pie chart by knowing that:

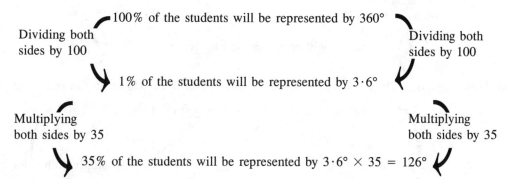

100% of the students will be represented by 360°

Dividing both sides by 100

1% of the students will be represented by 3·6°

Multiplying both sides by 35

35% of the students will be represented by 3·6° × 35 = 126°

Use the same technique to find the other angles:

Course	Percentage of Students	Calculation	Angle on Pie Chart
Mathematics	35	35 × 3·6	126°
Physics	25	25 × 3·6	90°
Chemistry	14	14 × 3·6	50·4°
Biology	19	19 × 3·6	68·4°
Environmental Sciences	7	7 × 3·6	25·2°

Check this column adds to 360°. It does!

We can now draw in the pie chart, which looks like this:

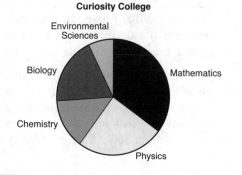

Curiosity College

EXAMPLE 4

At Destiny College, there are 245 students,
who are on the following courses:

87 Sociology
63 Media Studies
24 Catering
35 Child Care
19 Humanities
17 Psychology

> This time you can see that the numbers are not convenient ones! But never mind, we can use the same approach as before. The whole college will by represented by 360°.

245 students will be represented by 360°

Dividing
both sides by 245

Dividing
both sides by 245

1 student will be represented by $\frac{360}{245} \approx 1 \cdot 469°$

This doesn't turn out to be a convenient decimal either! Never mind! Do exactly as before, like this:

1 student will be represented by $\frac{360}{245}$ ($\approx 1 \cdot 469°$)

Multiply both sides by 87

Multiply both sides by 87

87 students will be represented by $\frac{360}{245} \times 87 \approx 127 \cdot 836°$

So, we can use the same technique to calculate the angles as follows:

Subject	Number of Students	Calculation	Angle on Pie Chart
Sociology	87	$\frac{360}{245} \times 87$	128°
Media Studies	63	$\frac{360}{245} \times 63$	92·5°
Catering	24	$\frac{360}{245} \times 24$	35°
Child Care	35	$\frac{360}{245} \times 35$	51·5°
Humanities	19	$\frac{360}{245} \times 19$	28°
Psychology	17	$\frac{360}{245} \times 17$	25°

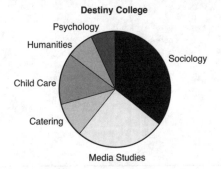

Destiny College

Psychology
Humanities
Child Care
Catering
Media Studies
Sociology

You can see that I have taken all the answers to the nearest half a degree, as this is about as accurate as I think I can draw an angle on my pie chart.

Adding the angles together, you can check that they do add to 360°. In some examples, where you have had to round answers to the nearest half a degree, you may find that your final total is very slightly different from 360°. This is called **rounding error**.

STATISTICS

Do not confuse 'rounding error' with making a 'mistake'. If your last column actually adds up to somewhere between, say, 359° and 361°, this is a consequence of taking the earlier answers to the nearest half a degree, and is perfectly acceptable. In practice, if you leave drawing the largest angle until last, the discrepancy will not be noticed.

EXAMPLE 5

At Excelsior College, the Principal has drawn a pie chart of the numbers of students at her college:

How many students are there on each course?

The Principal at Excelsior College has told me that there are 20 students doing Engineering.

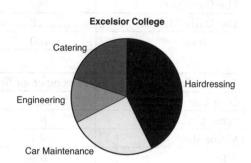

Excelsior College

When I measure the angle of that sector, it is 45°. So, I can write down a statement which I know to be true and continue from there, as we did before:

45° represents 20 students

Divide both sides by 45   Divide both sides by 45

1° represents $\frac{20}{45}$ students ($\approx 0\cdot4444$ students)

I can measure other angles from my pie chart and use the above information to find the numbers of students on each course.

Subject	Angle of Sector, as measured from the pie chart	Calculation	Number of Students
Engineering	45°	We were told this one!	20
Hairdressing	153°	$\frac{20 \times 153}{45}$	68
Car Maintenance	90°	$\frac{20 \times 90}{45}$	40
Catering	72°	$\frac{20 \times 72}{45}$	32

QUESTIONS 4.8

Newspaper	Number of Students
The Times	42
The Telegraph	49
The Independent	63
The Guardian	185
The Daily Mail	21
Total	360

1. Students at Advantage College are encouraged to read a newspaper. These are the papers that they claim to read.

Draw a pie chart of this information.

Newspaper	Number of Students
The Times	25
The Telegraph	38
The Independent	12
The Guardian	87
The Daily Mail	18
Total	180

2. Students at Brainwave College claim to read these newspapers.

Draw a pie chart of this information.

Type of Transport	Percentage of Students
Own Car	23%
Parents' Car	8%
Motor Bike	9%
Bike	6%
Bus	33%
Walk	21%

3. At Curiosity College, the principal has conducted a survey about how students travel to college. These are the results.

Draw a pie chart of this information.

Type of Transport	Number of Students
Own Car	83
Parents' Car	67
Motor Bike	19
Bike	17
Bus	34
Walk	25
Total	245

4. This is how students at Destiny College travel to college.

Draw a pie chart of this information.

5. At Excelsior College, the Principal has already drawn a pie chart of how students travel to school. There are 160 students at the college. Measure the angles of each sector, to find the number of students in each category.

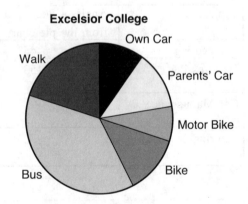

Excelsior College

6. A survey was carried out of 400 Year 11 pupils, to find out what they did at the end of Year 11.

204 stayed on at their old school 　　63 found a job
 88 went to a college 　　45 were still looking for a job

Draw a pie chart of this information.

7. A schoolboy is working on a statistics project. He goes to a large supermarket car park and records the country of make of the first 1000 cars there on one particular day. These are his results:

British　　345 　　French　　167
German　　226 　　Swedish　　45
　　　　　　　　　Japanese　217

Draw a pie chart of this information.

8. On his second visit to the supermarket, these were his results:

British	374	French	182	
German	209	Swedish	83	
		Japanese	152	

Draw a pie chart of this information.

Can he begin to draw any conclusions?

CUMULATIVE FREQUENCY

EXAMPLE 1

Alpha School has entered all its Year 11 pupils for French GCSE. These are their exam marks:

Mark (%)	Frequency
0–10	3
11–20	8
21–30	15
31–40	31
41–50	51
51–60	83
61–70	67
71–80	25
81–90	12
91–100	5

Total   300

The table tells us that three pupils scored 10 or less.

How many pupils scored 20 or less?

There is a temptation to say that the answer to this must be 8 pupils, but this is incorrect!
We must also include the 3 pupils who scored less than 10 marks, as they have scored less than 20 marks too!

So, 3 + 8 = 11 pupils have scored less than 20 marks.

How many pupils have scored less than 30 marks?
3 + 8 + 15 = 26 pupils have scored less than 30 marks.

Keeping a running total in this way is called finding the **Cumulative Frequency.**
It is best displayed in a table, like this:

Mark (%)	Freq	Marks	Cum Freq	
0–10	3	10 or less	3	3
11–20	8	20 or less	11	3 + 8
21–30	15	30 or less	26	3 + 8 + 15
31–40	31	40 or less	57	3 + 8 + 15 + 31
41–50	51	50 or less	108	3 + 8 + 15 + 31 + 51
51–60	83	60 or less	191	3 + 8 + 15 + 31 + 51 + 83
61–70	67	70 or less	258	3 + 8 + 15 + 31 + 51 + 83 + 67
71–80	25	80 or less	283	3 + 8 + 15 + 31 + 51 + 83 + 67 + 25
81–90	12	90 or less	295	3 + 8 + 15 + 31 + 51 + 83 + 67 + 25 + 12
91–100	5	100 or less	300	3 + 8 + 15 + 31 + 51 + 83 + 67 + 25 + 12 + 5

Total   300

This column is the Running Total.

We can display cumulative frequency information on a graph. Draw axes where the marks are along the horizontal axis. The cumulative frequency always goes along the vertical axis. Opposite 10 marks, plot the point 3 on the vertical axis. Against 20 marks, plot the point 11 on the vertical axis. When the points are plotted, join them with a smooth curve. The graph is called a **cumulative frequency curve** and will look like this:

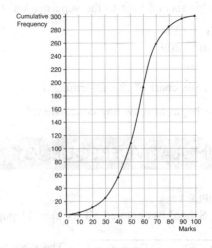

Cumulative frequency curves always have this same general shape, rather like an elongated 'S'. We can use our cumulative frequency curve to find several pieces of information.

Firstly, we can find the Median mark. Remember that the median is one type of average. It is the mark of the pupil in the middle. [Look back at the section on Mean, Median and Mode for a reminder before you read on!]

In theory, as we have an even number of pupils, we should look at the middle two people and take the mark that is half way between the two of them. In practice, we have such a large number of pupils that it is too difficult to use our graph to distinguish between the 150th and the 151st person! So, we can draw in this line (at 150 pupils) on the graph to help us find the Median like this:

So, we can read off that the median is 55 marks.

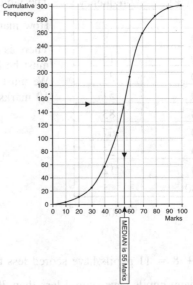

The median is the mark of the pupil in the middle. What if I look at the mark of the person who is one quarter of the way up the vertical axis?

Draw in a line at 75 pupils and then read off the mark, like this:

This value is called the **Lower Quartile** (the bottom quarter).

So, the lower quartile is 44 marks.

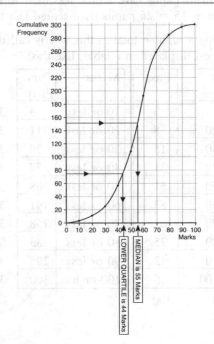

Now look at the mark of the person who is three-quarters of the way up the vertical axis.

Draw in a line at 225 pupils and then read off the mark, like this:

This value is called the **Upper Quartile** (the top quarter).

So, the upper quartile is 63 marks.

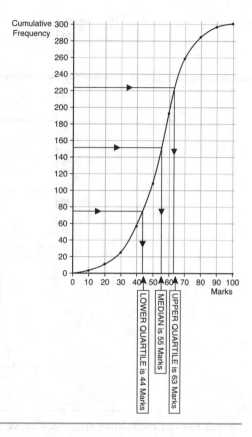

What do the upper quartile and lower quartile tell us?

Imagine the 300 pupils standing in a long line, in order of their exam mark, with those scoring least marks on the left and those scoring most on the right. We could represent the pupils in a diagram, like this:

Now ask the bottom 75 pupils and the top 75 pupils to sit down, like this:

Those pupils who are left standing are the middle half of Year 11.

The highest score of those still standing is   63 marks.
The lowest score of those still standing is   44 marks.   ....subtracting
                                                                   19 marks

So, they have scored within 19 marks of each other.

The difference between the Upper Quartile and the Lower Quartile is called the **Inter-Quartile Range**. It tells us something about the **spread** of the marks.

> Inter-Quartile Range = Upper Quartile − Lower Quartile

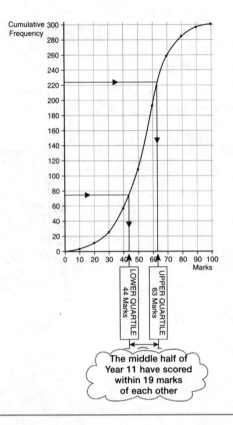

The middle half of Year 11 have scored within 19 marks of each other

We can use our cumulative frequency curve to answer other questions, such as:

(a) The pass mark was 35%. How many pupils scored less than the pass mark?
(b) A pupil had to score more than 72% to achieve a grade A. How many pupils were awarded a grade A?

Draw in two suitable lines on the cumulative frequency curve to help find the answers to these questions. Notice that, for this calculation, we start from the marks (along the horizontal axis) and work our way towards the cumulative frequency (along the vertical axis). The arrows, therefore, point the other way this time.

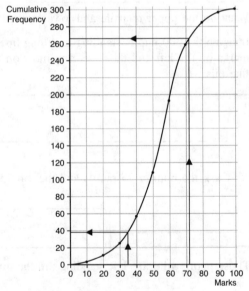

We can see from the cumulative frequency curve that about 38 pupils scored less than 35%. So 38 pupils failed the exam.

CAUTION!

> When we follow the arrows along from 72%, we get to about 265 pupils on the cumulative frequency axis.
>
> Clearly 265 pupils did not get a grade A!

265 pupils scored 72 marks or **less**.

So, 300 − 265 = 35 pupils scored **more** than 72 marks.

So, 35 pupils achieved a grade A.

STATISTICS

EXAMPLE 2

Mark (%)	Frequency
0–10	5
11–20	16
21–30	36
31–40	42
41–50	33
51–60	38
61–70	40
71–80	47
81–90	38
91–100	5
Total	300

At Beta School, just down the road, Year 11 pupils have also all been entered for French GCSE. These are their exam marks.

The cumulative frequency table looks like this:

Mark (%)	Freq	Marks	Cum Freq	
0–10	5	10 or less	5	5
11–20	16	20 or less	21	5 + 16
21–30	36	30 or less	57	5 + 16 + 36
31–40	42	40 or less	99	5 + 16 + 36 + 42
41–50	33	50 or less	132	5 + 16 + 36 + 42 + 33
51–60	38	60 or less	170	5 + 16 + 36 + 42 + 33 + 38
61–70	40	70 or less	210	5 + 16 + 36 + 42 + 33 + 38 + 40
71–80	47	80 or less	257	5 + 16 + 36 + 42 + 33 + 38 + 40 + 47
81–90	38	90 or less	295	5 + 16 + 36 + 42 + 33 + 38 + 40 + 47 + 38
91–100	5	100 or less	300	5 + 16 + 36 + 42 + 33 + 38 + 40 + 47 + 38 + 5

Total   300

We can plot the cumulative frequency curve and use this to work out:
(a) the median mark
(b) the upper quartile
(c) the lower quartile
(d) the inter-quartile range.
What conclusion can you draw about the two schools?

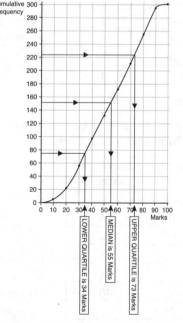

So, we can read off from our Cumulative Frequency Curve:

(a) the median is 55 marks

(b) the upper quartile is 73 marks

(c) the lower quartile is 34 marks

(d)   Upper Quartile = 73 marks
           Lower Quartile = 34 marks .....subtracting
       Inter-Quartile Range = 39 marks

The Inter-Quartile Range is 39 marks. So, the middle half of Year 11 (at Beta School) have scored within 39 marks of each other.

Remember that the Inter-Quartile Range at Alpha School was 19 marks. So, the middle half of

STATISTICS

Year 11 at Alpha School have scored within 19 marks of each other. The pupils at Alpha School are of a similar ability to each other. At Beta School there is a greater range of ability between the pupils. Notice that the median is the same for both schools. It is the **spread** of marks which is different between the two schools.

QUESTIONS 4.9

1. These are the GCSE Science marks at a particular school:

Mark (%)	Frequency
0–10	4
11–20	2
21–30	9
31–40	16
41–50	23
51–60	33
61–70	47
71–80	79
81–90	22
91–100	5
Total	240

Fill in a cumulative frequency table and draw a cummulative frequency curve and use this to find:

(a) the median mark.
(b) the upper quartile.
(c) the lower quartile.
(d) the inter-quartile range.
(e) the number of pupils who failed the exam, if the pass mark was 42%.
(f) the number of pupils who obtained a grade A, if the mark needed was 82% or better.

2. These are the GCSE English marks at a particular school:

Mark (%)	Frequency
0–10	3
11–20	8
21–30	20
31–40	49
41–50	94
51–60	51
61–70	82
71–80	15
81–90	24
91–100	4
Total	350

Fill in a cumulative frequency table and draw a cumulative frequency curve, which will enable you to find:

(a) the median mark.
(b) the upper quartile.
(c) the lower quartile.
(d) the inter-quartile range.
(e) the number of pupils who have failed the exam, if the pass mark is 35%.
(f) the number of pupils who have achieved a grade A if you need 75% or more for a grade A.

3. A coach company has kept some records of the number of passengers on its London to Birmingham direct route. These are the figures for 150 journeys:

Number of Passengers	Number of Journeys
0–5	3
6–10	5
11–15	14
16–20	25
21–25	41
26–30	40
31–35	15
36–40	4
41–45	3
Total	150

Fill in a cumulative frequency table and draw a cumulative frequency curve, which will enable you to find:

(a) the median number of passengers.
(b) the upper quartile.
(c) the lower quartile.
(d) the inter-quartile range.
(e) the number of journeys where the coach company loses money, if they need to carry at least 13 passengers to break even.

4. The results of a Maths exam for two classes in year 9 were as follows:

Class A: Median = 62 marks Inter-Quartile Range = 9 marks	Class B: Median = 62 marks Inter-Quartile Range = 27 marks

What do you think you could deduce about these two classes from these results?

STATISTICS **IS** ABOUT

COLLECTING THE DATA:

Deciding what data to collect
Deciding on the size of the sample
Doing a survey
Compiling a questionnaire
Making a tally chart

DISPLAYING THE DATA

Drawing bar charts
Drawing pie charts
Drawing frequency polygons
Drawing scatter graphs
Drawing cumulative frequency curves

ANALYSING THE DATA

Finding the Average (Mean, Median or Mode)
Grouping data – if necessary, to make it easier to handle
Looking for correlation by drawing Scatter Graphs
Finding the Range – the overall spread of the data
Finding the Inter-Quartile Range – a measure of the spread of the data

PROBABILITY

What is the probability that the school bus will be late tomorrow?
What is the probability that my car will have to stop at the next set of traffic lights?
What is the probability that I will die?
What is the probability that the next vehicle past my house will be a lorry?
What is the probability that the next vehicle past my house will be red?
What is the probability that you will ......

How **likely** do you think each of these events is?

The **chance** of an event happening is called the **probability** of that event happening.

PROBABILITY: PREDICTIONS AND EXPERIMENTS

We are going to do three experiments. Before we do any experiments, try some **predictions**!

A prediction is saying what you **think** will be the outcome of the experiment, before you actually **do** the experiment.

EXPERIMENT 1: ONE COIN TOSSED 50 TIMES
If you toss a coin 50 times, how many heads and how many tails do you think you would get?

EXPERIMENT 2: TWO COINS TOSSED 60 TIMES
If you toss two coins together 60 times, how many times do you think you would get two Heads? How many times would get one Head? How many times would you get no Heads at all?

EXPERIMENT 3: TWO DICE ROLLED 100 TIMES
If you throw two dice and record the total score, what possible scores are there? If you did this 100 times, how many times would you score 12?

Fill in your predictions in the following tables, making sure that all your totals are correct.

EXPERIMENT 1: One coin tossed 50 times

I predict		Heads
I predict		Tails
This should total	50	

EXPERIMENT 2: Two coins tossed 60 times

I predict		2 Heads
I predict		1 Head
I predict		0 Heads
This should total	100	

EXPERIMENT 3: Two dice rolled 100 times

I predict the score of 2		times
I predict the score of 3		times
I predict the score of 4		times
I predict the score of 5		times
I predict the score of 6		times
I predict the score of 7		times
I predict the score of 8		times
I predict the score of 9		times
I predict the score of 10		times
I predict the score of 11		times
I predict the score of 12		times
This should total	100	

DOING THE EXPERIMENTS

You have made your predictions, now do the experiments!

Record your results using the five bar gate counting system, or tally chart. Every fifth Head, put a diagonal line through, to make the 'gate'. This makes counting up at the end very easy.

Heads: ⊬⊓ ⊬⊓ ⊬⊓ ⊬⊓ ||| ⏜ You can easily see that this totals 23. ⏝

Now do the experiments, recording the results in the following tables, making sure that all your totals are correct:

EXPERIMENT 1: One coin tossed 50 times

	Tally	Total
Heads		
Tails		
	This should total	50

EXPERIMENT 2: Two coins tossed 60 times

	Tally	Totals
Two Heads		
One Head		
No Heads		
	This should total	60

EXPERIMENT 3: Two dice rolled 100 times

	Tally	Totals
Scores of 2		
Scores of 3		
Scores of 4		
Scores of 5		
Scores of 6		
Scores of 7		
Scores of 8		
Scores of 9		
Scores of 10		
Scores of 11		
Scores of 12		
	This should total	100

COMPARING PREDICTIONS WITH EXPERIMENTAL RESULTS

EXPERIMENT 1: Tossing One Coin 50 times

You probably predicted 25 Heads and 25 Tails – most people do! A coin is used at the start of some sports matches to decide which team goes first. Both sides are happy with tossing a coin as no-one gains an unfair advantage. The coin is equally likely to land Heads as it is to land Tails, provided, of course, that no-one has tampered with the coin to make it land Heads, say, more often than Tails! This would make the coin '**biased**'. Usually, coins are '**unbiased**' or '**fair**'.

H   T   There are only two possible outcomes
                            and they are equally likely to happen.

So, the probability of getting a Head is one half and the probability of getting a Tail is also one half. You can shorten this to:

$p(Tail) = \frac{1}{2}$ $p(Head) = \frac{1}{2}$

I asked pupils in my class to do Experiment 1 and these are the results that they obtained:

Heads	24	27	26	18	29	26	26	22	19	22	29	23	25	24	21
Tails	26	23	24	32	21	24	24	28	31	28	21	27	25	26	29

Although 25 Heads and 25 Tails is the most sensible prediction, only one pupil obtained this result. Many pupils believe that their experiment **should** always give 25 Heads and 25 Tails, as if this result was in some way "The Correct Answer". All of the results above are "correct", as they all happened. There will naturally be some variation in experimental results such as these.

Find the average number of Heads for my class. Find the average number of Tails for my class. What can you say about your answer? Ask more people to do Experiment 1 and find the average of all their results. What answer would you expect this time?

EXPERIMENT 2: Tossing Two Coins 60 times

Many pupils predict:

20	2 Heads
20	1 Head
20	0 Heads

This seems a very reasonable prediction, but when my class did experiment 2, their results did not agree with this prediction.

Two Heads	11	14	18	15	17	13	15	13	14	17	11	14	11	17	12
One Head	35	31	27	34	31	30	34	30	31	29	30	28	36	27	30
One Head	14	15	15	11	12	17	11	17	15	14	19	18	13	16	18

You can see that One Head appears to come up about twice as often as Two Heads or No Heads.

Let's look carefully at how the coins can land:

First   Second
Coin   Coin

H   H

H   T ⎫
               ⎬ There are two ways that one head can be obtained.
T   H ⎭

T   T

This shows that there are **FOUR** different outcomes (HH, HT, TH, TT) which are **EQUALLY LIKELY,** not three (Two Heads, One Head or No Heads).

EXPERIMENT 2 AGAIN

I asked my class to do experiment 2 again, this time recording their results in a new table.
HT would mean Head on the first coin and Tails on the second coin.
TH would mean Tails on the first coin and Head on the second coin.
And these two results would therefore be recorded separately this time.

These are their new results:

HH	15	13	15	13	16	17	15	15	11	17	12	15	17	18	11
HT	11	14	13	17	13	12	19	14	14	21	16	17	18	16	18
TH	15	21	17	17	13	15	12	19	16	8	16	14	11	15	17
TT	19	12	15	13	18	16	14	12	19	14	16	14	14	11	14

HH, HT, TH and TT are equally likely outcomes. We have tossed the two coins 60 times with each repetition of the experiment, so we should now expect each outcome to happen 60 ÷ 4 = 15 times each experiment. You can see by looking at the experimental results from my class that this is what is happening, give or take some variation in experimental results.

So, we can now calculate the probabilities of these outcomes, as follows:

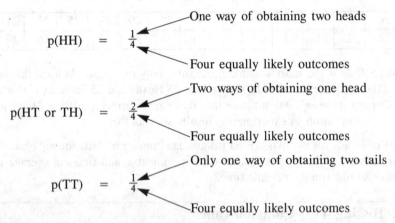

One way of obtaining two heads

$$p(HH) = \frac{1}{4}$$

Four equally likely outcomes

Two ways of obtaining one head

$$p(HT \text{ or } TH) = \frac{2}{4}$$

Four equally likely outcomes

Only one way of obtaining two tails

$$p(TT) = \frac{1}{4}$$

Four equally likely outcomes

Notice that these three probabilities add up to one.

$$\frac{1}{4} + \frac{2}{4} + \frac{1}{4} = \frac{4}{4} = 1$$

This must be the case, because we have included all the possible outcomes.

EXPERIMENT 3: Throwing Two Dice 100 Times

My class's results are:

Score of 2	2	4	2	6	4	2	6	2	2	2	4	2	1	2	5
Score of 3	10	7	8	7	4	4	8	2	5	6	8	6	9	6	4
Score of 4	8	7	11	7	6	14	8	7	8	11	5	8	12	11	4
Score of 5	11	13	7	10	13	11	15	17	10	13	8	5	13	12	11
Score of 6	12	17	11	11	10	13	14	17	16	10	16	16	10	13	15
Score of 7	19	18	22	17	19	13	13	14	12	12	16	20	22	16	20
Score of 8	16	14	13	15	16	15	8	15	14	13	17	20	10	17	9
Score of 9	9	10	12	13	15	10	14	12	14	7	6	11	9	5	11
Score of 10	6	4	9	4	6	6	3	8	5	11	10	8	6	10	10
Score of 11	6	3	5	5	6	9	7	6	6	11	7	4	6	7	9
Score of 12	1	3	0	5	1	3	4	0	8	4	3	0	2	1	2

You can see that the scores of 6, 7 and 8 came up much more often than 2, 3, 11 or 12.

Each pupil has drawn a bar chart of their results. The first three pupil's results looks like this:

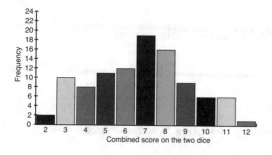

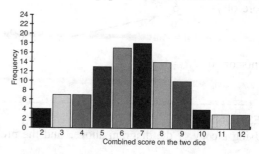

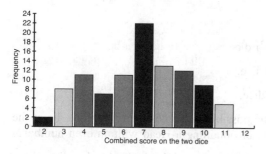

You can see that all the bar charts are of the same general shape. The scores of 2, 3, 11 and 12 have not come up that often, and there are many more scores of 6, 7 and 8.

In this case there are 36 different EQUALLY LIKELY outcomes. If I roll a red die (This is the correct word for one dice!) and a blue die, then I can record all of the different outcomes in this table:

Score on the Red Die

	1	2	3	4	5	6
1	2	3	4	5	6	7
2	3	4	5	6	7	8
3	4	5	6	7	8	9
4	5	6	7	8	9	10
5	6	7	8	9	10	11
6	7	8	9	10	11	12

Score on the Blue Die

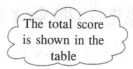

The total score is shown in the table

This kind of diagram is called a **possibility space diagram**, because it shows all the possible outcomes.

There is only one way of scoring 2 because you have to get a one on the red die and a one on the blue die.

So, p(scoring 2) = $\frac{1}{36}$

there is only one way to score 2

out of 36 different equally likely outcomes

Draw a new copy of the above table. Shade in all the combinations which give you a score of 7

You should find that three are six different ways of scoring a total of 7:

1 on the blue die and 6 on the red die
2 on the blue die and 5 on the red die
3 on the blue die and 4 on the red die
4 on the blue die and 3 on the red die
5 on the blue die and 2 on the red die
6 on the blue die and 1 on the red die.

p(score of 7) = $\frac{6}{36}$ ← there are six different ways of scoring 7

← out of 36 different equally likely outcomes

So, p(score of 7) = $\frac{6}{36} = \frac{1}{6}$

QUESTIONS 5.1

1. Using a copy of the diagram above, find the probability of scoring 5 with two dice.

2. Find the probability of scoring 10 with two dice.

3. Find the probability of scoring "a double".

4. Find the probability of scoring 10 or more with two dice.

5. Find the probability of scoring at least 8 with two dice.

6. Find the probability of scoring 5 or less with two dice.

7. Draw a possibility space diagram which gives all the possible outcomes for rolling one die at the same time as tossing one coin. What is the probability of obtaining a Head with an even number?

8. Use your diagram from question 7. What is the probability of obtaining a number less than three with a Tail?

9. Use your diagram from question 7. What is the probability of obtaining a 6 or a Head or both?

10. What is the probability of scoring a total of 1 with two dice?

11. What is the probability of scoring a number from 2 to 12 (inclusive) with two dice?

DEFINITION OF PROBABILITY

From the work we have done so far, we can move towards a more formal definition of probability:

p(an event happening) = $\dfrac{\text{Number of ways this event can happen}}{\text{Total number of equally likely outcomes}}$

Your answer to question 10, therefore, should be:

p(Score of total of 1 with two dice) = $\dfrac{0}{36}$ = 0

As you cannot score just 1 with two dice this is an impossibility.

The probability of an impossible event is zero.

p(an impossibility) = 0

Your answer to question 11 should be:

p(Scoring between 2 and 12 with two dice) = $\dfrac{36}{36}$ = 1

This covers all the possible scores, so this outcome is a certainty.

The probability of a certain event is one.

p(a certainty) = 1

THE PROBABILITY SCALE

We can put all probabilities onto a Probability Scale, which goes from 0 to 1, like this:

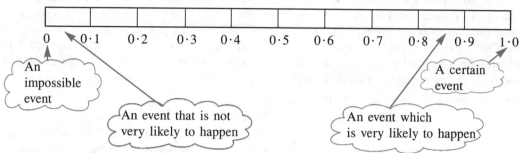

We have calculated a lot of probabilities so far, but our answers have been left as fractions. To place each event on the Probability Scale, it is easier to turn each fraction into a decimal.

p(scoring 7 with two dice) = $\frac{6}{36}$ [Remember that this means 6 **divided** by 36]

Use your calculator to do the division. So $6 \div 36 = 0 \cdot 16666\ldots$

We could give this to two decimal places as $0 \cdot 17$ and we can now put this probability onto the Probability Scale:

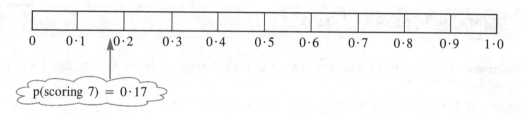

QUESTIONS 5.2

Make a copy of the Probability Scale. Calculate the probabilities of the following events and turn your fractions into a decimal, so that you can place each event on the Probability Scale.

1. What is the probability of choosing a Heart from a shuffled pack of 52 playing cards?

2. What is the probability of choosing a Red card from a shuffled pack of cards?

3. What is the probability of choosing a King?

4. What is the probability of choosing a Diamond from a pack of cards?

5. What is the probability of choosing a Diamond from a pack of cards where someone has lost the 7 of Spades from the pack?

6. What is the probability of choosing a Spade from the pack without the 7 of Spades?

7. What is the probability of choosing a '7' from the pack without the 7 of Spades?

8. What is the probability that it will rain tomorrow?

9. What is the probability that you will sneeze tomorrow?

10. What is the probability that if you drop a drawing pin that it will land with its point up?

EXPERIMENTAL PROBABILITIES

You will by now have realised that the last three questions are different from those that we have looked at so far. In the questions that involve dice, coins and playing cards, it is possible to find all the equally likely outcomes. For question 8, we know that either it will rain tomorrow or it will not. But these two outcomes are not equally likely. At some times of the year it is much more likely to rain than at other times, but even then it does not rain every other day! We could only begin to answer question 8 by making note each day for a long time whether it rained or not. The more days we looked at, the more reliable would be our answer. We could use the fraction:

$$p(\text{of rain tomorrow}) = \frac{\text{Number of days it has rain}}{\text{Number of days we've observed}}$$

to calculate an estimate of this probability. There can be no "right answer" for this type of probability as there is for dice, coins and cards. Also, your estimate will vary according to the season, which country you live in and even which part of that country.

To work out the probability of the drawing pin landing pointing up, we could throw it in the air and record how it lands for one hundred times. We could use the fraction:

$$p(\text{landing point up}) = \frac{\text{Number of times it landed point up}}{\text{Number of times we threw it up in the air}}$$

This is called the **Relative Frequency** and would give us a good measure of the probability of this event happening. Again, the more times you repeated the experiment the more accurate would be your answer for the probability of the drawing pin landing point up.

ESTIMATED PROBABILITIES

What is the probability that I will beat Arnold at tennis? What is the probability that I will beat Betty at tennis?

I could play both of them say ten times each, then use the fraction:

$$p(\text{beating Arnold}) = \frac{\text{number of matches that I beat Arnold}}{10}$$

to give an answer. Or, I could just make an intelligent guess, or estimate of how likely I am to win. I know that I am a better player than Arnold, so I believe that I have a good chance of beating him. I estimate that:

$$p(\text{beating Arnold}) = \frac{3}{4} = 0 \cdot 75$$

Betty, on the other hand has been working on her serve, so I don't think my chance of beating her is so good. I estimate that:

$$p(\text{beating Betty}) = \frac{1}{5} = 0 \cdot 2$$

ASSIGNING PROBABILITIES

To summarise, we can assign probabilities to events in different ways. Choose your method from this list depending on the situation you are dealing with. We can:

USE EQUALLY LIKELY OUTCOMES

With questions on dice, coins and playing cards, for example, we can work out the equally likely outcomes and from there the probabilities, using theory rather than experiment.

COLLECT DATA

We could collect data on how many children in the whole school were left-handed. We could use the relative frequency:

$$\frac{\text{number of left-handed pupil}}{\text{total number of pupils}}$$

to give us an estimate of the probability that a pupil chosen at random would be left-handed.

DO EXPERIMENTS

We could use an experiment to answer the question about the drawing pin landing point up and using the relative frequency to give us an estimate of the probability.

MAKE ESTIMATES

We have used a subjective estimate for the probabilities of my beating Arnold and Betty at tennis, using what I already know about the strengths and weaknesses of their game.

EXCLUSIVE EVENTS & EXHAUSTIVE EVENTS

I have a bag of sweets. In that bag there are 14 sweets, whose colours are as follows:

Red	Red	Blue	Yellow	Green	Green
Red	Red	Blue		Green	
Red	Red	Blue		Green	

I select a sweet without looking into the bag. The probabilities that I will choose a certain colour are:

$$p(\text{Red}) = \frac{6}{14} \qquad\qquad p(\text{Yellow}) = \frac{1}{14}$$

$$p(\text{Blue}) = \frac{3}{14} \qquad\qquad p(\text{Green}) = \frac{4}{14}$$

I am going to select only one sweet, without looking into the bag. If I select a Red sweet, for example, I do not select a Blue, or a Yellow or a Green one. So these different events are said to be **Mutually Exclusive**, because selecting Red **excludes** the other possibilities.

If I add these probabilities up:

$$p(\text{Red}) + p(\text{Blue}) + p(\text{Yellow}) + p(\text{Green}) = 1$$

$$\frac{6}{14} + \frac{3}{14} + \frac{1}{14} + \frac{4}{14} = \frac{14}{14} = 1$$

Take all four outcomes together and they are called **Exhaustive Events**, because they **exhaust** all the possibilities. Nothing else can happen. I can't, for example, take out a purple sweet, because there aren't any purple ones in the bag.

EITHER.... OR....PROBABILITIES

The probability that the sweet I select is either Red or Blue is calculated by adding the probabilities of Red or Blue from above

p(Selected Sweet is either Red or Blue) $= \frac{6}{14} + \frac{3}{14} = \frac{9}{14}$

This must be true because there are nine sweets out of the 14 which are either Red or Blue.

NOT .... PROBABILITIES

The probability that the sweet that I select is NOT Green, is the same as the probability that it is Red, or Blue or Yellow.

$$p(\text{Selected Sweet is NOT Green}) = P(\text{Red}) + P(\text{Blue}) + P(\text{Yellow})$$

$$= \frac{6}{14} + \frac{3}{14} + \frac{1}{14}$$

$$= \frac{10}{14}$$

We can also look at this another way, since:

p(Sweet is Green) + p(Sweet **Not** Green) = 1

So, p(Sweet **Not** Green) $= 1 - $ p(Sweet is Green)

$$= 1 - \frac{4}{14} = \frac{10}{14} \qquad \text{......as before.}$$

THE EXPECTED NUMBER

If you cut a pack of cards, what is the probability that the card you obtain would be a spade?

As there are four suits in each pack, each equally likely to turn up, the probability of obtaining a spade would be $\frac{1}{4}$.

If you repeated the experiment 20 times, how many times do you **expect** to obtain spades?

You would expect to obtain spades once every four goes, so

$\frac{1}{4} \times 20 = 5$ times

will give you the **expected number** of spades.

QUESTIONS 5.3

1. If I roll a die 180 times, how many 6's do I expect to get?

2. I toss a coin 120 times, how many heads do I expect?

3. I toss two coins together 120 times, how many times do I expect to get two heads?

4. I cut a pack of cards 100 times. How many times do I expect to get a Diamond?

COMBINED EVENTS AND TREE DIAGRAMS

When we tossed two coins together, we saw that there were four equally likely outcomes and we displayed them like this:

First Coin	Second Coin
H	H
H	T
T	H
T	T

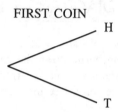

FIRST COIN

There is another very useful diagram that we can use to display this information. If we toss one coin first and look and see whether it has landed heads or tails, we can record the outcome like this:

The first coin can land either heads or tails. Whether it lands heads or tails makes no difference to how the second coin lands. These are said to be **independent** events.

So, we can complete the diagram, which is called a **tree diagram** because it has branches!

As p(head) = $\frac{1}{2}$ and p(tail) = $\frac{1}{2}$, I have put $\frac{1}{2}$ along each branch. I have added a "Possible Outcome" column and a "Probability" column as well.

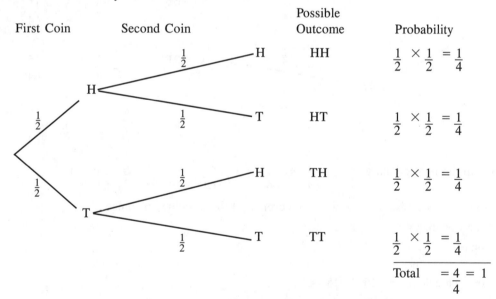

You can see that the probabilities are exactly the same as before, as long as we multiply the probabilities as we travel along a particular branch. Notice also, that the probabilities in the final column add up to one, as we have covered all the possible outcomes.

So, the tree diagram confirms that:

p(HH) = $\frac{1}{4}$ p(HT) = $\frac{1}{4}$ p(TH) = $\frac{1}{4}$ p(TT) = $\frac{1}{4}$

Tree diagrams can be used to calculate probabilities of two or more combined events.

QUESTIONS 5.4

1. The p(having a baby girl) = p(having a baby boy) = $\frac{1}{2}$.

What is the probability of having two children who are both girls? Hint: Draw a tree diagram similar to the one above for two coins.

2. In a family of two children, what is the probability of having one boy and one girl?

3. In a family of two children, what is the probability of having two children of the same sex?

4. Draw a tree diagram for a family of three children. What is the probability of :

(a) all the children being girls?   (d) two boys and one girl?
(b) all the children being boys?   (e) two girls and one boy?
(c) all the children being the same sex?

TREE DIAGRAMS 2: Replacing the ball

I have a bag of balls, where 5 are blue and 3 are red. I shake the bag, take a ball without looking into the bag, write down the colour of the ball and **then put the ball back in the bag**. I shake the bag and take a second ball from the bag and make a note of its colour too. I can record all possible outcomes on a tree diagram, as before.

First Ball	Second Ball	Possible Outcome	Probability
B ($\frac{5}{8}$)	B ($\frac{5}{8}$)	BB	$\frac{5}{8} \times \frac{5}{8} = \frac{25}{64}$
	R ($\frac{3}{8}$)	BR	$\frac{5}{8} \times \frac{3}{8} = \frac{15}{64}$
R ($\frac{3}{8}$)	B ($\frac{5}{8}$)	RB	$\frac{3}{8} \times \frac{5}{8} = \frac{15}{64}$
	R ($\frac{3}{8}$)	RR	$\frac{3}{8} \times \frac{3}{8} = \frac{9}{64}$

Adding up the last column gives: $\frac{25}{64} + \frac{15}{64} + \frac{15}{64} + \frac{9}{64} = \frac{64}{64} = 1$

Which must be the case because we have covered all the possible outcomes.

Using the tree diagram, we can see that:

p(two blues) = $\frac{25}{64}$

p(one of each colour) = $\frac{15}{64} + \frac{15}{64} = \frac{30}{64}$

p(two reds) = $\frac{9}{64}$

p(at least one red) = $\frac{15}{64} + \frac{15}{64} + \frac{9}{64} = \frac{39}{64}$

Or, another way of looking at this is to say that:

p(at least one red) = $1 - $ p(no reds) $= 1 - $ p(two blues)

$$= 1 - \frac{25}{64} = \frac{64}{64} - \frac{25}{64} = \frac{39}{64}$$

QUESTIONS 5.5

1. I am going to play my first tennis match against Arnold and my second match against Betty. Copy and complete this tree diagram, and answer the questions below. Remember that I have estimated my chances of beating Arnold and Betty as follows:

Prob(beating Arnold) = $\frac{3}{4}$ Prob(beating Betty) = $\frac{1}{5}$

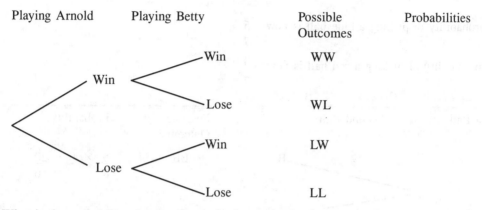

(a) What is the probability that I will win both matches?
(b) What is the probability that I will win only one match?
(c) What is the probability that I will win at least one match?
(d) What is the probability that I will win no matches at all?

2. A bag contains 10 coloured balls, 7 are yellow and 3 are green. I shake the bag, take a ball without looking, note its colour then put it back in the bag. I then shake the bag and take a second ball. Draw a tree diagram that will enable you to answer these questions.

(a) What is the probability that I will take two green balls?
(b) What is the probability that I will take two yellow balls?
(c) What is the probability that I will take one yellow and one green?
(d) What is the probability that I will take at least one green ball?

TREE DIAGRAMS 3: **Not** replacing the ball

I have a bag of balls, where 5 are blue and 3 are red. I shake the bag, take a ball without looking into the bag, write down the colour of the ball. **This time, I don't put the ball back in the bag**.

I shake the bag and take a second ball from the bag and make a note of its colour too. I can record all possible outcomes on a tree diagram, as before.

This time, I must think extremely carefully about the probabilities along each branch. **If** I have taken a **blue** ball first time, then there can be only 4 blue balls left in the bag, plus the 3 red balls. The contents of the bag are now as follows:

Blue   Red
Blue   Red
Blue   Red
Blue

So, the probability of picking a blue ball is now $\frac{4}{7}$

And the probability of picking a red ball is now $\frac{3}{7}$

If I had taken a **red** ball the first time, then there can be only 2 red balls left in the bag, plus the 5 blue ones. The contents of the bag are now as follows:

Blue   Red
Blue   Red
Blue
Blue
Blue

So, the probability of picking a blue ball is now $\dfrac{5}{7}$

And the probability of picking a red ball is now $\dfrac{2}{7}$

First Ball	Second Ball	Possible Outcome	Probability
	$\frac{4}{7}$ B	BB	$\dfrac{5}{8} \times \dfrac{4}{7} = \dfrac{20}{56}$
$\frac{5}{8}$ B	$\frac{3}{7}$ R	BR	$\dfrac{5}{8} \times \dfrac{3}{7} = \dfrac{15}{56}$
$\frac{3}{8}$ R	$\frac{5}{7}$ B	RB	$\dfrac{3}{8} \times \dfrac{5}{7} = \dfrac{15}{56}$
	$\frac{2}{7}$ R	RR	$\dfrac{3}{8} \times \dfrac{2}{7} = \dfrac{6}{56}$

Adding the final column gives: $\dfrac{20}{56} + \dfrac{15}{56} + \dfrac{15}{56} + \dfrac{6}{56} = \dfrac{56}{56} = 1$

So, we still have a total of one, which must be the case because we have covered all the possible outcomes, just as before!

Using the tree diagram, we can see that:

p(two blues) $= \dfrac{20}{56} = \dfrac{5}{14}$

p(one of each colour) $= \dfrac{15}{56} + \dfrac{15}{56} = \dfrac{30}{56} = \dfrac{15}{28}$

p(two reds) $= \dfrac{6}{56} = \dfrac{3}{28}$

p(at least one red) $= \dfrac{15}{56} + \dfrac{15}{56} + \dfrac{6}{56} = \dfrac{36}{56} = \dfrac{18}{28} = \dfrac{9}{14}$

Or, another way of looking at this is to say that:

p(at least one red) $= 1 - $ p(two blues)

$= 1 - \dfrac{20}{56} = \dfrac{56}{56} - \dfrac{20}{56} = \dfrac{36}{56} = \dfrac{18}{28} = \dfrac{9}{14}$ .....as before

QUESTIONS 5.6

1. I have a bag of balls, where 3 are red and 8 blue. I shake the bag and take a ball out of the bag without looking into the bag. **I don't put the ball back into the bag**. I shake the bag and take a second ball from the bag. Record all possible outcomes in a tree diagram.

(a) What is the probability of getting two reds.
(b) What is the probability of getting two blue.
(c) What is the probability of getting one of each colour?
(d) What is the probability of getting at least one red?

2. I have a bag of balls, where 2 are yellow and 7 are green. I shake the bag and take a ball out of the bag without looking into the bag. **I don't put the ball back into the bag**. I shake the bag and take a second ball from the bag. Record all possible outcomes in a tree diagram.

(a) What is the probability of getting two yellow.
(b) What is the probability of getting two green.
(c) What is the probability of getting one of each colour?
(d) What is the probability of getting at least one green?

ANSWERS

1.1
1. 259
2. 290
3. 540
4. 495
5. 96
6. 72

1.2
1. 52
2. 49
3. 531
4. 1608

1.3
1. 342
2. 349
3. 816
4. 843

1.3 ctd
5. 0.002923.....
6. 0.002865....
7. 0.001225....
8. 0.001186....

1.4
1

Hours and Minutes	Hours
3 hours 15 minutes	3·25 hours
4 hours 18 minutes	4·3
7 hours 42 minutes	7·7
1 hour 22 minutes	1·3666
2 hours 10 minutes	2·1666
6 hours 55 minutes	6·9166

2(a) 56·5mph
(b) 55·6mph
(c) 61·8mph
(d) 47·4mph

1.5
1. $a = -2°C$, $b = 2°C$, $c = -5°C$
   2°C, −2°C, −5°C
2. $a = 10°C$, $b = -8°C$, $c = -3°C$
   10°C, −3°C, −8°C
3. $a = -11°C$, $b = -12°C$, $c = 3°C$
   3°C, −11°C, −12°C
4. $a = -3°C$, $b = 0°C$, $c = -12°C$
   0°C, −3°C, −12°C
5. $8 - 5 = 3$
6. $4 - (-2) = 6$
7. $7 - (-4) = 11$
8. $5 - (-3) = 8$
9. $-3 - (-7) = 4$
10. $-2 - (-6) = 4$
11. $-£14 + -£20 = -£34$ .... so I owe £34
12. $-£9 + £4 = -£5$ ....so I owe £5

1.6
1. 6
2. −10
3. −9
4. −6
5. −2
6. −5
7. −3
8. 1
9. 5
10. −1
11. −7
12. 8
13. −3
14. 7
15. −13
16. −6
17. 11
18. −11
19. 12
20. 4
21. −10
22. 13
23. −3
24. −8

1.7
1(a) −6, −9, −12, −15
 (b) −4, −7, −10, −13
 (c) −3, −8, −13, −18
 (d) −5, −9, −13, −17
2. The two numbers are −2 and −5.

3.

Two Numbers	Their Sum	Their Product
6 and −7	−1	−42
−6 and 7	+1	−42
−6 and −7	−13	+42
4 and −9	−5	−36
−4 and −9	−13	+36
7 and −10	−3	−70

4(a) −36
(b) −4
(c) −100
(d) 6
(e) 21
(f) −4
(g) −84
(h) −4
(i) 35
(j) 8
(k) −68
(l) −3

1.8
1. Yes
2. No
3. Yes
4. Yes

1.9
1. 168
2. 60
3. 90
4. 36

1.10
1. 1, 2, 3, 4, 6, 8, 12, 16, 24, 48
2. 1, 2, 4, 5, 10, 20, 25, 50, 100
3. 1, 3, 9, 11, 33, 99
4. 1, 2, 23, 46

1.11
1. 4
2. 2
3. 9
4. 4

1.12
1. There are 25 prime numbers between 1 and 100: they are 2, 3, 5, 7, 11, 13, 17, 19, 23, 29, 31, 37, 41, 43, 47, 53, 59, 61, 67, 71, 73, 79, 83, 89, 97
2. $11 \times 13 = 143$, No
3. $17 \times 19 = 323$, No
4. $19 \times 23 = 437$, No

1.13
1. $50 = 2 \times 5 \times 5$
2. $52 = 2 \times 2 \times 13$
3. $60 = 2 \times 2 \times 3 \times 5$
4. $858 = 2 \times 3 \times 11 \times 13$

1.14
1. 121, 144, 169, 196, 225, 256, 289, 324, 361, 400
2. 529
3. 46·7856
4. 2246·76

1.15
1. 23
2. 31
3. 14.142...
4. 27

1.15 ctd
5. 3·162...
6. 10
7. 31·62....
8. 100

1.16
1. 1331, 1728, 2197, 2744, 3375, 4096, 4913, 5832, 6859, 8000
2. 50·653
3. 264·609....
4. 13481·272....

1.17
1. 21
2. 2·714...
3. 2·1544...
4. 4·6415...

1.17 ctd
5. 10
6. 21·544...
7. 46·415...
8. 100

1.18
1. 1, 3, 6, 10, 15, 21, 28, 36, 45, 55, 66, 78, 91, 105, 120, 136, 153, 171, 190, 210
2. $S = \dfrac{N(N + 1)}{2} = \dfrac{N^2 + N}{2}$

1.19
1(a) B is bigger
 (b) A is bigger
 (c) B is bigger
 (d) B is bigger
2(a) Any decimal starting 2·8***** For example 2·81
(b) Any decimal starting 4·5***** For example 4·57
(c) Any decimal starting 1·9***** For example 1·93
(d) Any decimal starting 0·3***** For example 0·34
(e) Any decimal starting 8·87***** For example 8·873
(f) Any decimal starting 0·125***** For example 0·1259
3(a) 5·35
(b) 2·605
(c) 17·5
(d) 3·7
(e) 3·7
(f) 6·85
4(a) 0·8
(b) 3·5
(c) 0·32
(d) 0·9
(e) 15·9
(f) same
(g) 0·54
(h) 0·2
(i) 6·61
(j) 12·2
(k) 2·95
5. Infinite number
6. Infinite number
7. Infinite number
8. Infinite number
9(a) fifty three point six eight
(b) nought point five two one
10(a) 8
(b) 4·07
(c) 6·4
(d) 7·9
(e) 11·95
11(a) 0·8, 1·0, 1·2, 1·4
(b) 0·75, 0·9, 1·05, 1·2, 1·35
(c) 4·11, 4·1, 4·09, 4·08, 4·07
12(a) same (b) same (c) same (d) 0·54 bigger (e) same (f) same

ANSWERS

1.20

1. 86·84
2. 523·44
3. 36·11
4. 3·15
5. 73·863
6. 4·612
7. 59·509
8. 2·719993
9. 273·173
10. 7042·058
11. 17·3
12. 6·35

13, 14 &15 Stories such as: I need 3.7 metres of material to re-cover a chair and 8.2 metres to re-cover a settee. How much material do I need altogether? You cannot talk about 3.7 felt tip pens!

1.21

1(a) 4 cm² (b) 2 cm² (c) 12 cm² (d) 3 cm²
2(a) 48 cm² (b) 4·8 cm² (c) 52 cm² (d) 5·2 cm²
(e) 256 cm² (f) 25·6 cm² (g) 300 cm² (h) 3 cm²
(i) 912 cm² (j) 9·12 cm²

1.22

1(c) 14·28 2(d) 100·1 3(c) 3·68 4(d) 0·72
5. 17·25 6. 215·67 7. 20·58
8. 41·454 9. 1·498 10. 0·19899

1.23

1(a) 0·5 cm (b) 0·25 cm (c) 0·75 cm (d) 0·75 cm
2(a) 9 cm (d) 6 cm (g) 8 cm (j) 1·2 cm
(b) 9 cm (e) 11 cm (h) 0·8 cm (k) 14 cm
(c) 6 cm (f) 11 cm (i) 12 cm (l) 1·4 cm

1.24

1(c) 2 3(d) 24·1 5. 30·4 7. 52·9 9. 32·776…
2(c) 1·4 4(c) 0·34 6. 5610 8. 710 10. 20·78….

1.26

1(a) £97·34 (b) £8·79 (to the nearest penny)
2. 20 cm long 3. x = 17·71 cm y = 6·16 cm
4. 11·76 kg 5. 11 parcels (30 cm of ribbon left over)
6. 3 shelves 7. 42.5 cm 8. 60 cm 9. 1.2 kg
10. 4·35 pounds 11. £12·69 12. 34·48 litres
13. Large: 17·1 grams per penny Medium: 17·35 grams per penny Small: 16.66 grams per penny The medium packet is the best buy.
14. Small: 5·83 ml per penny Large: 6·02 ml per penny The large size is the best buy.
15. 6·2 miles per litre 16. 33 miles per gallon

1.27

1(a) 0·5 (b) 0·333333… (c) 0·25 (d) 0·2
0·666666… 0·5 0·4
0·75 0·6
0·8

(e) 0·166666…. (f) 0·142857142…. (g) 0·125
0·333333… 0·285714285.. 0·25
0·5 0·428571428.. 0·375
0·6666… 0·571428571.. 0·5
0·83333… 0·714285714.. 0·625
0·857142857…. 0·75
0·875

(h) 0·1111… (i) 0·1 (j) 0·090909.. (k) 0·083333..
0·22222… 0·2 0·181818… 0·16666..
0·33333… 0·3 0·272727.. 0·25
0·44444… 0·4 0·363636.. 0·33333…
0·55555… 0·5 0·454545.. 0·416666…
0·66666.. 0·6 0·545454.. 0·5
0·7777… 0·7 0·636363… 0·58333…
0·88888… 0·8 0·727272… 0·6666..
0·9 0·818181.. 0·75
0·909090.. 0·8333…
0.91666..

2.

(a) $2\frac{1}{2}$ (b) $2\frac{1}{4}$ (c) $4\frac{1}{3}$ (d) $4\frac{3}{5}$ (e) 2
(f) $2\frac{1}{9}$ (g) $12\frac{3}{4}$ (h) $10\frac{2}{3}$ (i) $6\frac{2}{5}$ (j) $33\frac{1}{3}$

3.(a) $\frac{11}{4}$ (b) $\frac{10}{3}$ (c) $\frac{19}{3}$ (d) $\frac{47}{8}$ (e) $\frac{29}{6}$
(f) $\frac{11}{5}$ (g) $\frac{19}{3}$ (h) $\frac{18}{7}$ (i) $\frac{301}{3}$ (j) $\frac{235}{8}$

4.

(a) $\frac{1}{2} = \frac{5}{10}$ (b) $\frac{3}{4} = \frac{15}{20}$ (c) $\frac{18}{20} = \frac{9}{10}$
(d) $\frac{5}{6} = \frac{20}{24}$ (e) $\frac{3}{8} = \frac{15}{40}$ (f) $\frac{24}{30} = \frac{4}{5}$
(g) $\frac{2}{5} = \frac{8}{20}$ (h) $\frac{5}{8} = \frac{35}{56}$ (i) $\frac{24}{60} = \frac{2}{5}$ (j) $\frac{15}{36} = \frac{5}{12}$

1.29

1(b) $\frac{9}{10}$ (c) $\frac{7}{20}$ (d) $\frac{1}{9}$ (e) $\frac{1}{3}$
2. $\frac{3}{4}$ 3. 1 4. $\frac{7}{9}$ 5. $\frac{2}{7}$ 6. $\frac{1}{4}$ 7. $\frac{5}{9}$
8. $\frac{5}{6}$ 9. $\frac{5}{6}$ 10. $\frac{7}{8}$ 11. $\frac{7}{12}$ 12. $2\frac{43}{60}$ 13. $\frac{3}{5}$
14. $\frac{1}{5}$ 15. $\frac{1}{8}$ 16. $\frac{1}{10}$ 17. $2\frac{1}{6}$ 18. $2\frac{3}{20}$ 19. $1\frac{3}{4}$
20. $4\frac{9}{14}$ 21. $1\frac{5}{7}$ 22. $4\frac{1}{2}$ 23. $1\frac{5}{8}$ 24. $1\frac{5}{8}$ 25. $2\frac{13}{15}$

1.30

1. $\frac{3}{14}$ 2. $\frac{9}{40}$ 3. $\frac{15}{32}$ 4. $\frac{18}{75}$

1.31

1. $\frac{1}{6}$ 2. $\frac{1}{12}$ 3. $\frac{2}{15}$ 4. $\frac{6}{35}$
5. $\frac{2}{5}$ 6. $\frac{1}{2}$ 7. $\frac{5}{14}$ 8. $\frac{2}{3}$
9. $\frac{1}{8}$ 10. $\frac{5}{12}$ 11. $\frac{18}{5} = 3\frac{3}{5}$ 12. $\frac{50}{3} = 16\frac{2}{3}$
13. 2 14. $\frac{25}{3}$ 15. $\frac{25}{4} = 6\frac{1}{4}$ 16. $\frac{3}{5}$
17. $\frac{19}{2} = 9\frac{1}{2}$ 18. $\frac{34}{5} = 6\frac{4}{5}$ 19. $\frac{27}{20} = 1\frac{7}{20}$ 20. $\frac{25}{4} = 6\frac{1}{4}$

21(a) 10 galls (b) 12 galls 22(a) 36 litres (b) 54 litres
23. 387 boys 24. £1230
25. Abigail gets £600 Bruce gets £450 Caroline gets £750

1.32

1. $\frac{5}{4} = 1\frac{1}{4}$ 2. $\frac{4}{3} = 1\frac{1}{3}$ 3. $\frac{14}{3} = 4\frac{2}{3}$ 4. 1 5. $\frac{8}{9}$
6. $\frac{4}{3} = 1\frac{1}{3}$ 7. $\frac{4}{5}$ 8. $\frac{77}{24} = 3\frac{5}{24}$ 9. $\frac{35}{16} = 2\frac{3}{16}$ 10. $\frac{3}{4}$
11. 32 lengths 12. 27 lengths

1.34

1(a) (d) (g) (i) (j) are correct (b) (c) (e) (f) (h) are wrong
2(a) (iii) 1800 (b) (iii) 200 (c) (iv) 2000 (d) (iii) 8
3(a) 1200 (b) 35 (c) 1200 (d) 200 (e) 27 (f) 90 (g) 1·4
(h) 140 (i) 14000 (j) 3000
4. One £10 note and one £5 note.
7(a) 280 (b) 3500 (c) 16 000 (d) 4 (e) £3·59
(f) £32·35 or £32·36
8(a) £161·67 (b) £161·70 (c) £162

1.35

1 (a) 74·5 cm 2(a) 152·25 cm 3(a) 3·75 cm
(b) 75·5 cm (b) 152·75 cm (b) 3·85 cm
4(a) 2·25 cm and 4·65 cm (b) 2·35 cm and 4·75 cm
(c) 10·4625 cm² (d) 11·1625 cm²

1.36

1.

Number	1 decimal place	2 decimal places	3 decimal places
23·9355	23·9	23·93 or 23·94	23·935 or 23·936
344·29611	344·3	344·30	344·296
37·02698	37·0	37·03	37·027
0·07924	0·1	0·08	0·079
0·6047	0·6	0·60	0·605

2.

Number	1 significant figure	2 significant figures	3 significant figures
34·875	30	35	34·9
1689·63	2000	1700	1690
20 832	20 000	21 000	20 800
1·06428	1	1·1	1·06
0·0043923	0·004	0·0044	0·00439

3(a) 30 (b) 29·96436175 (d) 30·0 (e) 29·96 (f) 30·0
4(a) 13·4 cm (b) 13 cm

1.37

1.

Number	Number written as a power
243	3^5
9 ×	3^2 ×
2187	3^7

2.

Number	Number written as a power
729	3^6
3 ×	3^1 ×
2187	3^7

3.

Number	Number written as a power
2187	3^7
27 ×	3^3 ×
59049	3^{10}

4.

Number	Number written as a power
243	3^5
81 ×	3^4 ×
19683	3^9

1.38

1. $243 \div 27 = 3^5 \div 3^3 = 3^2$
2. $59049 \div 81 = 3^{10} \div 3^4 = 3^6$
3. $19683 \div 2187 = 3^9 \div 3^7 = 3^2$
4. $6561 \div 3 = 3^8 \div 3^1 = 3^7$

1.39

1(a) (i) 5^8 (a) (ii) 390 625
(b) (i) 8^5 (b) (ii) 32 768
(c) (i) 10^5 (c) (ii) 100 000
(d) (i) 2^{10} (d) (ii) 1024

2(a) 3^{15} 14 348 907   (g) 10^5 100 000
(b) 2^{12} 4096   (h) 2^{-1} $\frac{1}{2}$
(c) 10^8 100 000 000   (i) 2^{-5} $\frac{1}{32}$
(d) 2^{12} 4096   (j) 10^{-4} $\frac{1}{10000}$
(e) 3^6 729   (k) 10 10
(f) 2^4 16   (l) 2^6 64

3(a) False (b) True   (c) True   (d) False
4(a) $\frac{1}{2}$ (b) $\frac{1}{4}$ (c) $\frac{1}{8}$ (d) $\frac{1}{16}$ (e) $\frac{1}{10}$ (f) $\frac{1}{100}$
5(a) 10   (b) 4   (c) 8   (d) 12

1.40

1(a) 32   (b) 32   (c) 12   (d) 36   (e) 13   (f) 25
(g) 20 736 (h) 864   (i) $\frac{1}{25}$ (j) $\frac{1}{36}$
2(a) $6a^5$ (b) $6a^5b$ (c) $8x$ (d) $3a^3$ (e) $3a^{-3}$ (f) $a^{-1}b^7$
(g) $\frac{40}{3}b^6$ (h) $\frac{8b^5 + 2b^2}{a}$ (i) x^4y^6 (j) x^6y^9

1.41

1.

Calculation	Calculator Display on your calculator (For Example)		Standard Index Form
3000 × 5 000 000	1·5	10	$1·5 \times 10^{10}$
20 000 × 80 000 000	1·6	12	$1·6 \times 10^{12}$
250 000 × 3 000 000	7·5	11	$7·5 \times 10^{11}$
54 000 000 × 3 200 000	1·728	14	$1·728 \times 10^{14}$
0·000000004 ÷ 20 000	2	−13	2×10^{-13}
20 000 ÷ 0·000000004	5	12	5×10^{12}
6400 ÷ 0·000000004	1·6	12	$1·6 \times 10^{12}$
0·000000065 ÷ 20 000	3·25	−12	$3·25 \times 10^{-12}$

2(b) $3·1 \times 10^{-8}$ (c) $9·998 \times 10^5$ (d) $1·02 \times 10^{-2}$

3.

Number	Standard Index Form
23 000	$2·3 \times 10^4$
485 000 000 000	$4·85 \times 10^{11}$
3·71	$3·71 \times 10^0$
0·000000273	$2·73 \times 10^{-7}$
493 000	$4·93 \times 10^5$
3900	$3·9 \times 10^3$
0·0000000009	$9·8 \times 10^{-10}$
0·0000000526	$5·26 \times 10^{-8}$
0·000000000562	$5·62 \times 10^{-10}$
5 982 000	$5·982 \times 10^6$

4(a) $1·8923 \times 10^9$ (b) $7·4412 \times 10^{11}$ (c) 4×10^4
(d) $4·6 \times 10^4$ (e) $3·672 \times 10^9$ (f) $1·118 \times 10^{17}$
5. c, a, d, b   6. 5×10^2 seconds

1.42

1. Tony:

Subject	Mark	Mark out of 100	Percentage
Maths	$\frac{35}{50}$	$\frac{70}{100}$	70
Technology	$\frac{139}{200}$	$\frac{69·5}{100}$	69·5
Science	$\frac{15}{20}$	$\frac{75}{100}$	75
English	$\frac{39}{50}$	$\frac{78}{100}$	78
Music	$\frac{23}{25}$	$\frac{92}{100}$	92
Drama	$\frac{9}{10}$	$\frac{90}{100}$	90

2. Shreeti:

Subject	Mark	Mark out of 100	Percentage
Maths	$\frac{47}{50}$	$\frac{94}{100}$	94
Technology	$\frac{189}{200}$	$\frac{94·5}{100}$	94·5
Science	$\frac{19}{20}$	$\frac{95}{100}$	95
English	$\frac{19}{50}$	$\frac{38}{100}$	38
Music	$\frac{11}{25}$	$\frac{44}{100}$	44
Drama	$\frac{3}{10}$	$\frac{30}{100}$	30

3. 13% failed

1.43

Fraction	$\frac{1}{4}$	$\frac{6}{10}=\frac{3}{5}$	$\frac{8}{10}=\frac{4}{5}$	$\frac{9}{10}$	$\frac{7}{20}$	$\frac{13}{20}$	$\frac{7}{8}$	$\frac{1}{3}$	$\frac{2}{3}$	$\frac{27}{50}$	$\frac{23}{48}$	$\frac{175}{1000}$
Decimal	0·25	0·6	0·8	0·9	0·35	0·65	0·875	0·3333.	0·6666	0·54	0·479	0·175
Percentage	25	60	80	90	35	65	87.5	$33\frac{1}{3}$	$66\frac{2}{3}$	54	47.9	17.5

2. Chris Peters 36·1 %
Ian Anderson 25·1%
Rosalind Griffiths 38·9%

1.44

1. Archibald £3937·50   2. £588·50
Becky £2625·00
Clarence £2187·50
3. After 1 year £14 450   4. Sale price £552·50
After 2 years £12 282·50

5. £1233·75   6. Amy £6400
             Brian £8000
             Christopher £12 800
             Debbie £4800
7(a) £18 920   (b) £16 271·20   (c) £13 993·23
8(a) £12 720   (b) £13 483·20   (c) £14 292·19
9(a) £587·50   (b) £998·75   (c) £528·75   (d) £1116·25
10. £487·20

1.45

1. £120   2. £45   3. £400   4. 50 kg   5. 49.68 kg(!)
6. 80 kg   7. £1400   8. £320   9. £480   10. £16 000

1.46

1(a) 12·6%   (b) 59·5%
2(a) 30·8%   (b) 34·2%
3(a) 9·8%   (b) 54·5%   (c) 4·3%

1.47

1. Painting: 40% profit   Silver ring: 87·5% profit
Statue: 44% profit   Vase: 12·5% loss
Water Colour: 38·9% profit Pottery table lamp: 44·7% profit
Silver Pendant: 8·3% loss   Water Colour: 17·6% loss
2. 20·7%
3(a) 60 cm^2 (b) 5·5 cm & 13·2 cm (c) 72·6 cm^2
 (d) 12·6 cm^2(e) 21%   (f) 1·1 × 1·1 = 1·21
4(a) 126 cm^2 (b) 7·7 cm & 19·8 cm   (c) 152·46 cm^2
 (d) 26·46 cm^2 (e) 21%
 (f) 1·1 × 1·1 = 1·21
5. 13·5%   6. 2·5%   7. 2·4%

1.48

1(b) 1:6   (c) 1:144   (d) 25:2   (e) 1:50   (f) 1:5
 (g) 5:24   (h) 1:5   (i) 1:12   (j) 12:125
2(a) 1:6   (b) 1:10·5   (c) 1:4·8   (d) 1:20   (e) 1:13
 (f) 1:60   (g) 1:0·25   (h) 1:0·7   (i) 1:0·05
 (j) 1:422·222
3(a) 11:1   (b) 64:1   (c) 11·2:1   (d) 43·33:1
4(a) £200:£400   (b) £240:£360   (c) £200:£150
 (d) £468:£104   (e) £506:£644   (f) £100:£200:£300
 (g) £120:£180:£300 (h) £240:£336: £96
 (i) £375:£675:£75   (j) £122·50:£196: £294
5. 125 ml of juice   875 ml of water
6(a) 37·5 mph   (b) 112 km
7(a) 5 ounces   (b) 7·5 ounces   (c) 12·5 ounces
 (d) 42·5 ounces
8(a) 208 g   (b) 7·8 cm^3
9. 50 km
10(a) 6 m   (b) 18 cm
11(a) 750 m   (b) 76 cm
12(a) 660 km   (b) 500 km

2.1

1. 12a = 24
2. 5a + 7 (cannot be simplified any further) = 17
3. 6a + 6b = 30   4. 2a = 4
5. 2a + 4b = 16   6. 2a − 4b = −8
7. 2a + 3b = 13   8. 32a − 9b + 10c = 87
9. −4a + 2b = −2   10. 30 − a + 5b + c = 48
11. 21a = 42   12. 40a = 80
13. 40a^2 = 160   14. −40a^2 = −160
15. 120abc = 3600   16. −120abc = −3600
17. 120abc = 3600   18. −120abc = −3600
19. 8a^2 + 7a = 46   20. 2a^2 + 4a = 16
21. 4a = 8   22. 6ab = 36
23. 6b = 18   24. 6
25. −6b = −18   26. $\frac{7ab}{3}$ = 14
27. 21abc + 7ab = 672 28. 27abc + 7ab = 852
29. 3ab^2 = 54   30. 13a^{2}b^2 − ab^2 = 450

2.2

1. 9   2. 18   3. 2   4. 44   5. 28
6. 63   7. 56   8. 168   9. 1008   10. 101
11. 5   12. −10   13. 0   14. 0   15. 187
16. 45   17. 62·5 18. 16   19. 441   20. 441
21. 1   22. 0   23. 21   24. 3·25 25. −2·75
In questions 24 and 25 remember that:
(3a)^2 = (3a) × (3a) = 3 × a × 3 × a
but:
3a^2 = 3 × a × a

2.3

1. 20 + 5x   2. 6x + 48   3. 7x + 91
4. 3x − 24   5. 12x − 27   6. 20x + 35y + 15
7. 12x + 4 − 2y 8. 15x^2 + 18x 9. 30x^2 − 30xy + 18x
10. 28x^2 − 16xy + 12x

2.4

1. 34x + 23   2. −16x + 28   3. 51x + 21
4. −2x + 18   5. 5x + 17   6. 19x + 33
7. 7x − 28   8. 29x − 30   9. 38x^2 − 5x
10. 40x^2 − 77x

2.5

1. x^2 + 7x + 12   2. x^2 + 13x + 40   3. x^2 + 5x − 14
4. x^2 − 5x − 126   5. x^2 + x − 12   6. x^2 + 2x − 63
7. x^2 − 15x + 56   8. 2x^2 − 11x − 21 9. 3x^2 − 2x − 5
10. x^2 − 25

2.6

1. 5(x + 2)   2. 6(2x − 5)   3. 6(6x + 7)
4. 4(5y + 4)   5. 14(2x − 5)   6. 9(3 − 4x)
7. 6(15 − 8x)
8. 45 + 19x (no common factors, therefore doesn't
factorise)
9. 3(9x + 19)   10. 7(6x − y + 8)
11. 5(2x − 7y)   12. 5x(2x − 7y)
13. 4(3x − 4y + 7)   14. 3y(5x − y − 3)
15. 24(y − 3)   16. 6y(7x − 3y + 5)
17. 8x(13 − 5y − 7x)   18. 9y(7 − 3x − 5y)
19. 6xy(3 − 2x − 5y)   20. 7xy(3x − 5y − 4)

2.7

1. (x + 2)(x + 3)   11. (x − 1)(x + 5)
2. (x + 4)(x + 5)   12. (x − 7)(x − 4)
3. (x + 5)(x + 7)   13. (x + 5)(x − 2)
4. (x + 2)(x + 6)   14. (2x + 3)(x + 1)
5. (x + 1)(x + 7)   15. (2x + 1)(x + 4)
6. (x + 3)(x − 8)   16. (2x + 1)(x + 3)
7. (x + 8)(x − 2)   17. (3x + 1)(x + 4)
8. (x − 2)(x − 3)   18. (2x − 1)(x + 3)
9. (x − 5)(x + 4)   19. (x − 4)(x + 4)
10. (x − 5)(x − 3)   20. (x − 3)(x + 3)

2.8

1. x = 7   6. x = −6
2. x = 42   7. x = 9
3. x = 13   8. x = 19·26
4. x = −17   9. x = −4·78
5. x = −3   10. x = −7·21

2.9

1. x = 4   6. x = −3
2. x = 5   7. x = −4
3. x = 3   8. x = 3·5
4. x = −7   9. x = −2·5
5. x = 4   10. x = −6·2

2.10

1. x = 5   6. x = 3
2. x = −5   7. x = −4
3. x = 9   8. x = −5
4. x = 8   9. x = 2·3
5. x = 11   10. x = −0·8

2.11

1. x = 24   6. x = 10.2
2. x = −42   7. x = 4
3. x = 7   8. x = −3
4. x = 3   9. x = 7
5. x = −2   10. x = −3

2.12

1. x = 4   6. x = −2·2
2. x = 7   7. x = 0·7
3. x = −3   8. x = −3·4
4. x = −6   9. x = $\frac{1}{3}$
5. x = 4·5   10. x = −0·25

2.13
1. x = +2 and x = −2
2. no solutions
3. x = 0 and x = −4
4. x = −3 and x = 4
5. x = 0 and x = 5
6. x = 6.14 and x = −1.14
7. x = −3 and x = −4
8. x = −5 and x = −5
9. x = −1 and x = 6
10. x = 2 and x = 9
11. x = −3.41 and x = −0.59
12. x = 0 and x = −6

13. x = 0 and x = 4
14. x = $\frac{1}{2}$
    careful! 2x −1 = 0
    2x = 1   x = $\frac{1}{2}$
    and x = 3
15. x = +5 and x = −5
16. no solutions
17. x = −$\frac{1}{2}$ and x = −4
18. x = −4 and x = +6
19. x = −3 and x = 5
20. x = −6 and x = 4

2.14
1. x = 3·217
2. x = 7·165
3. x = 6·646
   x = 1·354

4. x = 3·405
   x = −4·405

2.15
1. x = 5 and y = 2
2. x = 7 and y = 1
3. x = 4 and y = 3
4. x = 2 and y = 5
5. x= 9 and y = 5

6. x = −4 and y = 3
7. x = 7 and y = 2
8. x = −5 and y = 2
9. x = −1 and y = −4
10. x = −5 and y = −3

2.16
1. a = x − b − c
2. d = $\frac{y}{e}$
3. x = $\frac{(z − b)}{a}$
4. x = a − b
5. x = 2a − b
6. x = 2a − b − y

7. a = $\frac{(y − x)}{b}$
8. a = $\frac{(3y − 2x)}{b}$
9. a = $\frac{(3y + 2x)}{b}$
10. x = $\frac{(ab − 3y)}{2}$

2.17
1. 3x − 7 = 89   x = 32
2. 13x + 5 = 226   x = 17
3. 3(x − 11) = 138   x = 57
4. 7(2x + 15) = 511   x = 29
5. 7(27 − x) = 56   x = 19
6. $\frac{x + 5 = 14}{9}$ x = 81
7. 5x + 9 = 7x – 135   x = 72
8. 2x + 7 = 5x – 98   x = 35
9. 19 − x = 3x – 149   x = 42
10. $\frac{4(x + 7) = 5x −71}{3}$ x = 27

2.18
1. 1·15 g/ cm³.
2. 45·6 mph
3. d = 2·4 m
    a = 4·4 m²
4. 392°F
5. 452·16 cm²
6. r = 7·98 cm
7   (a) h = 9·95 cm
    (b) r = 3·6 cm
8. 3 hours 10 minutes
9. 9.0688 g/cm³ = 9·07 (to 2 dec pl)
10. 145 minutes (to the nearest minute)
    = 2 hours 25 minutes

2.19
1(c) M = T × 2 + 1
(d)

Number of triangles	Number of matches
10	21
20	41
25	51
50	101
100	201
1000	2001
381	763

(e) Crosses at y=1

2(c) D = H × 4 + 2
(d)

Number of hexagons	Number of dots
10	42
20	82
25	102
50	202
100	402
1000	4002
372	1490

(e)   Crosses at y =2

3(c) M = H × 4 + 1
(d)

Number of houses	Number of matches
10	41
20	81
25	101
50	201
100	401
1000	4001
739	2957

(e) Crosses at y = 1

2.20
1. y = 3x + 4
2. y = 3x + 7
3. y = 4x −1
4. y = $\frac{1}{2}$x + 2

2.21
1. y = 9 − x
2. y = 9 − 2x
3. y = 14 − 3x
4. y = 7 − 2x

2.22
1. C = P × 9 + 3
So, when P = 46
C = 46 × 9 + 3
C = 417
So, Mrs Flowers will have to order 417 conifers.

2.23
1. The difference of the difference is always twice the co-efficient of the x-squared term.
2(a) y = x² + x
2(b) y = x² − x
2(c) y = 3x² + x
2(d) y = $\frac{3x² + x}{2}$

3. c = $\frac{3s²}{2} + \frac{s}{2}$

610 cards needed for 20 storeys
5612 cards needed for 61 storeys
5797 cards needed for 62 storeys

2.25
1(a) 1   (b) 2   (c) $\frac{1}{2}$ (d) −3   (e) $\frac{3}{13}$ (f) $\frac{-2}{7}$

2.26
1. y = 3x + 5
2(a) y = x + 1   (b) y = x −1   (c) y = 2x
(d) y = 2x + 1   (e) x = 3   (f) y = 1
(g) y = -x + 5   (h) y = 2x + 4
(i) y = $-\frac{1}{2}$x + 3

3(i) graph (a) is parallel to graph (e)
graph (b) is parallel to graph (f)
(ii) graph (c) is perpendicular to graph (d)
4.

Equation	Graph
y = x	g
y = 2x	f
y = 2x − 3	e
y = 7 − x	b
y = −5	h
y = −2x + 7	d
y = $\frac{1}{2}$x + 4	a
y = $-\frac{1}{2}$ x + 1	c

2.27

	ax + by = c form of the equation	Gradient	Cuts y-axis	y = mx + c form of the equation
1.	3x + 4y = 12	$-\frac{3}{4}$	+3	$y = -\frac{3}{4}x + 3$
2.	x + 5y = 10	$-\frac{1}{5}$	+2	$y = -\frac{1}{5}x + 2$
3.	2x − 3y = 12	$+\frac{2}{3}$	−4	$y = +\frac{2}{3}x − 4$
4.	−3x + 5y = 15	$+\frac{3}{5}$	+3	$y = +\frac{3}{5}x + 3$
5.	4x + 5y = 10	$-\frac{4}{5}$	+2	$y = -\frac{4}{5}x + 2$

2.28

1. x = 4, y = 2
2. x = 9, y = 1
3. x = 3, y = −1
4. x = 4, y = 11
5. x = 2, y = 3
6. x = 2·5, y = −3
7. x = −1, y = −2
8. x = −3, y = 0·5
9. x = 7, y = −0·25
10. x = $\frac{1}{3}$, y = −2

2.30

Equation	Solutions (where the graph crosses the x-axis)
1. y = x^2 + 3 = 0	no solutions
2. y = x^2 − 1 = 0	x = +1 and x = −1
3. y = x(x + 3) = 0	x = 0 and x = −3
4. y = x(x + 1) = 0	x = 0 and x = −1
5. y = (x + 2)(x − 2) = 0	x = −2 and x = +2
6. y = (x + 2)(x − 3) = 0	x = −2 and x = +3
7. y = x^2 + x − 2 = 0	x = −2 and x = +1
8. y = x^2 + x − 6 = 0	x = −3 and x = +2
9. y = x^2 + x − 7 = 0	x = 2·2 and x = −3·2*
10. y = x^2 − 2x − 6 = 0	x = 3·7 and x = −1·7*

*Approximately, reading from the graph
11(a) x=−1 and x=2   12(a) x=−1 and x=3
(b) x=3·19 and x=−2·19   (b) x=3·83 and x=−1·83

2.31

1(a) AB: 4 mph   (b) BC: 0 mph   (c) CD: 1·5 mph
(d) DE: 0 mph   (e) EF: 2 mph   (f) FG: 3 mph
2(a) 9 mph for 20 minutes, then stopped for 20 minutes, then 9 mph.
(b) 12 mph.
(c) Was Aaron mending a puncture on the grass and Beattie cycled by without seeing him when they crossed?
3(a) Between t = 16 seconds and t = 22 seconds.
(b) When t = 8 seconds and t = 28 seconds (approximately, reading from the graph).
(c) 1·875 m/s^2
(d) −2·5 m/s^2

2.32

1(a) 147 km   (b) 48 km
(c) 106 km   (d) 83 km
2(a) 94 miles   (b) 22 miles   (c) 72 miles   (d) 41 miles
3(i) (a) 36 litres   (b) 16 litres   (c) 25 litres
3(ii)(a) 8·8 gallons   (b) 7 gallons   (c) 4 gallons
4(i)(a) 57 kg   (b) 16 kg   (c) 88 kg
4(ii)(a) 10 stone 10 lb (b) 7 stone 8 lb   (c) 5 stone

3.1

1. a = 64°
2. b = 58°
3. c = 46°
    d = 67°
4. e = 60°
    f = 60°
    g = 60°
    h = 120°
5. i = 70°
    j = 58°
6. k = 106°
    l = 74°
    m = 32°
7. n = 44°
    p = 68°
    q = 112°
    r = 34°
8. s = 74°
    t = 37°

3.2

1.
a = 70°
b = 70°
c = 20°
d = 20°
e = 70°
f = 70°
g = 20°
h = 140°
i = 40°
j = 140°
k = 40°

2.
a = 65°

3.
a = 114°
b = 66°
c = 82°
d = 98°

4.
a = 118°
b = 62°
c = 118°

5.
a = 102°
b = 78°
c = 102°
d = 78°

6.
a = 32°
b = 116°
c = 32°
d = 32°

7.
a = 51°
b = 51°
c = 39°
d = 39°
e = 51°
f = 51°
g = 39°
h = 90°
i = 90°
j = 90°

8.
a = 123°

9.
a = 136°
b = 122°
c = 58°

10.
a = 39°
b = 116°
c = 25°
d = 39°

11.
a = 102°

12.
a = 34°
b = 63°
c = 34°
d = 105°

3.7

Polygon	Calculation	Interior Angle Sum
Equilateral Triangle	180° × 1	180°
Square	180° × 2	360°
Pentagon	180° × 3	540°
Hexagon	180° × 4	720°
Heptagon	180° × 5	900°
Octagon	180° × 6	1080°
Nonagon	180° × 7	1260°
Decagon	180° × 8	1440°
11-sided polygon	180° × 9	1620°
Dodecagon	180° × 10	1800°
N-sided Polygon	180° × (N − 2)	180N − 360°

3.8

2(a) rhombus   (b) x = 36°   y = 144°

3.9

2(a) infinite number (b) one   (c) 7   (d) none

3.10

1(a) order 4   (e) order 6
(b) order 2   (f) order 7
(c) order 2   (g) order 5
(d) order 2   (h) order 2

3.

NAME OF SHAPE	LINE SYMMETRY		ROTATIONAL SYMMETRY	
	Yes/No	Number of Lines	Yes/No	Order
Equilateral Triangle	Yes	3	Yes	3
Isosceles Triangle	Yes	1	No	-
Scalene Triangle	No	-	No	-
Square	Yes	4	Yes	4
Rectangle	Yes	2	Yes	2
Rhombus	Yes	2	Yes	2
Parallelogram	No	-	Yes	2
Kite	Yes	1	No	-
Trapezium	Possibly 1		No	-

Answers

3.11

1(a) 25·1 cm   (b) 53·4 cm   (c) 15·1 m
(d) 107 cm   (e) 244·9 cm   (f) 22·0 m
(g) 71·6 cm   (h) 439·6 cm
2(a) 49·7 cm   (b) 13·7 cm   (c) 2·5 cm
(d) 136·1 cm   (e) 0·8 m   (f) 107·8 cm
(g) 54·9 cm   (h) 34·7 cm
3. 483·6 m   4. 73·1 cm   5. 17·9 m
6. 502·4 cm   7. 37·7 m   8. 15·9 cm
9. 172·7 cm
10(a) 18·7 cm   (b) 15·9 cm   (c) 19·42 cm
(d) 23·42 cm   (e) 16·56 cm   (f) 22·84 cm

3.12

1(a) 153·9 cm²   (b) 95·0 cm²   (c) 32·2 m²
(d) 3629·8 cm²   (e) 12070·2 cm²   (f) 72·3 m²
(g) 1063·1 cm²   (h) 47119·6 cm²
2(a) 12·4 cm   (b) 15·7 cm
(c) 8·5 cm   (d) 19·5 cm
3(a) 3·3 m   (b) 34·8 cm
(c) 29·4 cm   (d) 26·5 cm
4. 161·4 cm²   5. 104·5 cm
6(a) 113·0 cm²   (b) 512·0 cm²
7. 1648·5 mm²   8(a) 45°   (b) 39·3 cm²
9(a) 36°   (b) 37·7 cm²
10 (a) 33·7 cm²   (b) 22·3 cm²   (c) 40·6 cm²
(d) 16·6 cm²   (e) 14·9 cm²   (f) 3·4 cm²

3.13

1. 10 cm²   2. 13 cm²   3. 29 cm²
4. 20 cm²   5. 34 cm²   6. 37 cm²

3.14

All answers are areas, measured in cm².
1. 4, 4, 8   4 + 4 = 8
2. 1, 4, 5   1 + 4 = 5
3. 1, 9, 10   1 + 9 = 10
4. 4, 9, 13   4 + 9 = 13
5. 9, 16, 25   9 + 16 = 25
6. 4, 25, 29   4 + 25 = 29

This is Pythagoras' Theorem! The areas of the two small squares add together to give the area of the large square. Now go on to read the next section on Pythagoras' Theorem.

3.15

1. a = 10 cm   6. f = 4·6 cm
2. b = 25 cm   7. g = 8·2 cm
3. c = 11·5 cm   8. h = 12·1 cm
4. d = 12·6 cm   9. i = 9·9 cm
5. e = 10·1 cm   10. j = 10·7 cm

3.16

1. 10·4 cm   7. No
2. 15·6 cm   8(a) 5·4 cm
3. 10·6 cm   (b) 5·1 cm
4. 19·2 cm   (c) 10·8 cm
5. 128·1 m   (d) 16·3 cm
6. 5·7 m

3.17

1

Angle	Sin	Cos	Tan
30°	0·5	0·866	0·577
60°	0·866	0·5	1·732
45°	0·707	0·707	1
15°	0·259	0·966	0·268
55°	0·819	0·574	1·428

2(a) 42·3°   (d) 18·5°
(b) 72·8°   (e) 32·3°
(c) 54·2°   (f) 40·6°

3(a) k = 6·4 cm   (b) m = 2·8 cm
(c) n = 8·4 cm   (d) p = 3·1 cm
(e) q = 8·5 cm (Use Pythagoras!)
(f) r = 10·6 cm (Use Pythagoras!)
(g) s = 4·9 cm   (h) t = 16·2 cm
(i) u = 15·3 cm
4(a) a = 24°   (e) e = 16°
(b) b = 55°   (f) f = 65°
(c) c = 44°   (g) g = 57°
(d) d = 42°   (h) h = 40°
5. height = 64 metres.
6. length = 7·8 metres
7(a) height = 6·9 cm   (b) area = 27·6 cm²
8. angle = 64°
9(a) angle = 33·2°
(b) 13·4 cm   (c) 53·6 cm²
10. x = 10·4 cm

3.18

1(a) 7.5 cm²   (d) 7.5 cm²
(b) 15 cm²   (e) 12 cm²
(c) 15 cm²   (f) 12 cm²
2(a) 30 cm   (c) 17.5 cm
(b) 16 cm   (d) 138 cm
3(a) 30 cm²   (c) 10 cm²
(b) 12 cm²   (d) 1128 cm²
4(a) 96 cm²   (c) 144 cm²
(b) 12 cm   (d) square, by 48 cm²
5(a) 480 cm²   (c) 900 cm²
(b) 30 cm   (d) square, by 420 cm²

3.19

1(a) 30 cm   (d) 30 cm
(b) 26 cm   (e) 62 cm
(c) 26·2 cm   (f) 42 cm
2(a) 30 cm²   (d) 40 cm²
(b) 36 cm²   (e) 204 cm²
(c) 38·28 cm²   (f) 29·25 cm²
3. 24 cm²
4(a) 7·5 cm²   (b) 7·5 cm²   (c) 7·5 cm²
(d) 15 cm²   (e) 18 cm²   (f) 11 cm²
5   (i) cm²   (ii) m²
(a) 10125   1·0125
(b) 13650   1·365

3.20

1(a) 168 cm³   (b) 120 cm³   (c) 12 cm³
(d) 40 cm³
2. Cuboid 1 holds 70 m³
Cuboid 2 holds 68.544 m³
Cuboid 1 holds most water.
3(a) 2 400 000 cm³ (b) 2·4 m³
4(a) 4 104 000 cm³ (b) 4·104 m³
6(a) 518·32 ml
(b) The label says 500 ml
(c) The dimensions given were the outside dimensions. We need to take into account the thickness of the carton itself and there might be a small amount of air in the carton.
7. 18 m³
8(a) 337·5 cm³   (b) 225 cm³   (c) 787·5 cm³
9(a) 72 cm³   (b) 252 cm³   (c) 408 cm³
10. 363 cm³ (to the nearest whole number)
11. 163 cm³ (to the nearest whole number)
12. 687 cm³ (to the nearest whole number)

3.21

1(a) The bearing of X from Y is 262°
(b) The bearing of Y from X is 82°
2(a) The bearing of X from Y is 312°
(b) The bearing of Y from X is 132°
3(a) The bearing of X from Y is 80°
(b) The bearing of Y from X is 260°
4(a) The bearing of X from Y is 140°
(b) The bearing of Y from X is 340°

ANSWERS

3.22

1(a) s = 1·9 km   (b) e = 2·55 km
2(a) s = 3·1 km   (b) w = 2·7 km
3(a) n = 2·4 km   (b) w = 2·95 km
4(a) distance = 2·4 km   (b) bearing = 264°

3.23

1. A(7, 1)   B(−1, −3)   C(−3, 5)   D(4, −7)   E(6, 7)
F(−7, −3)   G(−8, −7)   H(7, −4)   P(3, −1)
Q(0·5, −1)   R(−0·5, 2)   S(−0·5, −5·5)
2. (5, 11)
3. Parallelogram
4. B(4, 0), D(−4, 2)
5. S(−2, 5)
6. (−4, −7), (−6, 1) and (2, 3)
7(a) Parallelogram   (b) 34 units^2
8(a) Rhombus   (b) 84 units^2

3.24

1(a) $\begin{pmatrix} 4 \\ -2 \end{pmatrix}$ (b) $\begin{pmatrix} 0 \\ -4 \end{pmatrix}$ (c) $\begin{pmatrix} -4 \\ -5 \end{pmatrix}$ (d) $\begin{pmatrix} -5 \\ 0 \end{pmatrix}$ (e) $\begin{pmatrix} -4 \\ 3 \end{pmatrix}$ (f) $\begin{pmatrix} 5 \\ 3 \end{pmatrix}$

4. A′(5, 1)
B′(4, −11)
C′(−3, 4)
D′(0, −11)

5(a) $\begin{pmatrix} 2 \\ 3 \end{pmatrix}$, $\begin{pmatrix} -5 \\ -11 \end{pmatrix}$

(b) $\begin{pmatrix} -3 \\ -8 \end{pmatrix}$

(c) $\begin{pmatrix} 2 \\ 3 \end{pmatrix} + \begin{pmatrix} -5 \\ -11 \end{pmatrix} = \begin{pmatrix} -3 \\ -8 \end{pmatrix}$

6(a)

(I) $\begin{pmatrix} -5 \\ 3 \end{pmatrix}$ (ii) $\begin{pmatrix} 4 \\ 1 \end{pmatrix}$ (iii) $\begin{pmatrix} 3 \\ -5 \end{pmatrix}$ (iv) $\begin{pmatrix} -8 \\ -9 \end{pmatrix}$ (v) $\begin{pmatrix} 7 \\ 11 \end{pmatrix}$

(b) $\begin{pmatrix} 1 \\ 1 \end{pmatrix}$

(c)

$\begin{pmatrix} -5 \\ 3 \end{pmatrix} + \begin{pmatrix} 4 \\ 1 \end{pmatrix} + \begin{pmatrix} 3 \\ -5 \end{pmatrix} + \begin{pmatrix} -8 \\ -9 \end{pmatrix} + \begin{pmatrix} 7 \\ 11 \end{pmatrix} = \begin{pmatrix} 1 \\ 1 \end{pmatrix}$

3.25

3.	(a)	(b)	(c)	(d)
A(4, 7)	(−4, 7)	(4, −7)	(2, 7)	(4, −11)
B(6, 6)	(−6, 6)	(6, −6)	(0, 6)	(6, −10)
C(4, 5)	(−4, 5)	(4, −5)	(2, 5)	(4, −9)
D(4, 1)	(−4, 1)	(4, −1)	(2, 1)	(4, −5)

4 (a) Object	Image after reflection in the x-axis
A(1, 1)	A′(1, −1)
B(2, 4)	B′(2, −4)
C(4, 2)	C′(4, −2)
D(5, 6)	D′(5, −6)
E(7, 2)	E′(7, −2)
(x, y)	(x, −y)

(b) Object	Image after reflection in the y-axis
A(1, 1)	A″(−1, 1)
B(2, 4)	B″(−2, 4)
C(4, 2)	C″(−4, 2)
D(5, 6)	D″(−5, 6)
E(7, 2)	E″(−7, 2)
(x, y)	(−x, y)

5(a) (3, 5)
(b) y = x

6(a)

A(2, 7)	A′(2, −3)
B(6, 3)	B′(6, 1)
C(−4, 4)	C′(−4, 0)

(b)

A(1, 3)	A′(−7, 3)
B(−2, −2)	B′(−4, −2)
C(0, 0)	C′(−6, 0)

(c)

A(4, 1)	A′(−1, −4)
B(2, 6)	B′(−6, −2)
C(−2, 4)	C′(−4, 2)

(d)

A(6, −1)	A′(−2, 7)
B(1, −5)	B′(−3, −1)
C(4, −5)	C′(−4, 3)

3.26

2(a) Object	Image after rotation of 90° clockwise about the point (0, 0)
A(2, 1)	A′(1, −2)
B(3, 3)	B′(3, −3)
C(4, 2)	C′(2, −4)
D(5, 4)	D′(4, −5)
E(5, 1)	E′(1, −5)
(x, y)	(y, −x)

(b) Object	Image after rotation of 180° about the point (0, 0)
A(2, 1)	A″(−2, −1)
B(3, 3)	B″(−3, −3)
C(4, 2)	C″(−4, −2)
D(5, 4)	D″(−5, −4)
E(5, 1)	E″(−5, −1)
(x, y)	(−x, −y)

(c) Object	Image after rotation of 270° clockwise about the point (0, 0)
A(2, 1)	A‴(−1, 2)
B(3, 3)	B‴(−3, 3)
C(4, 2)	C‴(−2, 4)
D(5, 4)	D‴(−4, 5)
E(5, 1)	E‴(−1, 5)
(x, y)	(−y, x)

3(a) C′(3, −6)
(b) Centre of rotation (−5, 0)
(c) 90° clockwise
4(a) 90° anticlockwise about the point (1, 1)
(b) 45° clockwise about the point (−3, 1)
(c) 150° clockwise about the point (0, −1)
(d) 125° clockwise about the point (1, 1)

3.28

3(a) Scale Factor = 4, Centre of Enlargement (2, 2)
(b) Scale Factor = 2, Centre of Enlargement (7, 4)
(c) Scale Factor = 3, Centre of Enlargement (3, 5)
(d) Scale Factor = 2·5, Centre of Enlargement (1, 7)

4(i) Shape	Area of Object	Area of Image after an enlargement, scale factor 2
(a)	1	4
(b)	2	8
(c)	3	12
(d)	4	16
(e)	5	20
(f)	6	24
(g)	7	28
(h)	8	32

Area of Image = Area of Object $\times$ 4
Area of Image = Area of Object $\times$ 2^2
Area of Image = Area of Object $\times$ (Scale Factor)^2

4(ii) Shape	Area of Object scale factor 3	Area of Image after an enlargement,
(a)	1	9
(b)	2	18
(c)	3	27
(d)	4	36
(e)	5	45
(f)	6	54
(g)	7	63
h)	8	72

Area of Image = Area of Object $\times$ 9
Area of Image = Area of Object $\times$ 3^2
Area of Image = Area of Object $\times$ (Scale Factor)^2

(iii) Shape	Area of Object scale factor 4	Area of Image after an enlargement,
(a)	1	16
(b)	2	32
(c)	3	48
(d)	4	64
(e)	5	80
(f)	6	96
(g)	7	112
(h)	8	128

Area of Image = Area of Object $\times$ 16
Area of Image = Area of Object $\times$ 4^2
Area of Image = Area of Object $\times$ (Scale Factor)^2

3.29
3(a) Scale Factor = $\frac{1}{2}$, Centre of Enlargement (13, 1)
(b) Scale Factor = $\frac{1}{4}$, Centre of Enlargement (7, 5)
(c) Scale Factor = $\frac{1}{3}$, Centre of Enlargement (1, 5)

3.30
1. a and e; b and f; c and g
2. a and g; c and i; e and h
3(a) a = 8·25 cm b = 7·5 cm
(b) c = 8·8 cm d = 13·2 cm
(c) e = 12·6 cm f = 14·4 cm
4(a) a = 6 cm b = 4 cm
(b) c = 8 cm d = 7 cm
(c) e = 6 cm f = 4 cm
5. 22·5 cm
6. 8·16 cm

3.31
1. Rotation 90° anticlockwise about (0, 0).
2. Reflection in the x-axis.
3. Translation $\begin{pmatrix} 2 \\ -4 \end{pmatrix}$
4. Translation $\begin{pmatrix} 0 \\ -2 \end{pmatrix}$
5(a) T (b) Q (c) Y (d) Y (e) N (f) M (g) Y (h) X

4.1
1.

	Mean	Median	Mode
(a)	29·4	28	38
(b)	56·4	56·5	56 and 58
(c)	4·26	4·05	no mode
(d)	20·8	22	0

2. mean = 71·6 kg median = 68 kg
3. mean = 162·5 median = 163 cm
4. mean = 57·9 median = 57·5
5. mean = 2·75 median = 3 mode = 3
6. 36
7. 373 years 4 months
8(a) mean = 1 goal per game (b) 6 goals needed
9(a) mean = 16 marks (b) median = 16·5 marks
(c) mode = 17 marks
10(a) mean = 17·4 marks (b) median = 18 marks
(c) mode = 18 marks
11(a) mean = 18·4 marks (b) median = 19 marks
(c) mode = 19 marks
12(a) mean = 18·4 marks (b) median = 18·5 marks
(c) mode = 20 marks
(d) Remarkably similar results. The schools must have a similar intake of ability.

4.2
1(a)

Marks	Totals
0–9	0
10–19	3
20–29	8
30–39	13
40–49	16
50–59	7
60–69	10
70–79	11
80–89	9
90–99	3

(c) mean = 53·7 marks

2(a)

Number of Cars	Totals
0–9	1
10–19	4
20–29	16
30–39	22
40–49	13
50–59	10
60–69	9
70–79	3
80–89	5
90–99	3
100–109	3
110–120	1

(c) mean = 48 cars
(d) income will be about £87 600

4.3
1. mean = 63·2
2. mean = 65·2

4.4
1(a) mean = 72·9 (b) range = 49
2(a) mean = 72·4 (b) range = 89
(c) The mean is very nearly the same for each class, but the spread of marks is much greater in class 10B than in class 10A.

4.5
1(c) 72% (d) 53%
2(c) 73·5kg (d) 172 cm

4.6

1(d) mean = $57 \cdot 955$ = $58 \cdot 0$ (to one dec pl)

2(a)

Weight	Total
$39 \cdot 5 \leqslant w < 44 \cdot 5$	4
$44 \cdot 5 \leqslant w < 49 \cdot 5$	7
$49 \cdot 5 \leqslant w < 54 \cdot 5$	9
$54 \cdot 5 \leqslant w < 59 \cdot 5$	11
$59 \cdot 5 \leqslant w < 64 \cdot 5$	14
$64 \cdot 5 \leqslant w < 69 \cdot 5$	7
$69 \cdot 5 \leqslant w < 74 \cdot 5$	8

(d) mean = $51 \cdot 6333$ = $51 \cdot 6$ (to one dec pl)

4.7

1(a) 309 apples

(d) mean = $148 \cdot 656$ = $148 \cdot 7$ (to one dec pl)

2(a) 263 tomatoes

(d) mean = $70 \cdot 726$ = $70 \cdot 7$ (to one dec pl)

4.8

1.

The Times	$42°$
The Telegraph	$49°$
The Independent	$63°$
The Guardian	$185°$
The Daily Mail	$21°$

2.

The Times	$50°$
The Telegraph	$76°$
The Independent	$24°$
The Guardian	$174°$
The Daily Mail	$36°$

3.

Type of Transport	Angle (to the nearest half degree)
Own car	$83°$
Parents' car	$29°$
Motor Bike	$32 \cdot 5°$
Bike	$21 \cdot 5°$
Bus	$119°$
Walk	$75 \cdot 5°$

4.

Type of Transport	Angle (to the nearest half degree)
Own car	$122°$
Parents' car	$98 \cdot 5°$
Motor Bike	$28°$
Bike	$25°$
Bus	$50°$
Walk	$36 \cdot 5°$

5.

Type of Transport	Number of Students
Own car	16
Parents' car	20
Motor Bike	12
Bike	20
Bus	60
Walk	32

6.

stayed on at their old school	$183 \cdot 5°$
went to a college	$79°$
found a job	$56 \cdot 5°$
were still looking for a job	$40 \cdot 5°$

7.

British	$124°$
German	$81.5°$
French	$60°$
Swedish	$16°$
Japanese	$78°$

8.

British	$134.5°$
German	$75°$
French	$65.5°$
Swedish	$30°$
Japanese	$54.5°$

4.9

1(a) median = 68 marks

(b) upper quartile = 74 marks

(c) lower quartile = 52 marks

(d) inter-quartile range = $74 - 52$ = 22 marks

(e) 34 pupils have failed.

(f) $240 - 222$ = 18 pupils got grade A.

2(a) median = 53 marks

(b) upper quartile = 63 marks

(c) lower quartile = 42 marks

(d) inter-quartile range = $63 - 42$ = 21 marks

(e) 52 pupils fail the exam.

(f) $350 - 322$ = 28 pupils achieve a grade A

3(a) median = 24 passengers

(b) upper quartile = 28 passengers

(c) lower quartile = 18 Passengers

(d) IQR = $28 - 18$ = 10 passengers

(e) 15 journeys they made a loss.

4. The middle half of Class A have scored within 9 marks of each other. The middle half of Class B have scored within 27 marks of each other. You could conclude that pupils in Class A are of a similar ability to each other. There is a greater range of ability in the pupils of Class B. You might conclude that Class A is a set, whereas Class B is a mixed ability class.

5.1

1. $\frac{4}{36} = \frac{1}{9}$ 2. $\frac{3}{36} = \frac{1}{12}$ 3. $\frac{6}{36} = \frac{1}{6}$ 4. $\frac{6}{36} = \frac{1}{6}$

5. $\frac{15}{36} = \frac{5}{12}$ 6. $\frac{10}{36} = \frac{5}{18}$

7.

	1	2	3	4	5	6
H	H 1	H 2	H 3	H 4	H 5	H 6
T	T 1	T 2	T 3	T 4	T 5	T 6

$\frac{3}{12} = \frac{1}{4}$ 8. $\frac{2}{12} = \frac{1}{6}$ 9. $\frac{7}{12}$ 10. 0   11. 1

5.2

1. $\frac{1}{4}$ 2. $\frac{1}{2}$ 3. $\frac{4}{52} = \frac{1}{13}$ 4. $\frac{13}{52} = \frac{1}{4}$ 5. $\frac{13}{51}$

6. $\frac{12}{51} = \frac{4}{17}$ 7. $\frac{3}{51} = \frac{1}{17}$

5.3

1. 30 times   2. 60 times   3. 30 times   4. 25 times

5.4

1. p(2 girls) = $\frac{1}{4}$

2. p(1 boy, 1 girl) = $\frac{2}{4} = \frac{1}{2}$

3. p(same sex) = $\frac{1}{4} + \frac{1}{4} = \frac{1}{2}$

4(a) p(all girls) $= \frac{1}{8}$

(b) p(all boys) $= \frac{1}{8}$

(c) p(same sex) $= \frac{1}{8} + \frac{1}{8} = \frac{1}{4}$

(d) p(two boys, one girl) $= \frac{3}{8}$

(e) p(two girls, one boy) $= \frac{3}{8}$

5.5

1(a) $\frac{3}{20}$

(b) $\frac{12}{20} + \frac{1}{20} = \frac{13}{20}$

(c) $\frac{16}{20} = \frac{4}{5}$

(d) $\frac{4}{20} = \frac{1}{5}$

2(a) $\frac{9}{100}$

(b) $\frac{49}{100}$

(c) $\frac{21}{100} + \frac{21}{100} = \frac{42}{100} = \frac{21}{50}$

(d) $\frac{51}{100}$

5.6

1(a) $\frac{6}{110} = \frac{3}{55}$

(b) $\frac{56}{110} = \frac{28}{55}$

(c) $\frac{24}{110} + \frac{24}{110} = \frac{48}{110} = \frac{24}{55}$

(d) $\frac{54}{110} = \frac{27}{55}$

2(a) $\frac{2}{72} = \frac{1}{36}$

(b) $\frac{42}{72} = \frac{7}{12}$

(c) $\frac{14}{72} + \frac{14}{72} = \frac{28}{72} = \frac{7}{18}$

(d) $\frac{70}{72} = \frac{35}{36}$

Index